8

Oxford, United Kingdom

September 6–9th 2016

Proceedings

Eighth meeting

Of the

European Society

For

Chlamydia Research

Editors:

Colette O'Neill

Ian N. Clarke

Patrick Horner

Barbara Van Der Pol

COMMITTEES

Local Organising Committee:

Ian N. Clarke	Sarah Howie
Patrick Horner	Gary Entrican
Colette O'Neill	Richard Hayward
Peter Marsh	Nick Thomson
Katy Turner	Robin Bailey
Janet Wilson	David Longbottom
Charles Lacey	Kevin Dunbar
David Mabey	Aura Andreasen
Martin Holland	Tariq Sadiq

European Scientific Committee:

Ian N. Clarke	(Chair, UK)
Patrick Horner	(Co-Chair, UK)
Servaas Morré	(The Netherlands)
Angelika Stary	(Austria)
Per-Anders Mårdh	(Finland)
Matthias Maas	(Austria)
Judit Deák	(Hungary)
Konrad Sachse	(Germany)
Gilbert Greub	(Switzerland)

International Representative:

Barbara Van Der Pol	(Sponsor Liaison, USA)

Sponsors

The European Society for Chlamydia Research would like to recognise the following companies for their generous support of our meeting.

Gold sponsors

Silver sponsors

Bronze sponsors

Non-commercial sponsors

PREFACE

We are very pleased to welcome you to the UK and the Eighth meeting of the European Society for *Chlamydia* Research. This is the first time that the meeting has been hosted in the UK and we have chosen Oxford for the occasion. The meeting is a unique forum in *Chlamydia* research with inclusive and wide participation from the research community. We have exciting presentations of the latest research data, keynote expert speaker reviews and we hope that these set the scene and provide the opportunity to exchange ideas and initiate collaborations in a warm and friendly atmosphere.

The theme for the meeting is *"Applying Chlamydia basic science, pathogenesis research and evolving diagnostics to improving control programmes"*. The intention is to create an environment where basic scientists, epidemiologists, public health specialists and clinicians will come together to discuss the latest advances in research and thus not only better inform future research collaborations but also current public health interventions. The meeting concludes with a clinical day which can be attended independent of the conference and is specifically targeted at clinicians, microbiologists and public health specialists. We are hopeful that the meeting will have a major impact on the current delivery of *Chlamydia* control programmes and help facilitate advances in our understanding of basic science.

We have striven to engage conference attendees with different career stages, cultures and experiences and backgrounds. We are exceedingly pleased by the number and quality of the abstracts. For the first time we used an online abstract submission and scoring system, each abstract was scored independently by three local committee members. The aim was to generate an unbiased programme that reflects the nature of interests amongst the participants. We hope that by including a rich variety of perspectives we can maximise participation. Thus we are very pleased to note the expansion of research in non-chlamydial species. To maximise participation in the oral programme we have also decided to try out some new concepts in addition to the 'clinical day'. Within the programme we plan to have intensive short presentations with broader discussions in the sessions on serology and diagnostics. Whilst competition for oral presentations was intense the poster sessions play host to some of the most dynamic and important interactions that take place at conferences and so must not be missed. Accordingly, we have scheduled two afternoon sessions dedicated to poster presentations so that delegates assigned to poster sessions will get the opportunity to meet with other poster presenters and discuss their work.

We are very much looking forward to an exciting meeting and thank you in advance for your active participation.

We wish you all a productive and memorable experience in Oxford,

Ian N. Clarke, Patrick Horner, Barbara Van Der Pol

The organisers

ACKNOWLEDGEMENTS

To fulfil our not-for-profit scientific mission the European Society for *Chlamydia* Research relies on significant personal commitment from members of the European Scientific Committee and the Local organising committee. We are very grateful for the efforts of past and present committee members who have followed this tradition and made this conference possible. In addition, the meeting would not be possible without the generous contribution of support from industry donors and non-commercial organisations who are highlighted in the programme book and here in the abstract book. Since Paddy and I agreed to host the meeting in 2008 the financial landscape has changed dramatically with the great recession, the deepest in the UK since the 1930s and then followed by austerity and faltering recovery. This has had a major impact on science funding and investment in research across the world. In this climate the support of donors to the viability of the meeting is critical so please visit our sponsors stands and engage with them.

In addition to these important benefactors I would like to highlight the contribution of a number of key individuals. Firstly, my colleagues and co-organisers Dr. Paddy Horner and Dr. Bobbie Van Der Pol who have been deeply involved in the organisation at all levels and their dedication, enthusiasm, hard work and energy had been a key factor in bringing the meeting to life. Bobbie's critical contribution has been in recruiting sponsors without whom the meeting would not be viable. Our conference is co-badged with BASSH and I am extremely grateful to Dr Daniel Richardson (Brighton) who has helped guide us through the complex process of conference organisation with sage advice. We are also very grateful to the committee members (European and Local) and the keynote speakers for agreeing to attend the conference and providing abstracts. This generosity is underscored by the fact that all have foregone expense re imbursement which has made the conference financially viable and allowed us to provide bursaries to support postgraduate students/post docs from outside the EU and USA to attend. I am extremely grateful to all committee members, without whose involvement this event would not have been possible, all have contributed from abstract reviewing to chairing sessions and so this is genuinely a major team effort.

The conference would not have been possible without help from my team in Southampton, most important amongst which has been the tireless and tenacious support from my PA, Mrs Leanne Palmer. I am also very grateful to Mrs. Cynthia Prince and Ms. Rachel Skilton who designed and wrote the website with help from Dr. Colette O'Neill. Colette has subsequently organised and maintained the website and taken on the role of chief editor for this abstract book and the programme book. My sincere thanks also to Dr. Pete Marsh (Public Health England, Southampton) for his continued support and collegiality and to Cate Winstanley (PhD student) and Dr. Sarah Pearson for their thoughtfulness and good citizenship in supporting us.

These are major tasks that she has performed with exemplary skill. I wish to thank (in advance) our medical students Ed Coates (Southampton) and Annabelle Clarke (Brighton) who will help with the smooth running of oral sessions.

Last, but by no means least, we are grateful for the wonderful original artistic designs for the conference logos by Georgina Horner which we have used for the abstract book, the programme book, business cards and posters to advertise this event.

I hope this meeting will be a memorable experience for you all and will lead to new initiatives and collaborations in research.

Ian N. Clarke

Chair, Organising Committee ESCR 2016

TABLE OF CONTENTS

Page

Committees i

Sponsors ii

Preface iii

Acknowledgements iv

Contents page v

Session 1: Molecular Biology 1

Session 2: Cell Biology 14

Session 3: Vaccines 25

Session 4: Immunology 29

Session 5: Animal and cellular models of *C. trachomatis* infection 34

Session 6: Other chlamydial species 40

Session 7: Trachoma 53

Session 8: Epidemiology 60

Session 9: Serology 65

Session 10: Diagnostics 71

Clinical research day 80

Poster Session A 94

Poster Session B 147

Author index 205

TUESDAY MORNING, 6TH SEPTEMBER

SESSION 1:

Molecular Biology

Chairs:
David Nelson & Nick Thomson

09.15 – 09.45

KEYNOTE: RAPHAEL VALDIVIA

Genetic analysis of *Chlamydia* pathogenesis

Raphael Valdivia, Barbara Sixt, Victoria Carpenter, Duke University School of Medicine, Durham NC 27510, USA

Species of *Chlamydia* are the etiologic agent of endemic blinding trachoma, the leading cause of bacterial sexually transmitted diseases, significant respiratory pathogens, and a zoonotic threat. Their dependence on an intracellular growth niche and their peculiar developmental cycle are major challenges to elucidating their biology and virulence traits. The last five years has seen tremendous advances in our ability to perform a molecular genetic analysis of *Chlamydia* species. Major achievements include the generation of large collections of mutant strains, now available for forward- and reverse-genetic applications, and the introduction of a system for plasmid-based transformation enabling complementation of mutations; expression of foreign, modified, or reporter genes; and even targeted gene disruptions. This talk will summarize the current status of the molecular genetic toolbox for *Chlamydia* species, with a focus on the function of effector proteins as revealed by forward and reverse genetics applications. We will describe *C. trachomatis* mutants defective for various aspect of immune signaling and cell death regulation, and a characterization of the bacterial and host factors mediating such processes.

09.45-10.00:Transposon Mutagenesis in *Chlamydia trachomatis* reveals Key Factor for Lateral Gene Transfer

Kelly Harrison, Scott Labrie, Greg Peterson, Jason Wickstrum, Scott Hefty.
University of Kansas, Lawrence, KS, USA

Background/ Introduction

Random mutagenesis is a powerful approach for discovery of genetic components associated with specific biological phenotypes. Random genetic mutagenesis in *Chlamydia* has been limited to chemical approaches that typically result in numerous genetic lesions and some difficulty associating multiple mutations with specific phenotype.

Objectives

Transposon mutagenesis can provide singular insertion of a genetic marker that typically disrupts the function of a gene for which transposon has inserted. To evaluate the ability of a transposon system to function in *Chlamydia*, a non-replicative plasmid encoding for both a transposase and transposon was used for transformation.

Method

The hyper active form of the *Himar* transposase (C9) was cloned into a plasmid vector that also contained β-lactamase flanked by cognate inverted repeats. The plasmid was transformed into *Chlamydia* using standard approaches with antibiotic selection through multiple passages. Arbitrary PCR and DNA sequencing was performed on resistant cultures. Southern blot also performed to evaluate the single insertion of transposon. Confocal microscopy was used to evaluate basic bacterial and inclusion morphology of transposon mutants. Lateral gene transfer with C. suis (Tet^R) and *C. trachomatis* CT339::Tn or CT383/84::Tn (Amp^R) was also performed.

Results

The transposon system developed is functional in *C. trachomatis* and allows for singular insertions. A relatively small library of mutants was generated with most exhibiting growth morphologies similar to wild-type *C. trachomatis*. Transposon insertion into CT696 yielded a slow growing *C. trachomatis* with few bacteria that were disassociated from normal inclusion growth. Transposon insertion in to CT339, which share sequence similarity to competence factor ComEC/A, demonstrated an inability to allow for lateral gene transfer supporting the importance in this process.

Conclusions

This transposon system is functional in *C. trachomatis*; however, poor transformation efficiency and few genes that may tolerate disruption limited high throughput potential. Despite this limitation, these mutants revealed interesting biological phenotypes. Repeated transformations are expected to generate defined mutant library in a relatively short period of time and effort.

10.00-10.15: Characterization of a temperature sensitive aminoacyl-tRNA synthetase *Chlamydia trachomatis* mutant

Julie A Brothwell[1], Barry D Stein[2], David E Nelson[1]
[1]*Indiana University School of Medicine, Indianapolis, IN, USA,* [2]*Indiana University-Bloomington, Bloomington, IN, USA*

Background/ Introduction

Proteomic and transcriptomic studies indicate that many aminoacyl-tRNA synthetases and all tRNA species are present in EB despite their transcription only beginning in early-mid development. In addition, global inhibition of early protein synthesis by chloramphenicol blocks inclusion maturation and predisposes the inclusion to host immune defenses.

Objectives

The importance of individual translation substrates during the developmental cycle has not been previously explored due to the essentiality of the genes involved. To circumvent this, we utilized a conditional *gltX* mutant to characterize how the lack of a particular aminoacyl-tRNA species affects chlamydial growth and inclusion development.

Method

An ethyl methanesulfonate (EMS) mutagenized *C. trachomatis* L2 library was screened for mutants that formed inclusions at 37°C, but failed to form mature inclusions at 40°C. Mapping of several mutants using whole genome sequencing and counterselection lateral gene transfer identified a $gltX^{ts}$ mutant and generated an isogenic recombinant that lacked the $gltX^{ts}$ allele but that maintained all the other mutant alleles. Temperature shift assays identified when *gltX* function became essential for growth. Progeny and genome copy numbers were enumerated for the wild-type parent, $gltX^{ts}$ and its recombinant. Inclusion ultrastructure was visualized by transmission electron microscopy.

Results

Although $gltX^{ts}$ exhibited normal growth kinetics at 37°C, very few progeny were produced by $gltX^{ts}$ at 40°C compared to the wild-type parent and isogenic recombinant. $gltX^{ts}$ genome replication did not appreciably increase at the non-permissive temperature relative to the input, indicating that genome replication was impaired. Additionally, inclusions typically contained more than 1 RB at the end of the developmental cycle, indicating that differentiation from EB into RB and at least one cell division were possible. Inclusion growth and progeny production at 40°C could be rescued when shifted to 37°C prior to 18 hours post infection.

Conclusions

Chlamydia EB contain the requisite proteins and protein precursors to allow differentiation into RB. Unlike models of persistence where genome replication continues in the absence of division, our data suggests that the lack of functional GltX stalls both protein and DNA synthesis.

10.15-10.30: chlamydial polymorphic membrane proteins (Pmps) form functional oligomers

Alison Favaroni, Soeren Luczak, Elisabeth Becker, Johannes Hegemann
Heinrich-Heine-University, Duesseldorf, Germany

Background/ Introduction

Pmps are the biggest family of *Chlamydia* adhesins and are very promising candidates for vaccine development. *C. trachomatis* and *C. pneumoniae* have 9 and 21 Pmps respectively, characterized by multiple repeats of GGA(I,L,V) and FxxN motifs, and resemble autotransporter structures with the passenger domain (PD) responsible for protein functions.

Objectives

A better understanding of the functional properties of Pmp proteins is instrumental for the development of a vaccine. Thus, we want to test our model which suggests the interaction and oligomerization of Pmp proteins with relevance to adhesion.

Method

C. pneumoniae D-Pmp21, a subdomain of the naturally occurring M-Pmp21 with adhesive capacity, and a motif-mutated D-Pmp21 were tested for oligomerization via Size-Exclusion Chromatography (SEC) and Transmission Electron Microscopy (TEM) and for adhesive properties toward human epithelial cells.
Different domains of *C. trachomatis* Pmps were tested for interaction via Far-Western dot-blot, pull-down assays and MicroScale Thermophoresis measurements (MST). Blue-native gels, 2D SDS-PAGE, SEC and TEM were performed to analyze the formation and the structure of complexes. Oligomers were tested for their adhesion capacity.
In vivo Pmp interactions were tested via Immunoprecipitation (IP) from infectious EBs.

Results

C. pneumoniae D-Pmp21 formed amyloid-like oligomers. Oligomer formation was dependent on the presence of FxxN motifs and was required for adhesion. *In vivo* Pmp21 interaction with other Pmps could be detected on EBs via IP. Moreover, *C. trachomatis* Pmp fragments also interacted with other Pmps. They formed high molecular weight (hMW) homomeric and heteromeric complexes. TEM analysis showed that homomeric complexes formed small filaments, while heteromeric complexes generated significantly longer filaments.
The complexes displayed differences in adhesion strength to human cells. Interestingly, adhesion-incompetent fragments are located in the adhesive fractions when interacting with an adhesion-competent fragment.

Conclusions

These data indicate that *C. pneumoniae* D-Pmp21 can form amyloid-like structures able to bind human cells. Moreover, *C. trachomatis* Pmps interact with each other, forming homo- and heteromeric filamentous structures, likely increasing their functional capacity.
Currently, we perform experiments aiming at characterizing Pmp oligomers *in vivo*.

10.30-10.45: Identification and characterization of novel persistence genes in *Chlamydia trachomatis*

Matthew K Muramatsu[1], Julie A Brothwell[1], Tim E Putman[2], Daniel D Rockey[2], Barry D Stein[3], David E Nelson[1]

[1]Indiana University School of Medicine, Indianapolis, Indiana, USA, [2]Oregon State University, Corvallis, Oregon, USA, [3]Indiana University, Bloomington, Indiana, USA

Background/ Introduction

Various stimuli induce *C. trachomatis* to enter a viable but nonculturable state termed persistence. Tryptophan depletion via IFN-γ induction of indoleamine 2,3-dioxygenase is the most well-studied and relevant stimulus to human disease. Only urogenital serovars are able to utilize indole and serine to synthesize tryptophan and reactivate from persistence.

Objectives

With the exception of tryptophan synthase (*trpBA*), no chlamydial genes have been definitively linked to persistence *in vitro*. Transcriptomic and proteomic analysis indicates global changes occur when *C. trachomatis* enters persistence. Thus, we sought to identify additional genes that *C. trachomatis* utilizes to enter, maintain and reactivate from persistence.

Method

HeLa cells were pretreated with IFN-γ and infected with isolates from an EMS mutagenized library. Susceptible to IFN-γ mediated persistence (Sip) mutants were identified as having reduced IFU counts following reactivation from persistence with indole as compared to the untreated control. Infectious progeny production was assessed for all the Sip mutants in tryptophan replete conditions. Healthy Sip mutants were whole genome sequenced, and the causative mutations were mapped using a marker-less recombination strategy based on LGT. Inclusion morphology following reactivation was assessed by TEM and fluorescent microscopy. Infectious progeny following reactivation with either indole or tryptophan were compared.

Results

Several Sip mutants were identified from the persistence screen. All mutants were determined to have normal growth kinetics in tryptophan replete conditions as compared to the parent L2-GFP strain. The causative mutations in three of the Sip mutants were mapped to *trpB*, CTL0225, and CTL0694, corresponding to the β-subunit of tryptophan synthase, a putative integral membrane protein, and putative oxidoreductase, respectively. Additionally all the mapped Sip mutants made smaller inclusions and still contained aberrant RB following reactivation with indole, indicating a possible defect in reactivation. This was confirmed by the reduced IFU production following reactivation with either indole or tryptophan.

Conclusions

We have identified two additional genes necessary for *C. trachomatis* to either maintain or reactivate from persistence, indicating that persistence is a complex phenotype. Additionally, CTL0225 and CTL0694 share sequence identity to an amino acid transporter and *cysJ* in *E.coli*, respectively, suggesting a need for additional nutrients during persistence.

10.45-11.00: RNA-sequencing of iron-starved *C. trachomatis* reveals key players in iron metabolism and indicates induction of a general stress response that precedes the persistent state

Amanda J. Brinkworth, Nicholas D. Pokorzynski, Rey A. Carabeo
School of Molecular Biosciences, College of Veterinary Medicine, Washington State University, Pullman, WA, USA

Background/ Introduction

Since iron is essential for the growth and development of *Chlamydia*, its acquisition and accumulation must be carefully regulated. Immediate transcriptional responses to iron limitation have not yet been characterized in detail, leaving a gap in the current knowledge of how *Chlamydia* regulates its response to changes in iron availability.

Objectives

Because the fast-chelating agent 2,2'-Bipyridyl efficiently and homogeneously starves *Chlamydia* of iron, we use it here to determine the immediate transcriptional response to iron starvation. This study provides the first evidence of an iron-dependent regulon for *Chlamydia trachomatis*, and also provides clues to the molecular events that precede iron-induced persistence.

Method

2,2'-Bipyridyl (BpdI) treatment of *C. trachomatis* at 12h p.i. for only 3h is sufficient to induce up-regulation of the iron-responsive *ytg* operon, well in advance of the formation of aberrant RBs. Primary and secondary transcriptional responses to iron starvation were compared by RNA-sequencing from *C. trachomatis* between 12h post-infection and 12+3h BpdI, and between 12+6h BpdI and 18h post-infection, respectively. Ion Torrent reads were aligned to the *C. trachomatis* L2/434/Bu genome using Rockhopper 2.0.3. Differential expression was determined from upper quartile-scaled normalization values using a DESeq algorithm that assumes an FDR of 1% when p-values are < 0.05.

Results

Several transcripts whose products are known to coordinate metals for their function were immediately induced in response to iron starvation, including the *ytg* operon and the iron-sulfur cluster synthesis operon *sufBCD*. The primary response also included an increase in transcripts involved in carbon metabolism, tryptophan salvage, lipid metabolism, and energy storage. Interestingly, few transcripts were downregulated during the primary response. Comparison of 12+6h BpdI treatment with 18h infection did not reveal an obvious secondary response, but instead induced a significant delay in the expression of several mid-to-late cycle genes, including the type III secretion-related genes *lcrD, lcrE*, and *tarP*.

Conclusions

The immediate transcriptional response to iron starvation was determined for *C. trachomatis*. The pattern of induction is consistent with that of *ytg* operon. Upregulated transcripts also indicate that *Chlamydia* attempts to accumulate amino acids and energy substrates upon iron starvation to allow aberrant RBs to recover rapidly from delayed growth.

11.30-11.45: Genomic history of *Chlamydia trachomatis*: historic separation, contemporary mixing and a conspicuous absence of antibiotic resistance

James Hadfield[1], Simon Harris[1], Helena Seth-Smith[1,2], Surendra Pramar[3], Patiyan Andersson[4], Philip Giffard[4], Julius Schachter[5], Jeanne Moncada[5], Hamid Jalal[3], Matthew Burton[6], David Mabey[6], Anthony Solomon[6], Magnus Unemo[7], Peter Marsh[8], Ian N. Clarke[9], Nicholas Thomson[1], The *C. trachomatis* Global Consortium[1]

[1]*Pathogen Genomics, The Wellcome Trust Sanger Institute, Cambridge, UK,* [2]*Functional Genomics Center, University of Zürich, Zürich, Switzerland,* [3]*Public Health Laboratory Cambridge, Addenbrookes Hospital, PHE, Cambridge, UK,* [4]*Menzies School of Health Research, Darwin, Australia,* [5]*Department of Laboratory Medicine, University of California, San Francisco, USA,* [6]*Clinical Research Department, London School of Hygiene & Tropical Medicine, London, UK,* [7]*WHO Collaborating Centre for Gonorrhoea and other STIs, Örebro University Hospital, Orebro, Sweden,* [8]*Public Health Laboratory Southampton, PHE, Southampton, UK,* [9]*Molecular Microbiology, University of Southampton, Southampton, UK*

Background/ Introduction

Chlamydia trachomatis is the world's most prevalent bacterial sexually transmitted infection and leading infectious cause of blindness, yet it is one of the least understood human pathogens, in part due to the difficulties in culture, accessing the DNA and a lack of available tools for genetic manipulation.

Objectives

Our objective was to extend the previous observations made by us and others using limited data sets to understand in high resolution the evolutionary and recombination dynamics of *Chlamydia trachomatis*.

Method

We used a multitude of approaches to gain access to the genomic data, culture and culture independent approaches, and included isolates that reflect as full range as possible of geographic, temporal and disease causing isolates.

Results

Sequencing of 563 genomes sampled over 50 years and from 20 countries allowed detailed exploration of recombination and evolutionary dynamics. We demonstrate that the lymphogranuloma venereum lineage is substantially younger than previously suggested implying that the species has undergone a number of severe evolutionary bottlenecks and subsequent modern expansions that impact on our view of how this pathogen has and continues to evolve. Finally, at a time when nearly every pathogen is becoming increasingly drug resistant, we find absolutely no evidence of circulating antimicrobial resistance alleles despite continually increasing prevalence.

Conclusions

Whilst genomic data has its limitations and at a time when genomic tools are being developed and being used on *Chlamydia trachomatis* genomic data still has more to give to reveal the subtleties in the way this successful pathogen is evolving.

11.45-12.00: *Chlamydia trachomatis* whole-proteome microarrays for antigenic target identification

Katrin Hufnagel, Smiths Lueong, Martina Willhauck-Fleckenstein, Beiping Miao, Angelika Michel, Julia Butt, Michael Pawlita, Jörg D. Hoheisel, Tim Waterboer
German Cancer Research Center (DKFZ), Heidelberg, Germany

Background/ Introduction

Persistent infections with *Chlamydia trachomatis* (*Ct*) can cause cervicitis, pelvic inflammatory disease, tubal factor infertility and may contribute to cancer development in humans. The host immune system recognizes and responds to different proteins of the complex pathogen by producing antibodies. These antibody responses can show infection- or disease state-specific patterns.

Objectives

We aim to develop high-density protein arrays for *de novo* identification of antigens distinguishing e.g. infected from non-infected individuals, acute from chronic infections, or infected cancer patients from infected cancer-free individuals.

Method

Using Multiple Spotting Technique, we have developed high-density protein microarrays expressing *in situ* the entire *Ct* proteome comprising 895 open reading frames. For systematic antigen identification, pools of serum samples were applied onto the microarray and *Ct*-specific antibodies were identified. In preliminary experiments, we incubated the microarrays with samples from women (i) seronegative in *Ct* serological assays, (ii) with recently acquired or (iii) persistent *Ct* infection and (iv) from cervical cancer patients.

Results

We successfully expressed more than 90% of all *Ct* proteins. Through comparison of antibody reactivity patterns, we identified antigens which were commonly recognized by all known *Ct*-seropositive samples. Other antigens reacted only with samples from cervical cancer patients, or only with *Ct*-infected cancer-free individuals. In addition we identified antigens distinguishing persistent from recently acquired infections. The *Ct* antigen chaperonin GroEL, a known marker for persistence, reacted only with samples from patients with a persistent infection. Most known *Ct*-seronegative samples showed no reactivity with any of the *Ct* proteins, except for few *Ct*-seronegative samples from cervical cancer patients.

Conclusions

High-density protein microarray is a promising tool for *de novo* antigen identification. After identifying and characterizing the first antigen panels we aim to validate the selected antigens in sero-epidemiological case-control studies using low-density, high-throughput Luminex suspension array technology.

12.00-12.15: chlamydial transcription during IFN-gamma mediated persistence is dependent on the tryptophan content of the transcribed gene

Scot P. Ouellette, Kelsey J. Rueden, Lisa A. Rucks
University of South Dakota, Vermillion, SD, USA

Background/ Introduction

Human chlamydial species are exquisitely sensitive to tryptophan (trp) limitation. While the phenotypic effects of trp limitation, via IFN-gamma mediated IDO induction, are well characterized (e.g. blocked progression through the developmental cycle, enlarged RBs, blocked division), little is known about the mechanism *Chlamydia* uses to induce this persistent growth state.

Objectives

We previously observed by microarray analysis that chlamydial transcription was globally elevated during IFN-gamma mediated trp limitation (Ouellette et al., 2006). We hypothesized that the transcription pattern is dependent on the trp content of the transcribed gene.

Method

Human epithelial HEp2 cells were infected with *C. pneumoniae* AR39. Infected cells were left untreated (UTD) or were treated with IFN-gamma. At 24h and 48h post-infection (pi), nucleic acid samples were collected. Total RNA was DNased and reverse-transcribed whereas total genomic DNA was isolated from duplicate samples. Separate samples were processed for immunofluorescence (IFA). RT-qPCR was performed against a panel of genes, and transcription was normalized to gDNA as previously described (Ouellette et al., 2006).

Results

We began by looking at transcription of *euo*, which exhibits elevated transcription during IFN-gamma mediated persistence, as a way of validating that persistence was induced: IFA confirmed this. We next assayed a panel of genes that were either rich or poor in trp codons. We observed that transcription of genes with multiple trp codons was generally increased during trp limitation whereas genes with no trp codons were unchanged or decreased under these conditions. We did observe exceptions to this rule, but the exceptions were predictable and followed the same trp rule depending on position within operons or within large genes.

Conclusions

Chlamydia lacks a stringent response, which most bacteria use to respond to amino acid limitation. Our observations suggest that *Chlamydia* has either evolved a unique response to trp limitation or that its response represents a de-repressed state due to the lack of a stringent response.

12.15-12.30: Genetic analysis of *Chlamydia muridarum* interferon-gamma resistance

Amanda M. Giebel[2], Shuai Hu[1], Krithika Rajaram[2], Ryan Finethy[3], Evelyn Toh[1], Julie A. Brothwell[1], Richard P. Morrison[4], Sandra G. Morrison[4], Robert J. Suchland[5], Barry D. Stein[2], Jorn Coers[3], David E. Nelson[1]
[1]*Indiana University School of Medicine, Indianapolis, IN, USA,* [2]*Indiana University, Bloomington, IN, USA,* [3]*Duke University Medical Center, Durham, NC, USA,* [4]*University of Arkansas for Medical Sciences, Little Rock, AR, USA,* [5]*University of Washington, Seattle, WA, USA*

Background/ Introduction

Chlamydiae have evolved mechanisms to circumvent species-specific host immune responses. For example, *C. muridarum* is highly interferon-gamma (IFN-g) resistant in mice whereas *C. trachomatis* is IFN-g sensitive. This is important because IFN-g sensitivity impacts modeling of human *Chlamydia* infections in mice. Genes that mediate *C. muridarum* IFN-g resistance are unknown.

Objectives

To identify *C. muridarum* IFN-g resistance genes and characterize the cognate host defense pathway(s), which inhibit *C. trachomatis*, but not *C. muridarum,* in mice.

Method

IFN-g sensitive (Igs) mutants were identified by screening 2976 EMS mutagenized *C. muridarum* isolates in +/- IFN-g conditions. Development of Igs mutants was compared by one-step growth curve assays +/- IFN-g in McCoy cells. Igs phenotypes were linked to specific mutations via genome sequencing, genetic suppressor analysis, and lateral gene transfer. Virulence of select Igs and suppressor mutant isolates was compared in a C57BL/6 mouse genital tract infection model. The mechanism of interferon sensitivity of one Igs mutant was interrogated using a combination of chemical inhibitors of specific interferon effector pathways, knockout cell lines, and inducers of apoptosis and necrosis.

Results

Thirty-one Igs mutants were identified. The most sensitive mutant, Igs4, produced 7-fold fewer inclusions and 41-fold fewer progeny in IFN-g-treated cells at 24hpi. Utilizing a suppressor and a recombinant strategy the Igs4 phenotype was mapped to a mutation in the putative inclusions membrane gene, *tc0574.* Igs4, but not Igs4 suppressors, were strongly attenuated in the mouse genital tract. Surprisingly, IFN-g sensitivity of Igs4 was not rescued when various IFN-g-stimulated effector pathways including iNOS, Phox, IRG, perforin 2, or autophagy were inactivated or inhibited. However, Igs4 was profoundly sensitive to extrinsic and intrinsic inducers of apoptosis in the absence of IFN-g.

Conclusions

We have identified a putative inclusion membrane gene that appears to mediate *C. muridarum* IFN-g and apoptosis resistance. More broadly, phenotypes of the Igs mutants we have characterized suggest that IFN-g resistance of *Chlamydia* spp. is complex and may reflect prolonged pathogen-host co-evolution.

12.30-12.45: *Chlamydia trachomatis* infection associated immune responses and genital pathology is tegulated by host microRNAs

Rishein Gupta, Tanvi Arkatkar, Jonathon Keck, JiehJuen Yu, M Neal Guentzel, James P Chambers, Bernard P Arulanandam
South Texas Center for Emerging Infectious Diseases and Center for Excellence in Infection Genomics, University of Texas at San Antonio, One UTSA Circle,, San Antonio, Texas, USA

Background/ Introduction

In humans, genital *Chlamydia trachomatis* (Ct) infection may lead to reproductive sequelae including fibrosis and inflammation. While the role of host molecular regulators namely microRNAs (miRs) is not well examined, the contribution of downstream immune pathways/ genes leading to genital tissue exacerbation and tissue remodeling is known.

Objectives

Given the regulatory link between miRs and immunity, in this study, we determined signatures of host miRs and the mechanistic contribution of selected miRs in immune responses and subsequent development of pathology in *Chlamydia muridarum* (Cm) infection.

Method

C57BL/6 wild type (WT) were intravaginally infected with Cm and cellular infiltrates (flow cytometry), miRs and putative targets (real-time PCR and mass spectrometry) and genital pathology was analyzed. *In vivo* and *ex vivo* experiments using miR agonists and antagonists for gain and loss of function respectively were performed. Down-selected miRs were validated (real-time PCR) in cohorts of Ct infected women with reproductive sequelae including infertility.

Results

Cm infection in WT genital tract significantly regulated selected miRs. Amongst these, miRs-125b, -182, -214 and 30c were subjected to *in vitro* knockdown analyses with specific inhibitors and resulted in significant increase in Cm infectivity. *In vivo* miR-214 was observed to regulate intracellular adhesion molecule (ICAM)-1 and neutrophil infiltration affecting development of upper genital pathology. Importantly, significant changes in expression of selected miRs in Ct D infected women was indicative of the translational relevance of these miRs. Regulation of Ct associated immune responses by downselected miRs was further established using 'gain and loss of function' approaches in infected mice.

Conclusions

Overall, these findings provides evidence for regulation of immune responses via host miRs in genital Cm/ Ct infection. Ongoing efforts in our laboratory include the specific role of these miRs signatures affecting antigen specific immunity and subsequent development of upper genital pathology.

12.45-13.00: Gene deletion by FRAEM with the use of a novel suicide vector

Konrad E Mueller, Katerina Wolf, Kenneth A Fields
University of Kentucky, Lexington, Kentucky, USA

Background/ Introduction

Although chemical mutagenesis and group II intron insertions demonstrate the tractability of *Chlamydia trachomatis* for genetic manipulation, these methods produce a limited range of genomic modifications. However, the competence of the bacterium and its propensity for genomic recombination suggest the potential applicability of more-versatile genetic techniques such as allelic exchange.

Objectives

This work aimed to develop and utilize a novel suicide vector for use in *C. trachomatis* which would enable plasmid curing as well as gene deletion and sequence insertion by homologous recombination. Fluorescent markers would provide the ability to evaluate the success of the mutagenesis process by microscopy.

Method

The chlamydial suicide vector was assembled with all *pgp1-8* genes of the native chlamydial pL2 plasmid previously shown to enable the maintenance of transformation vectors in *C. trachomatis*. However, expression of *pgp6* was modified to be regulated by the TetR repressor-operator system. In order to direct homologous recombination to specific sites of the chlamydial genome, 3-kilobase sequences flanking target genes were assembled around a dual cassette encoding both GFP and β-lactamase and introduced into the suicide vector. *trpA* encoding tryptophan synthase and subsequently *ctl0063*, *ctl0064*, and *ctl0065* encoding effector and effector-related proteins were targeted for deletion.

Results

In the presence of anhydrotetracycline inducer, transformed *C. trachomatis* maintained the suicide vector throughout multiple passages. Removal of inducer resulted in the loss of the suicide vector and the generation of pL2 plasmid-cured chlamydial populations. Transformation of the modified suicide vector carrying the targeting sequence for *trpA* successfully produced green-fluorescent *C. trachomatis* lacking the *trpA* gene and expressing the expected tryptophan-auxotrophic phenotype. Mutagenesis progress was monitored by fluorescent microscopy as enabled by the presence of *gfp* and *mCherry* in the dual cassette and suicide-vector backbone, respectively. Subsequent attempts to delete *ctl0063*, *ctl0064*, and *ctl0065* were also successful.

Conclusions

All attempts at gene deletion produced observable mutants one passage after successful transformation. Thus, in addition to a method of curing plasmids, control of *pgp6* expression resulted in a novel suicide vector enabling efficient reverse genetics in *C. trachomatis* through fluorescence-reported allelic exchange mutagenesis (FRAEM).

TUESDAY AFTERNOON, 6TH SEPTEMBER

SESSION 2:

Cell Biology

Chairs:
Richard Hayward & David Longbottom

14.00 – 14.30

KEYNOTE: RICHARD HAYWARD

New insights into host and pathogen reorganisation during *Chlamydia trachomatis* entry into host cells

Richard D Hayward, Institute of Structural and Molecular Biology, Birkbeck & University College London, Malet Street, London WC1E 7HX

The unusual biphasic lifecycle of the *Chlamydiae* is underpinned by transitions between two bacterial forms of distinct morphology and function; the elementary (EB) and reticulate (RB) body. Both forms of the bacteria employ a type III secretion system (T3SS) to translocate effector proteins across host membranes to promote cell entry and intracellular replication, respectively. Our recent cell biology experiments supported by electron and cryo-electron tomography have provided fresh insights into *Chlamydia*-host interactions.

Our re-analysis of EB structure by cryo-electron tomography revealed a polarised architecture, with distinct membrane and protein structures occupying opposite hemispheres. One hemisphere is characterised by a tubular inner membrane invagination, while the other exhibits asymmetric periplasmic expansion to accommodate an array of T3SSs. This is reminiscent of the array formed in RBs at the 'pathogen synapse', a remarkable structure linking the bacterial, inclusion and host endoplasmic reticulum membranes. Strikingly, EBs orient with their T3SS-containing pole facing the target cell, enabling direct contact with the plasma membrane. Since membrane-embedded T3SSs were captured in both cell-free and cell-associated states, we used cryo-electron tomography and sub-tomogram averaging to derive the intact structure of the primordial *C.trachomatis* T3SS in the presence and absence of host membrane contact at ~3nm resolution. Comparison of the averaged structures demonstrated a marked compaction of the basal body occurs when the needle tip contacts the host cell membrane. Compaction is coupled to the stabilisation of the cytosolic sorting platform-ATPase complex, which is associated with the cytoplasmic face of the T3SS core. This revealed the first structure of a bacterial T3SS engaged with a eukaryotic host, and a 'pump action' conformational change underpinning effector injection.

In addition to these insights into bacterial structure, our data also demonstrate that contact triggers unexpectedly diverse alterations in host membrane and cytoskeletal architecture including macropinosomes, actin-rich filopodial extensions and phagocytic cups. Once encapsulated into tight early vacuoles, EB polarity and the T3SS are temporarily lost. Building on these studies, our complementary cell biology data derived from quantitative fluorescence microscopy will be presented. These characterise a dominant macropinocytosis-like pathway underlying *C.trachomatis* entry that involves not only Rac1 but implicates additional host components that mechanistically couple phosphoinoside signalling, actin reorganisation and membrane deformation during cell invasion.

14.30-14.45: The role of gap junction mediated antigen transport in *Chlamydia* induced oviduct pathology

Srikanth Manam[1], Sophie La Salle[1], Yong Zhang[2], Michael Holtzman[2], Bruce J Nicholson[3], Kyle H Ramsey[1], <u>Ashlesh K Murthy</u>[1]

[1]*Midwestern University, Downers Grove, IL, USA,* [2]*Washington University at Saint Louis School of Medicine, Saint Louis, MO, USA,* [3]*University of Texas Health Science Center at San Antonio, San Antonio, TX, USA*

Background/ Introduction

We have shown previously that *Chlamydia*-specific CD8[+] T cells do not significantly affect bacterial clearance but cause oviduct pathology. This suggests the possibility that chlamydial peptides are presented to CD8[+] T cells by uninfected cells, but begs the question: "How do uninfected cells acquire chlamydial peptides"?

Objectives

We examined the hypothesis that gap junction mediated antigen transport (GMAT) via channels formed by connexin (Cx) proteins, predominantly Cx43 expressed on oviduct epithelium, contributes to this effect.

Method

HeLa cells were engineered to express functional Cx43 (HeLa-Cx43) or mutant Cx43 (HeLa-Cx43-T154A). The presence of chlamydial antigens in uninfected cells neighboring *Chlamydia*-infected cells was evaluated by immunofluorescent microscopy. The transport of ovalbumin or chlamydial antigens from HeLa cells to mouse antigen presenting cells, and subsequent activation of antigen-specific CD8[+] T cells was evaluated. In parallel, Cre-Lox technology was used to generate mice (Foxj1Cre-Cx43flox mice) with a conditional deficiency of Cx43 only in ciliated columnar epithelia of oviduct, not uterine horns. Bacterial shedding, immune response and upper reproductive pathology was evaluated in these mice following vaginal *C.muridarum* infection.

Results

HeLa-Cx43, not HeLa or HeLa-Cx43-T154A, displayed chlamydial antigens in uninfected cells neighboring *Chlamydia*-infected cells. HeLa-Cx43 efficaciously transferred $Ova_{257-264}$ or chlamydial antigens to co-cultured mouse APC, which subsequently activated respective antigen-specific CD8[+] T cells. Lower and upper genital tract chlamydial burden, splenic antigen-specific total cellular cytokine response and serum antibody response were comparable between Foxj1Cre-Cx43flox and WT mice. However, TNF-a production from *Chlamydia*-specific splenic CD8[+] T cells on days 8, 10, and 14 after infection, and the incidence and severity of oviduct, not uterine horn, pathology on day 80 after infection in Foxj1Cre-Cx43flox mice was significantly reduced compared to WT animals.

Conclusions

These results demonstrate the role of GMAT in rendering uninfected cells targets for attack by *Chlamydia*-specific CD8[+] T cells. Importantly, these results provide compelling experimental evidence for a role of GMAT in immunopathogenesis of mucosal pathogens, and unravel a new target for intervention to reduce clinically important pathologies.

14.45-15.00: Focal Contact Maturation to a Unique *Chlamydia*-designed Adhesive Structures in Infected Cells Require Contractile Forces Provided by the Molecular Motor Myosin II

Antonio T. Pedrosa[1,2], Rey Carabeo[1]
[1]*Washington State University, Pullman, WA, USA,* [2]*The University of Aberdeen, Aberdeen, UK*

Background/ Introduction

The ability of epithelial cells to extrude as part of the homeostasis of the epithelium or in response to infection is detrimental to *Chlamydia* because the pathogen spends the majority of its developmental cycle in the non-infectious stage. *Chlamydia* has an uncharacterized mechanism to neutralize premature epithelial exfoliation.

Objectives

We intend to extend our previous observation that revealed the evolution of focal adhesions (FA) to stable adhesive structures that may be distinct from normal focal adhesions. Here, we implicate the contractile forces provided by myosin II in this evolution, and identify the molecular participants.

Method

We monitored the mechanical forces exerted along the FAs in infected cells using quantitative intramolecular FRET across a tension sensor probe (Vin-TS) that has the FRET-compatible fluorophores mTFP1 and Venus. Blebbistatin and vinculin-knockout cells were used to evaluate myosin II and vinculin involvement in FA number and morphology.

Results

We observed the alterations to focal adhesions in infected cells involves at least two distinct steps - a chloramphenicol-resistant step that affects FA numbers, and a chloramphenicol-sensitive stage when a co-factor is produced to facilitate FA maturation indicated by a switch in morphology. A loss of FRET at focal adhesions was observed with Vin-TS, but not mutants unable to bind F-actin, indicating tension transmission along the actin filament through vinculin, and potentially through the talin protein to promote FA maturation. Consistent with the role of vinculin, FAs remained morphologically unchanged in *Chlamydia*-infected vinculin-knockout cells relative to infected wild type cells.

Conclusions

The creation of unique adhesive structures in *Chlamydia*-infected cells involves a mechanism that requires contractile forces to be transmitted to vinculin. The effects on FA morphology indicate that this mechanism is related to the unidentified co-factor that accelerates the formation of the *Chlamydia*-specified adhesive structures in the infected cell.

15.00-15.15: Diverse host-pathogen metabolism in productive and persistent *Chlamydia trachomatis* infection

Kensuke Shima[1], Inga Kaufhold[1], Thomas Eder[2], Nadja Käding[1], Nis Schmidt[1], René Deenen[3], Karl Köhrer[3], Thomas Rattei[2], Jan Rupp[1]
[1]*Department of Infectious Diseases and Microbiology, University of Lübeck, Lübeck, Germany,*
[2]*Division of Computational Systems Biology, University of Vienna, Vienna, Austria,* [3]*Biological and Medical Research Center (BMFZ), Heinrich-Heine-University Düsseldorf, Düsseldorf, Germany*

Background/ Introduction

Severe clinical sequelae such as pelvic inflammatory disease are linked to chronic inflammation which can be caused by persistently *Chlamydia trachomatis* infected cells. In productive and persistent *C. trachomatis* infection, *C. trachomatis* has to acquire host metabolites to survive in host due to truncated metabolic pathways in *C. trachomatis*.

Objectives

Persistent infection has been investigated in different environmental stimuli. However, little is known about the regulation of host and chlamydial metabolism in different persistent infection models. In this study we investigate how host and chlamydial metabolism are regulated in productive and persistently *C. trachomatis* infected cells.

Method

Interferon-γ (IFN-γ), penicillin and deferoxamine (DFO) were used to induce persistent *C. trachomatis* infection. We used transmission electron microscopy (TEM) to show morphology of *C. trachomatis* in different infection models. Glycolytic activity and other metabolic markers were measured by Seahorse cellular metabolic analyzer (XF-Analyzer) and two-photon microscopy (2-LSM) in real time. The chlamydial transcriptome was sequenced using Illumina HiSeq technology. Gene expression in each persistence model was compared to productive infection.

Results

In productive *C. trachomatis* infection, we could show the increased HIF-1α and glucose transporter-1 proteins. In accordance with this regulation, glucose metabolism was significantly enhanced in productive *C. trachomatis* infection compared to non-infected control cells. Furthermore, HIF-1α protein and glycolysis were differentially regulated in IFN-γ, penicillin and DFO induced persistent *C. trachomatis* infections. In addition, 2-LSM and transcriptome analyses revealed that chlamydial metabolism and gene expression were differentially regulated in three different persistent *C. trachomatis* infections.

Conclusions

Host and chlamydial metabolism is differentially regulated in various infectious environments and these diverse metabolic characteristics might influence chlamydial growth, progeny and characteristics of persistent infection.

15.15-15.30: Manipulation of host nuclear architecture by *Chlamydia trachomatis*

Maud Dumoux, Oliver Martin, Maya Topf, Richard D Hayward
Institute of Structural and Molecular Biology, Birkbeck and University College London, London, UK

Background/ Introduction

During the lifecycle, the inclusion occupies a significant proportion of the cytoplasmic volume and consequently competes with and repositions host cell organelles. As the inclusion is anchored at the microtubule organising centre, the expanding inclusion is apposed to the host cell nucleus, and deforms its shape.

Objectives

We investigated the potential consequences of inclusion-induced deformation of the host nucleus on nuclear organisation and function.

Method

We have applied electron and confocal microscopy, including quantitative approaches, in combination with cell biology techniques incorporating the use of knockout cell lines, nuclear transport assays and fluorescence *in situ* hybridisation.

Results

Our data reveal that chlamydial infection and the pressure exerted by the inclusion drives profound alterations in the organisation of the nuclear envelope, inducing polarisation. Critically, these changes reflect active modifications, and are not simply a passive response of the host cell to the presence of the inclusion apposed to the nucleus. We demonstrate that the infection-associated changes in nuclear envelope organisation signal alterations in host genome organisation and sub-nuclear architecture, impacting on host gene expression, recombination and repair. We show that impairment of this sequence of events modulates bacterial infectivity.

Conclusions

We demonstrate a novel mechanism of cell subversion during chlamydial infection, showing that *C.trachomatis* induces changes in nuclear envelope structure that promote inclusion biogenesis and hijack host cell gene expression.

16.00-16.15: Identification of members of the chlamydial divisome which link septum formation and peptidoglycan remodelling

Nicolas Jacquier[1], Patrick H. Viollier[2], Gilbert Greub[1]

[1]Institute of Microbiology, University Hospital Center and University of Lausanne, Lausanne, Switzerland, [2]Department of Microbiology & Molecular Medicine, Institute of Genetics & Genomics in Geneva (iGE3), Faculty of Medicine / CMU, University of Geneva, Geneva, Switzerland

Background/ Introduction

Bacterial cell division is usually organized by the well conserved protein FtsZ, a bacterial homologue of tubulin. FtsZ accumulates at the midcell in a structure called a Z-ring and recruits other proteins involved in cytokinesis. Interestingly, *Chlamydiales* lack a sequence homologue of FtsZ, but, nevertheless divide by binary fission.

Objectives

We could recently show that the actin homologue MreB, its regulator RodZ and the Pal-Tol complex localize at the division septum in *W. chondrophila*, a *Chlamydia*-related bacterium, in a process depending on peptidoglycan biosynthesis. In this study, we further investigated the link between peptidoglycan biosynthesis and divisome formation in *Chlamydiales*.

Method

For this purpose, we performed various screens to describe potential interactors of both RodZ and peptidoglycan. Immunoprecipitation and mass spectrometry analysis allowed us to identify several candidates that are conserved in all *Chlamydiales* and that might play a role in the coordination of septum formation and peptidoglycan remodeling.

Results

We could confirm that some of these candidates localize to the division septum in *W. chondrophila*. Moreover, these proteins were able to bind peptidoglycan *in vitro* and induce division defects upon heterologous overexpression in an *E. coli* system. These proteins can thus interact with both the chlamydial divisome and peptidoglycan.

Conclusions

Our results indicate that the newly identified proteins of the divisome machinery we might play an important role in the coordination of peptidoglycan remodeling and divisome formation during chlamydial cell division. These proteins might thus be targets for antibiotics specifically targeting *Chlamydiales*, avoiding development of resistance in other bacteria.

16.15-16.30: A 2-pyridone amide potently inhibits *Chlamydia trachomatis* virulence and uncouples infectivity from progeny production

Wael Bahnan[1], Jim Silver[1], James Good[2], Fredrik Almqvist[2], Sven Bergström[1]
[1]*Molecular biology department, Umeå University, Umeå, Sweden,* [2]*Department of Chemistry, Umeå University, Umeå, Sweden*

Background/ Introduction

Our lab has shown that modulating chlamydial pathogenesis using chemical genetics is a valid method for studying molecular details of infection. At the core of chlamydial pathogenesis is the generation of infectious progeny. To our knowledge, no anti-chlamydial drugs have blocked the generation of infectious progeny without affecting growth/inclusion phenotypes.

Objectives

The aim of this study is to understand how a 2-pyridone small molecule can disrupt chlamydial differentiation into infectious progeny, without affecting growth or inclusion phenotype. We also aim to identify genetic mutations that can re-couple infectivity and progeny formation that was disrupted by 2-pyridones.

Method

Microscopic analysis (TEM, confocal, fluorescent and light microscopy) were used to study the effect of compound 21a (Good et al 2016) on the inclusion morphology and efficacy of infectious progeny production in re-infection experiments. Compound 21a-treated bacteria were assayed for adhesion and invasion using established microscopy-based protocols. The transcriptional activity of 21a treated bacteria was analysed by RT-PCR. Mouse infections were done intra-vaginally and the infected mice were swabbed and monitored for bacterial burden until the infections were cleared. All animal infections were done abiding by ethical regulations stated by Swedish guidelines.

Results

Treatment of *C. trachomatis* infected cells with 21a leads to inhibition of infectivity, without disrupting general progeny formation. Compound 21a-treated bacteria associate to and invade HeLa cells but fail to initiate transcription of key early-cycle genes, rendering them unable to create inclusions. The compound 21a-mediated attenuation in HeLa cells was validated by an attenuation of infection in a vaginal infection model. Mechanistic analysis suggests that the uncoupling of infectivity and progeny formation can be partially restored by single amino acid mutagenesis of the RNAse III and SNF2 Helicase Loci, which convey resistance to compound 21a as well as other 2-pyridones.

Conclusions

In this work, we present evidence that *C. trachomatis* infectivity can be uncoupled from progeny formation, using a small molecule in wild-type bacteria. We provide data describing the 2-pyridone mediated attenuation and show that mutations in the RNAseIII and Helicase genes restore infectivity despite drug treatment.

16.30-16.45: *Chlamydia* infection alters barrier function of the epithelium

Ana T. Nogueira[1,2], Kristin M. Braun[3], Rey Carabeo[1]
[1]*Washington State University, Pullman, Washington, USA,* [2]*The University of Aberdeen, Aberdeen, UK,* [3]*University of London, London, UK*

Background/ Introduction

Chlamydia encounters the squamous stratified epithelium in the lower genital tract before it ascends to the columnar epithelium in the upper genital tract. The interaction with the stratified epithelium of the lower genital tract remains unexplored, and data regarding its consequences on the course of infection and histopathology are lacking.

Objectives

We aim to characterize the interaction of *Chlamydia* with the stratified epithelium and investigate the changes to the protective barrier function of the epithelium during infection. We link the inhibition of epithelial sheet migration during infection to the disorganization of cell adhesion structures observed in infected cells.

Method

The stratified squamous epithelium in a 3D culture model is used to explore interaction between the epithelium and *Chlamydia*. The basal layer is targeted for infection to recapitulate the microabrasions often found in the lower genital tract. These breaks in the epithelial barrier serve as portals for a number of mucosal pathogens, such as *Chlamydia* and HPV. Effects of *Chlamydia* infection on the barrier function and epithelial sheet migration, and reorganization of the select markers for focal adhesions and hemidesmosomes were evaluated quantitatively using migration and wound healing assays, and live-cell imaging.

Results

Chlamydia can successfully infect the basal layer and disseminate throughout the epithelium. Infection disrupted the formation of a compact and well-organized multilayer epithelium and epithelial restitution, thus compromising the protective function of this epithelium. We explored this by demonstrating that *Chlamydia*-infected cell sheets could not close the wound in comparison to uninfected sheets. During collective migration, the cells rely more on hemidesmosome remodeling, instead of focal adhesions. Tracking the hemidesmosome-specific marker beta-4 integrin, we observed a marked disorganization of this protein in infected cells, indicating that in addition to focal adhesions in single-cell migration, *Chlamydia* also interferes with hemidesmosome functions.

Conclusions

Sparse infection was sufficient to influence the behavior of neighboring uninfected cells, leading to abnormal coordination of collective migration. We propose a model whereby *Chlamydia* targets the hemidesmosomes of the cells in the basal layer to alter their dynamics and organization.

16.45-17.00: Lipid metabolism as a novel antibiotic target in *Chlamydia*

Sergio A. Mojica[1], Olli Salin[1], Robert Bastidias[2], Naresh Sunduru[1], Mattias Hendenström[1], Raphael Valdivia[2], Mikael Elofsson[1], Åsa Gylfe[1]
[1]*Umeå University, Umeå, Västerbotten, Sweden,* [2]*Duke University, Durham, North Carolina, USA*

Background/ Introduction

The type II fatty acid synthesis (FASII) pathway is essential for bacterial lipid biosynthesis and continues to be a promising target for novel antibacterial compounds. Recently, *Chlamydia* has been demonstrated to be capable of FASII and this pathway is indispensable for chlamydial growth.

Objectives

We present evidence that acylated sulfonamides target chlamydial FASII by inhibiting the function of FabF.

Method

We have performed a High-Content-Screen with *C .trachomatis* infected cells and identified acylated sulfonamides as potent (IC_{50} = 3-12 µM) growth inhibitors of the bacteria. The compounds are bactericidal, have a narrow antimicrobial spectrum, and act by a different mechanism than Sulfamethoxazole. *C. trachomatis* strains resistant to acylated sulfonamides were isolated by serial passaging a wild type strain in low compound concentrations. Whole genome sequencing was performed on ten plaque purified isolates from two independently isolated resistant populations, showing predominant mutations in the *fabF* gene. NMR and DARTS in-vitro studies were carried out to access protein-small molecule interactions.

Results

All resistant strains harbored single nucleotide substitutions leading to amino acid substitutions in the lipid synthesis enzyme FabF, part of the chlamydial FASII pathway. The isolation of independent mutants containing substitutions in the *fabF* gene, both predicted to be near the active site, suggested that the FabF protein may be the subcellular target of acylated sulfonamides. Subsequent protein-small molecule interaction studies have determined that acylated sulfonamides directly bind to FabF *in vitro*. Recently developed genetic tools will allow us to continue to assess the importance of FabF and the FASII pathway for resistance to acylated sulfonamides.

Conclusions

Independently obtained acylated sulfonamide resistant mutants with FabF mutations as well as in-vitro protein-small molecule interaction studies strongly suggest acylated sulfonamides target the FabF enzyme directly. This work may contribute to answering key questions about the importance of FASII to development and may provide a lead towards a new antimicrobial.

17.00-17.15: The Rsb phosphoregulatory network controls availability of Sigma66 and influences growth and development in *Chlamydia trachomatis*

Christopher C Thompson[1], Derek Fisher[2], Myra McClure[1]
[1]*Imperial College London, London, UK,* [2]*Southern Illinois University, Carbondale, IL, USA*

Background/ Introduction

Switch-protein kinase modules are common effectors of energy and stress responses in bacteria. Analogues of a commonly studied pathway from *Bacillus subtilis*, are conserved in the *Chlamydia trachomatis* genome. Putative components include an anti-sigma factor (RsbW), two system antagonists (RsbV1/2), and potential phosphatases (RsbU, CT589, CT259).

Objectives

At the onset of this study, no regulated target of the *Chlamydia* Rsb network had been identified.

Method

In vitro association assays (bacterial two hybrid and SPR) were used to assess interactions between RsbW and either the chlamydial sigma factors or the system antagonists (RsbV1 or RsbV2). Interactions were validated via phenotypic studies in which the expression of module components were elevated via ectopic expression or knocked out.

Results

RsbW associated with both Sigma66 and RsbV1, though association with RsbV1 was dependent on ATP and was abrogated upon the phosphorylation of RsbV1. RsbU was shown to dephosphorylate RsbV1.

In cell culture experiments, ectopic expression of RsbW correlated to decreased expression of Sigma66-dependent genes, and a decreased growth profile. Ectopic expression of RsbV1 exhibited an opposite correlation, in which Sigma66-dependent gene expression was elevated and a more rapid growth profile was observed. Genetic deletion of *rsbV1* phenocopied over-expression of RsbW.

Conclusions

RsbW is both an anti-sigma factor of Sigma66 and a kinase of RsbV1. Association of RsbW and RsbV1 requires ATP. ATP levels could trigger liberation of Sigma66 from RsbW, resulting in increased growth, whereas low ATP levels could drive RsbW towards association with Sigma66, resulting in a slower development.

WEDNESDAY MORNING, 7TH SEPTEMBER

SESSION 3:

Vaccines

Chairs:

Charles Lacey and Kyle Ramsey

08.30 – 9.00

KEYNOTE: MICHAEL STARNBACH

A mucosal *Chlamydia trachomatis* vaccine stimulates protective memory T cells

Michael N. Starnbach. Harvard Medical School, Boston, MA 02115, USA.

Many non-mucosal vaccines are poorly protective against mucosal pathogens, presumably because they do not generate mucosa-tropic memory cells. Few mucosal vaccines are in clinical use because live vaccine vectors pose safety risks and killed or molecular antigens (Ags) are weak immunogens when applied to intact mucosa. Adjuvants can potentially overcome this poor immunogenicity, however, conventional mucosal adjuvants possess unfavorable safety profiles. We have developed an adjuvanted vaccine against *Chlamydia trachomatis*. Genital *Ct* infection induced protective immunity that depended on interferon-γ (IFN-γ) producing CD4 T-cells, whereas mucosal exposure to UV-inactivated *Ct* (UV-*Ct*) generated tolerogenic *Ct*-specific regulatory T-cells, resulting in exacerbated bacterial burden upon *Ct* challenge. However, mucosal immunization with UV-*Ct* complexed with charge-switching synthetic adjuvant particles (cSAP) did not exert the tolerogenic effect of UV-*Ct* alone but elicited long-lived protection. This differential effect of UV-*Ct*-cSAP versus UV-*Ct* was because the former was presented by immunogenic CD11b⁺CD103⁻ dendritic cells (DCs), while the latter was acquired by tolerogenic CD11b⁻CD103⁺ DCs. Genital protection was achieved after intrauterine or intranasal, but not subcutaneous vaccination and was inducible in conventional and humanized mice. Regardless of vaccination route, UV-*Ct*-cSAP induced robust systemic memory cells. However, only mucosal vaccination induced a wave of *Ct*-specific effector T-cells that seeded the mucosa during the first week and established resident memory T cells (T_{RM}). Without T_{RM}, mice were suboptimally protected, even when circulating memory cells were abundant. For optimal *Ct* clearance, both early seeding by T_{RM} and infection-induced recruitment of a second wave of circulating memory cells were required. Thus, using a novel mucosal vaccine platform, we demonstrate that protection against *Ct* depends on synergistic actions of two memory T cell subsets with distinct migratory properties.

09.00-09.15: A novel, second-generation lipid adjuvant in combination with recombinant polymorphic membrane protein D protects against intra-vaginal *Chlamydia trachomatis* infection in mice

Wayne Paes[1,2], Naj Brown[1], Marek Brzozowski[2], Rhea Coler[3], Steve Reed[3], Darrick Carter[3], Paul Kaye[1], Charles Lacey[1]

[1]*Centre for Immunology and Infection, University of York, York, UK,* [2]*York Structural Biology Laboratory, University of York, York, UK,* [3]*Infectious Disease Research Institute, Seattle, USA,* [4]*Department of Health Sciences, University of York, York, UK*

Background/ Introduction

Due to the paucity of robust clinical data, protective immunological parameters against *Chlamydia trachomatis* (Ct) infections have been derived from animal models, where pathogen-specific Th1-type immunity has been the main focus of antigen prioritization and vaccine development. However, few studies highlight a role for antibodies in protection against Ct infection.

Objectives

Our study aimed to:
(i) Investigate the efficacy of recombinant polymorphic membrane protein D (rPmpD) as a vaccine candidate against sexually transmitted Ct infection
(ii) Perform the first preclinical evaluation of a novel, rationally designed TLR4 agonistic second-generation lipid adjuvant (SLA) in vivo

Method

Female C57BL/6 mice were immunized subcutaneously on day 0 with 5μg/dose of three SLA formulations (aqueous-SLA-AF, oil-in-water emulsion-SLA-SE or liposomal-SLA-LSQ) in combination with 5μg/dose rPmpD or 2×107 inclusion forming units (IFU) of UV-inactivated Ct serovar E/Bour EBs. Vehicle-immunized control groups were also included. Boosting was conducted on days 21 and 42. Three weeks post final immunization, mice were challenged intra-vaginally with 4.5×108 IFU of Ct serovar D/UW3/Cx EBs. Cervico-vaginal swabs were obtained on days 1, 3, 7, 14 and 22 post-challenge, and total IFU/well were enumerated on Hak cell monolayers to determine resistance to infection and mean bacterial load.

Results

We show that:
1. SLA is a novel class of adjuvant that may be more widely used in future preclinical Ct vaccine development, and that the magnitude of SLA-induced Th1-type immunity is formulation-dependent.
2. Significant protection against intra-vaginal Ct challenge can be achieved by subcutaneous immunisation with rPmpD in combination with SLA, quantified both as early resistance to infection and mean bacterial load over a longer-term period.
3. Significantly enhanced resistance to infection and reduced shedding were also observed in the absence of SLA-induced Th1-biased cellular responses, correlating with the presence of robust rPmpD-specific serum and cervico-vaginal IgG titres.
4. Antibodies induced by immunisation with rPmpD recognise Ct elementary bodies (EBs).

Conclusions

Our study demonstrates that anti-rPmpD antibodies may play a significant role in mediating protection against urogenital Ct challenge, and highlights the utility of structure-based approaches to adjuvant design. Our results also emphasize the need for a more detailed mechanistic understanding of antibody-mediated mechanisms of protection in future Ct vaccine development.

09.15-09.30: Multivalent vaccine based on extended VD1 regions of the Major Outer Membrane protein promotes high titered neutralizing antibodies targeting the *Chlamydia trachomatis* C-complex

Anja W. Olsen[1], Ida Rosenkrands[1], Martin J. Holland[2], Frank Follmann[1], Peter Andersen[1]
[1]*Statens Serum Institut, Copenhagen, Denmark,* [2]*London School of hygiene & Tropical Medicine, London, UK*

Background/ Introduction

Recently, we presented a novel immunorepeat vaccine technology for generating high titered and broadly reactive antibodies. We recombinantly engineered a multivalent vaccine construct based on VD4's and their surrounding constant segments within the B- and B-related complex serovars. This construct exhibited broad neutralizing activity and importantly antibody mediated protection.

Objectives

To target the *Chlamydia* C-complex with a multivalent vaccine construct based on VD1s.

Method

Immunorepeats (homologous and heterologous) of extended VD1 regions of C-complex serovars were designed and produced recombinantly in *E. Coli*. Mice were vaccinated with 25 µg of the different constructs adjuvanted with cationic liposomes (CAF01), and sera were isolated after the 3rd vaccination. Immunogenicity and specificity of monomers and multimers were compared. The specificity of the B-cell response was investigated using panels of 9-mer peptides, with 8aa overlap, spanning the extended regions of SvA, SvI, SvIa and SvJ. Furthermore, *in vitro* neutralization of chlamydial infectivity by the mouse antisera was assayed on Syrian Hamster Kidney (HaK) cells.

Results

The VD1 immunorepeats promoted strong antibody responses directed against both conserved and variable segments of serovar A, I, Ia and J. Strong *in vitro* neutralization capacity was found and we identified a vaccine construct capable of cross-neutralizing both ocular (SvA) and genital (SvJ) strains.

Conclusions

We identified a novel vaccine construct capable of targeting serovars of the C-complex by VD1 specific neutralizing antibodies. These results support the overall strategy to construct a broadly protective *Chlamydia* subunit vaccine, targeting both ocular and genital infections, by combining VD1 and VD4 specific neutralizing antibodies.

WEDNESDAY MORNING, 7TH SEPTEMBER

SESSION 4:

Immunology

Chairs:
Alison Quayle & Martin Holland

09.30 – 10.00

KEYNOTE: WILL GEISLER

Immune Responses in Human chlamydial Infection and Their Association with Protective Immunity and Immunopathology

WM Geisler. Departments of Medicine and Epidemiology, Division of Infectious Diseases, University of Alabama at Birmingham.

Chlamydia trachomatis infection is a major global public health concern, causing significant reproductive morbidity in women. Research from animal models forms much of the basis for our current understanding of immunity to *Chlamydia* and *Chlamydia*-associated immunopathology. Limited natural history and epidemiological studies of human chlamydial infection provide support that humans can eradicate *Chlamydia* without treatment and develop protective immunity (of unclear duration). However, immune responses against *C. trachomatis* may also contribute to immunopathology of the reproductive tract in humans. Ethical considerations are a major challenge in studying the natural history of untreated *Chlamydia* in humans and the immune responses that contribute to protection and pathology.

Systemic and mucosal immune responses and immune cell phenotypes have been characterized in *Chlamydia*-infected humans, but there are only limited studies investigating immune responses associated with clinical correlates of protection and clinical manifestations of immunopathology. This Keynote presentation will review immune responses, humoral and cellular, in human chlamydial infection and their association with protective immunity and immunopathology.

10.00-10.10: Detection of a chlamydial metabolite by STING regulates inflammasome activation in response to *C. trachomatis* infection

Steve J Webster[1], Sven Brode[1], Lou Ellis[1], Tim Fitzmaurice[1], Matthew Elder[1], Nelson Gekara[2], Pani Tourlomousis[1], Clare Bryant[1], Simon Clare[4], Ronnie Chee[3], Hill JS Gaston[1], Jane C Goodall[1]
[1]University of Cambridge, Cambridge, UK, [2]Umea university, Umea, Sweden, [3]Royal Free Hospital, London, UK, [4]Sanger Institute, Cambridge, UK

Background/ Introduction

Immunopathology associated with *Chlamydia* infection is highly dependent on the inflammatory cytokines interferon-β and IL-1β. However, mechanisms regulating canonical and non-canonical inflammasome activation that control the maturation of IL-1β and induce pyroptosis in response to infection are poorly understood.

Objectives

Identify host and pathogen factors that contribute to the induction of canonical and non-canonical inflammasome activation in macrophages infected with *C. trachomatis*.

Method

Macrophages were prepared from the bone marrow of mice with genetic deficiencies in; caspase-1, caspase-11 or both, the NADPH oxidase system or STING. Macrophages were infected with live or gamma-irradiated (attenuated) *C. trachomatis* at an MOI of 20 IFU/cell for defined incubation periods. Inflammasome activation was determined by ELISA of macrophage supernatants for IL-1β release, proteolytic processing of IL-1β analysed by western blotting and cell death assayed by LDH release. Intracellular bacterial load was determined by fluorescent antibody labelling of *Chlamydia* LPS. Transfection of cyclic di-AMP or LPS was done in serum free optiMEM using Fugene transfection reagent.

Results

Proteolytic cleavage and release of IL-1β in response to *C. trachomatis* infection was caspase-1 dependent and independent of caspase-11. Intriguingly, pyroptosis occurred by either caspase-1 or caspase-11 dependent mechanisms, confirming activation of the non-canonical inflammasome. Both canonical and non-canonical inflammasomes required type-1 interferon receptor signalling. NADPH oxidase deficient macrophages harboured elevated bacterial burdens and displayed an increased type-1 interferon signature and hyper-inflammasome activation- demonstrating that *Chlamydia* replication is a contributing factor to inflammatory responses. Accordingly, attenuated *C. trachomatis* failed to initiate inflammasome activation, but responses could be recovered by transfection of the metabolite cyclic di-AMP in a STING dependent manner.

Conclusions

We have identified that *C. trachomatis* replication, controlled by NADPH oxidase, initiates STING dependent inflammasome activation via detection of a chlamydial metabolite. Thus *C. trachomatis* replication and metabolism are key factors that determine host inflammatory responses and contribute to the understanding of chlamydial latency, immunopathology and potential *Chlamydia* vaccine adjuvants.

10.10-10.20: *Chlamydia* induces epithelial-mesenchyme transition that causes reproductive complications and provides a co-factor for human papilloma virus-related cervical carcinoma

Joseph U Igietseme[1,2], Tamas Nagy[3], Yusuf Omosun[2,1], Olga Stuchlik[1], Matthew S Reed[1], James Partin[1], Qing He[2,1], Kahaliah Joseph[1], Debra Ellerson[1], Zenas George[1], Francis O Eko[2], Claudiu Bandea[1], Jan Pohl[1], Carolyn M Black[1]
[1]*Centers for Disease Control & Prevention (CDC), Atlanta, GA, USA,* [2]*Morehouse School of Medicine, Atlanta, GA, USA,* [3]*University of Georgia, Athens, GA, USA*

Background/ Introduction

Chlamydia trachomatis genital infection in women causes severe reproductive complications and is a strong co-factor for human papilloma virus (HPV)-associated cervical carcinoma. The observation that *Chlamydia* induces epithelial-mesenchyme transition (EMT) through caspase-mediated miRNA dysregulation, suggests that EMT plays a role in the pathogenesis of infertility and co-factor in cervical carcinoma.

Objectives

We tested the hypothesis that the pathogenesis of *Chlamydia*-induced infertility and its role as a co-factor for HPV-associated cervical epithelial carcinoma required EMT induction. We investigated EMT induction by *Chlamydia* and the ability of EMT inhibitors to prevent chlamydial complications and promotion of HPV-related cervical carcinoma in a mouse model.

Method

Immunofluorescence staining of primary murine epithelial cells (C57epi.1 line) for EMT markers was performed on *C. trachomatis* L2-infected (MOI = 1) and non-infected monolayers after 72h. The HPV 16 E6/7 transgenic mouse that requires estrogen as co-factor for accelerated development of invasive cervical carcinoma, was infected 2-3 times intra-genitally with 10^5 inclusion-forming units (IFU)/ mouse. The reproductive tissues (cervix, uterine horns and oviducts) were analyzed histopathologically (H&E staining) to determine whether chronic genital chlamydial infection could replace estrogen in disease pathogenesis. The pan-caspase inhibitor, Z-VAD-FMK and the control Z-FA-FMK were used in culture and *in vivo* at 50 mM.

Results

Chlamydia induced EMT *in vitro* and *in vivo*, involving caspase activation, Dicer cleavage inactivation, and altered expression of key miRNAs and transcription factors that regulate epithelial functional integrity, fibrosis and tumorigenesis. The pan-caspase inhibitor, Z-VAD-FMK prevented *Chlamydia*-induced EMT and the reproductive pathologies, including tubal inflammation, hydrosalpinx and infertility in mice. Additionally, similar to estrogen, *Chlamydia* promoted reproductive tract epithelial hyperplasia in the HPV 16 E6/E7 transgenic mouse model of cervical carcinoma, implicating *Chlamydia* as a co-factor for HPV-related reproductive carcinoma. Thus, EMT is a central pathogenic event underlying the complications of genital chlamydial infection and its co-factor role in carcinoma.

Conclusions

Our results indicate that chlamydial induction of pathologic EMT in the reproductive epithelium alters fertility-related epithelial functions, and promotes fibrosis and tumorigenesis. This provides a novel understanding of the molecular pathogenesis of *Chlamydia*-induced infertility and its co-factor role in HPV-related cervical carcinoma that may lead to disease biomarkers and therapies.

10.20-10.30: A novel trivalent antigen consisting of type III secretion proteins, BD584, protects against *Chlamydia*-induced immunopathology of the upper genital tract

David C Bulir[1], Steven Liang[1], Sylvia Chong[2], James B Mahony[1,2]
[1]M. G. DeGroote Institute for Infectious Disease Research, Hamilton, Ontario, Canada, [2]St. Joseph's Research Institute, Hamilton, Ontario, Canada

Background/ Introduction

The chlamydial type III secretion system (T3SS) is composed of surface exposed and secreted proteins. Vaccines composed of T3SS proteins in other gram-negative bacteria have showed significant protection against disease caused by Yersinia, Salmonella, and Shigella spp., yet limited studies have explored chlamydial T3SS proteins as antigens.

Objectives

To examine the protective effect of immunization with a novel chlamydial trivalent T3SS (BD584) antigen against *Chlamydia*-induced immunopathology we immunized mice with BD584 then challenge with live C. *muridarum*.

Method

The N-terminal 100 amino acids of CopB and CopD were fused to full length CT584 and cloned into an expression vector containing an N-terminal polyhistidine tag. Fusion protein BD584 was purified on a Ni-NTA agarose column and analyzed via SDS-PAGE and size exclusion chromatography (SEC). Eight week old female C57/BL6 mice were immunized intranasally (IN) with various amounts of BD584 antigen with 10 μg of CpG adjuvant in 15 μL of PBS while control mice received PBS alone. Immunizations were performed twice, 6 weeks and 3 weeks prior to challenge with C. *muridarum*.

Results

SDS-PAGE revealed that BD584 was greater than 95% pure and SEC revealed that it formed higher order structures with an apparent molecular weight corresponding to a hexamer. Only 2 of 10 ovaries from mice immunized with 20 μg of BD584 showed hydrosalpinx compared to 9 of 10 ovaries for the control group. Immunization with doses of greater than 40 μg of BD584 resulted in decreased protection compared to the 20 μg group, but was partially protective when compared to the control group.

Conclusions

Immunization with BD584 antigen significantly protected mice from the development of hydrosalpinx as compared to control mice. BD584 represents a novel serovar cross-reactive antigen for prevention against infection and/or *Chlamydia*-induced immunopathology. Studies to elucidate the mechanism of protection associated with BD584 are currently under way.

WEDNESDAY MORNING, 7TH SEPTEMBER

SESSION 5:

Animal and cellular models of
C. trachomatis infection

Chairs:
Dorothy Patton & Daisy Vanrompay

11.15 – 11.45

KEYNOTE: KYLE RAMSEY

A review of animal models of chlamydial infection

Kyle H. Ramsey, PhD. Basic Science Division, Department of Microbiology and Immunology, Midwestern University, Downers Grove, Illinois, USA

Those interested in the study of chlamydial infections are fortunate that several animal models exist. Whether one desires to study urogenital, ocular, respiratory or systemic infection, an excellent animal model is available for this purpose. However, one needs only to remember that no single model is known to possess all the qualities that allow for a perfect mimic of human chlamydial infection or disease and at the same time allows for the large scale experimentation necessary to accomplish immunization experiments or to study pathogenesis in detail.

There seems to be consensus amongst investigators that non-human primates (NHP) can most closely mimic human ocular and urogenital chlamydial infection. First, they can be readily infected in the eye and the lower female urogenital with human isolates of *Chlamydia trachomatis*. The anatomy, physiology and microbiota of the NHP lower urogenital tract are similar to those of humans. They also possess a similar 28-30 day estrous cycle. No hormonal manipulation is required to induce susceptibility to infection and, importantly, the manifestations of chlamydial disease are similar to that seen in humans. Finally, the host response in NHP seems to also mirror that which is known in humans. However, the high cost, ethical issues and the logistical and practical challenges of housing and maintaining NHP colonies restricts widespread use of the NHP to a role in a final confirmatory platform - prior to human vaccine testing, for example.

Another model for the study of chlamydial lower urogenital infection, as well as of ascending infection and accompanying upper tract pathology, is inoculation of guinea pigs with the *C. caviae*. The agent of guinea pig inclusion conjunctivitis (or GPIC) is the only known strain of *C. caviae* and appears to be highly host specific. As the name implies, GPIC also causes conjunctivitis in guinea pigs when inoculated onto the eye and hence also mimics primary chlamydial conjunctivitis in humans. The GPIC agent is a natural pathogen of guinea pigs and is transmitted when animals are housed in close quarters. Artificial inoculation of GPIC intravaginally causes infection that mimics lower urogenital infection in humans and, like the NHP, no hormonal manipulation is needed to render animal susceptible to the infection. Likewise, the guinea pig has a similar anatomy, physiology, and a 15-18 day estrous cycle. Additional strengths of this model are that urogenital infection can be transmitted sexually and, like humans, neonatal guinea pigs can acquire chlamydial pneumonitis from an infected mother during parturition. Host immunity, susceptibility to reinfection and the type of immunity needed to resolve infection all seems to mimic what is known for human infection. Two aspects of this model arguably limit its usefulness: the genetic dissimilarity of *C. caviae* when compared to *C. trachomatis* and a limited immunological reagent and guinea pig strain repertoire with which to study, in depth, the host immune response and immunopathogenesis.

Lastly, the mouse can be infected in the lower urogenital tract with either human isolates of *C. trachomatis* or with the natural rodent pathogen, *C. muridarum*. The former is almost strictly dependent upon hormonal manipulation with depo-injected progestins or ovarectomy whereas the latter is enhanced by such manipulation but is not strictly dependent upon it. Both mouse models have the advantage that the mimicked natural route of transmission (intravaginal inoculation) results in shedding from the lower genital tract. In addition, in the *C. muridarum* model, the infection will routinely ascend the upper genital tract to induce significant acute and chronic pathological manifestations that in many ways also mimic an acute episode of *C. trachomatis* pelvic inflammatory disease in humans. However, it should be noted that careful selection of mouse strain and *C. trachomatis* genotype can also result in similar upper genital tract infection and immune-mediated pathology. Even still, there is limited evidence regarding the induction of chronic reproductive sequelae in mice following *C. trachomatis* infection as that induced in humans, whereas the naturally mouse-adapted strain *C. muridarum* can produce comparable reproductive pathology following intravaginal infection in mice. The small size, ease of handling, relative low cost and the plethora of immunological reagents, transgenic and gene knockout mice available make *both* of these models ideal for detailed studies on pathogenesis and for large scale screening of vaccine candidates prior to assessment in larger animal models or humans.

In summary, there are many animal models to study chlamydial infection. One need only to deliberately and wisely choose the model and interpret carefully the results in light of what is known of human chlamydial infection and disease. With this in mind, the lack of a perfect model, or even a perfectly agreed upon model, should not be a hindrance to the *in vivo* study of chlamydial pathogens for it is likely that the most reliable results will be garnered from a broad view of correlating findings in one or more animal models with observations from human studies.

11.45-12.00: Prime-boost immunization strategy for induction of mucosal immunity in the minipig model of human genital *C. trachomatis* infection

Emma Lorenzen[1,2], Frank Follmann[1], Sarah Bøje[1,2], Karin Erneholm[1,2], Anja W. Olsen[1], Jørgen S. Agerholm[2], Gregers Jungersen[3], Peter Andersen[1]
[1]Statens Serum Institut, Copenhagen, Denmark, [2]University of Copenhagen, Copenhagen, Denmark, [3]National Veterinary Institute, Copenhagen, Denmark

Background/ Introduction

International efforts in developing a vaccine against *Chlamydia trachomatis* have high¬lighted the need for novel immunization strategies for the induction of genital immunity. An ideal *Chlamydia* vaccine should elicit cell mediated and humoral immunity expressed in the genital mucosal, however, traditional injectable vaccination regimes are poor inducers of mucosal immunity.

Objectives

To develop an immunization strategy for optimal induction of systemic and mucosal genital immunity against *C. trachomatis* in the advanced minipig model of human genital *Chlamydia*.

Method

We evaluated an intramuscular (IM) prime/intranasal (IN) boost vaccination strategy in a Göttingen Minipig model with a reproductive system very similar to humans. The vaccine was composed of *C. trachomatis* subunit antigens based on the VD4 region of MOMP formulated in the Th1/Th17 promoting CAF01 adjuvant. Systemic and mucosal antibody responses were monitored by ELISA (IgG, IgA and secretory component (SC)) pre and post vaginal chlamydial infection. The systemic cell mediated immune response was evaluated through interferon gamma and Interleukin 17A (IL-17A) levels in the supernatant of re-stimulated PBMCs. The vaginal chlamydial load was evaluated by qPCR on vaginal swabs.

Results

IM priming immunizations with CAF01 induced a significant cell-mediated interferon gamma and IL-17A response and a significant systemic high-titered neutralizing IgG response. Following genital challenge, intranasally boosted groups mounted an accelerated, highly significant genital IgA response that correlated with enhanced bacterial clearance on day 3 post infection. By detecting antigen-specific SC, we showed that the genital IgA was locally produced in the genital mucosa. The was a significant inverse correlation between the vaginal IgA SC response and the vaginal chlamydial load suggesting that vaginal IgA in the minipig model is involved in protection against *C. trachomatis.*

Conclusions

This study showed that by combining IM immunizations with IN booster immunizations, not only a strong systemic immune response was established, but also a significant SIgA response in the genital tract of female minipigs, correlating with accelerated clearance of a genital *C. trachomatis* infection.

12.00-12.15: Development of a human urethral equivalent to study *Chlamydia trachomatis* invasion

Bart Versteeg[1], Lenie van den Broek[2], Sylvia Bruisten[1], Margriet Mullender[3], Henry de Vries[1], Sue Gibbs[2]

[1]Public Health Service, Amsterdam, The Netherlands, [2]Department of Dermatology VU University Medical Centre (VUMC), Amsterdam, The Netherlands, [3]Department of Plastic, Reconstructive and Hand Surgery, VU University Medical Center (VUMC), Amsterdam, The Netherlands

Background/ Introduction

Chlamydia trachomatis (Ct) genovars D-K cause non-invasive urogenital infections, which often remain asymptomatic. Little is known about the invasion of the epithelial layer and the subsequent effects of Ct on the epithelium in humans.

Objectives

The objective of this study was to develop a human urethral 3D *in vitro* equivalent to gain a better insight into the invasiveness of Ct in host tissue.

Method

Human urethral equivalents were constructed by seeding primary urethral keratinocytes and fibroblasts on top of and into a collagen matrix. Urethral cells were isolated from urethral clinical specimens of transgender patients undergoing gender surgery at VUMC. Urethral equivalents were incubated with a Ct genovar D strain, by placing a Ct impregnated nylon gauze on top of each model. Standard Ct cell culture, existing of HeLa cells grown on coverslips, were used as a control to assess growth of Ct strains used for infections of the urethral equivalents. Ct invasion was assessed after 2, 4 and 6 days of incubation

Results

Urethral equivalents consisted of a fully differentiated urethral epithelium on a urethral fibroblast populated collagen hydrogel. The epithelium consisted of multiple differentiated cell layers resembling native urethral tissue. We successfully infected urethral equivalents with a Ct genovar D strain. Ct invasion and expansion was detected in the epithelial layer, but not in the underlying collagen matrix, at 2, 4 and 6 days post infection. Morphological changes of the urethral equivalent could be observed at 2, 4 and 6 days post infection compared to non-infected urethral equivalents, whereby it appeared that the epithelial layer grows around the invaded Ct bacteria.

Conclusions

We were able to construct a urethral equivalent resembling native urethral tissue. Moreover, these urethral equivalents could successfully be infected by a Ct genovar D strain, making this a promising life model to investigate the human pathogenesis of urogenital Ct infections.

12.15-12.30: Characterization and *Chlamydia* infection of primary human Fallopian tube epithelial cells grown in air-liquid interface

Uma Nagarajan, Catherine O' Connell, Amy Kiathanapaiboon, Emily Powell, Jeeho Kim, Leslie Fulcher, Holly Chamberlain, Victoria Madden, Priscilla Wyrick, Mehmet Kessimer, Mathew Zerden, Scott Randell, Toni Darville
University of North Carolina, Chapel Hill, NC, USA

Background/ Introduction

Genital *Chlamydia trachomatis* infection can result in immunopathology and severe tissue damage leading to infertility. chlamydial infection may also contribute to the induction of Fallopian tube cancers. A significant barrier to investigating chlamydial pathogenesis is the inability of human strains to elicit oviduct disease in mice.

Objectives

To develop an in vitro human Fallopian tube epithelial (FTE) cell culture model to study human immune responses and strain-specific virulence factors.

Method

Fallopian tube explants obtained via salpingectomy from pre-menopausal women were dissociated and cells were cultured on plastic for 3-5 days in bronchial-epithelial cell growth media for expansion. Cells were transferred to air-liquid interface (ALI) culture on a PTFE MillicellCMÒ membrane. Once confluent, an ALI was established by removing media from the apical surface. Mucoid secretions were apparent and ciliated cells appeared between 8-12 days after transfer to ALI culture. Cultures were characterized by histology, confocal microscopy, SEM and TEM. Cells were infected with *C. trachomatis* strains or stimulated with TLR ligands and induction of inflammatory responses was analyzed by RT-PCR.

Results

Histology and EM revealed polarized secretory and ciliated epithelial cells that closely resembled the *in vivo* morphology. Proteomic analysis of apical secretions identified >250 proteins, including mucins (MUC9, MUC16, MUC5B and MUC5A), and innate defense proteins (complement, proteases and anti-proteases). Basal expression of TLR2 and TLR4 was low. TLR3 expression was high. Poly IC treatment induced IFN beta, CXCL10 and IL-6. Infection was easily established in cells passaged 8-12 days after transfer to ALI (20-40% infection) while cells passaged for 28 days proved more resistant (<10%). Infection correlated with high CXCL10 but marginal increases in IL-6 and IFN beta expression.

Conclusions

We have established an ALI FTE cell culture model that recapitulates key morphological and functional features of the *in vivo* epithelium and have optimized parameters for infection with clinically relevant *C. trachomatis* strains.

WEDNESDAY AFTERNOON, 7ᵀᴴ SEPTEMBER

SESSION 6:

Other chlamydial species

Chairs:
Gilbert Greub & Mirja Puolakkainen

13.30 – 14.00

Keynote: Peter Timms

The animal *Chlamydiae*: Recent developments and new insights

Borel, N[1]., Entrican, G[2]., Di Francesco, A[3]., Jelocnik, M[4]., Laroucau, K[5]., Longbottom, D[2]., Polkinghorne, A[4]., Reinhold, P[6]., Sariya, L[7]., Taylor-Brown, A[4]., <u>Timms, P[4].</u>, Zhou, J[8]., et al.

[1] University of Zurich, Switzerland, [2] Moredun Institute, Scotland, [3] University of Bologna, Italy, [4] University of Sunshine Coast, Australia, [5] ANSES, Maisons-Alfort, France, [6] Federal Research Institute for Animal Health, Jena, Germany, [7] Mahidol University, Thailand, [8] Lanzhou Veterinary Research Institute, China.

There are currently 12 designated species of *Chlamydia* and 11 of these infect animals, naturally. Some of these have a single host species, while others have a very broad host range, including humans. *C.psittaci* is one of the oldest designated chlamydial species (1968; although it has been narrowed over time) and is best known for causing serious zoonotic disease in humans, in addition to infecting birds. Recent studies have rapidly expanded our understanding of *C.psittaci* genomic diversity, clinical pathology, host-pathogen interaction and anti-bacterial immunity. While *C.psittaci* mainly infects psittacine birds and poultry, it has also been reported in cattle, sheep, swine, horses, goats, cats, wildlife and laboratory rodents. One of the more significant recent changes has been the addition of several new avian species of *Chlamydia*, *C.avium*, *C.gallinacea* and *C.ibidis* (Candidatus), infecting psittacines, pigeons and domestic poultry. The opportunity to study infection and disease in the natural host, something not easily done in human infections, has resulted in improved understanding of the complexity of pathogenic mechanisms, pathophysiological interactions and systemic consequences in the bovine host, as just one example. An area of particular interest is the observation of tetracycline resistance in *C.suis*. This presumably relates to the high use of tetracycline in pig production but does demonstrate the ability of *Chlamydia* to genuinely become antibiotic resistant. Given that there has been in vitro transfer of this resistance from *C.suis* to clinical strains of *C.trachomatis*, it demonstrates the potential public health concerns. Studies performed on *C.suis* pig isolates have demonstrated a tetracycline resistance phenotype associated with the genomic island carrying *tet*(C) resistance gene in a range of European countries. Reports suggest that tet resistant *C.suis* is a chronic gastrointestinal infection in these pigs.

An interesting area has been the discovery that *Chlamydiae* (mainly *C.pneumoniae*) also infect cold blooded animals such as snakes, crocodiles, iguanas and frogs. *C.pneumoniae* can be a chronic, asymptomatic infection but it can also cause severe granulomatous inflammation of the internal organs. Swabs were commonly positive by PCR at both choana and cloaca sites from a variety of snakes. While some of the snake *C.pneumoniae* genotypes are similar to previously identified lineages, several new reptilian lineages have also been identified. The potential link between *C.pneumoniae* infections in snakes, frogs, koalas and Australian indigenous people continues to be intriguing.

Perhaps the species with the most diverse host range is *C.pecorum*, infecting several domestic animals such as sheep, cattle and pigs but also wild ruminants and of course koalas. The diversity of hosts is only matched by the diversity of genetic lineages infecting these hosts. The advent of cheaper whole genome sequencing approaches (an improvement over the previous dependence on *omp*A genotyping) is starting to unravel the association of genotype, host and disease, as well as potential cross-host transmission events in this species. Because of the devastating impact of chlamydial infections in the koala, work has progressed toward the development of a vaccine against *C.pecorum* in this wild host. While there are obvious shortcomings of using a wild animal such as the koala to develop a vaccine (eg. lack of a suitably wide range of immunological tools) it also has many advantages, such as, (a) a wide range of genetic strains infecting the host (cf *C.trachomatis* vaccines for humans) to enable homologous versus heterologous protection studies, (b) evaluating protection against infections acquired by natural mechanisms (eg. sexual transmission), (c) evaluating vaccines not only in naïve individuals but also currently infected individuals, (d) evaluating protection against disease as well as infection. Progress with the development of a *C.pecorum* vaccine in koalas is providing some useful insights into not only this species but other chlamydial species and hosts. While the diversity and biology of this genus is the most well-characterised in this rapidly expanding phylum, there is still a lot to uncover in terms of tissue tropism and pathogenesis, and novel species and their impact.

14.00-14.15: *Chlamydia psittaci*, not *Chlamydia trachomatis*, type III secretes effectors that remodel the inclusion membrane and target the inner nuclear membrane of the host and bystander cells

Daniel Phillips[1], Sergio Mojica[1], Kelley Hovis[1], Heather Huot-Creasy[1], Joanna Carneiro da Silva[1], Jacques Ravel[1], Ru-ching Hsia[1], Kathy Wilson[2], Patrik M Bavoil[1]
[1]*University of Maryland, Baltimore, MD, USA*, [2]*Johns Hopkins University, Baltimore, MD, USA*

Background/ Introduction

Chlamydia species cause infections in humans ranging from prevalent, often asymptomatic genital infections caused by *Chlamydia trachomatis* to relatively rare, life-threatening zoonotic infections caused by avian *Chlamydia psittaci*. All *Chlamydia* spp. type III-secrete effector proteins that interact with host targets. Among these, 59-107 Inc proteins target the host-derived inclusion membrane.

Objectives

We aim to elucidate distinct developmental and pathogenic pathways that are used by different *Chlamydia* species and are based on the specific properties of orthologous type III secreted effectors. Our findings will provide a platform for interfering with pathogenesis as well as potential biomarkers of infection and disease in humans.

Method

We have used a combination of 'omic (genomics and proteomics), cell, molecular and evolutionary biology methods, as well as *Chlamydia*-specific methods to identify molecular and subcellular targets of two effectors of *Chlamydia psittaci* (IncA/Cps, SinC) that have well characterized orthologs in *C. trachomatis* (IncA, CT694), and investigate their function. For this, we have developed highly specific polyclonal antisera for antibody-based detection (e.g., immunofluorescence, immunoblot, immunogold) and have applied *in vivo* BioID analysis (biotinylation of effector-proximal targets and mass spectrometry identification of biotinylated peptides) and an *in vitro* liposome tubulation assay to identify SinC subcellular targets and to characterize IncA/Cps function.

Results

This comprehensive approach has led to the characterization of novel, unprecedented properties of these two type III secreted effectors of *C. psittaci*. IncA/Cps uniquely displays a functional membrane-remodeling BAR-like domain related to SNX-BAR of eukaryotic sorting nexins. IncA/Cps contributes to the formation of retromer-like tubules extending outward into the cytosol, around and through the nucleus and outside of the host cell into neighboring uninfected bystander cells. SinC targets LEM-domain proteins of the nuclear inner membrane of infected cells, and, remarkably, that of neigboring uninfected cells. Our preliminary results suggest that SinC is translocated to neighboring cells via IncA/Cps-laden retromer-like tubules.

Conclusions

a) IncA/Cps, the first BAR protein described in a prokaryote, contributes to the remodeling of the inclusion membrane extending it inward into the inclusion lumen, and outward into the cytosol via retromer-like tubules; b) SinC targets LEM-domain proteins of the inner nuclear membrane, with potential consequences on essential host functions.

14.15-14.30: Molecular Characterization of detected *C. pneumoniae* strains in Moroccan patients with cardiovascular diseases

Loubna Elyazouli[1 ,3], Naima Elmdaghri[1], Hicham Hejaji[2], Mohamed Bouazza[4], Aziz Alami[2], Abdelouahed Amraoui[4], Nadia Dakka[3], Fouzia Radouani[1]
[1]Institut Pasteur, Chlamydiae and Mycoplasmas Laboratory,, Casablanca, Morocco, [2]Cardiovascular Surgery Service , Ibn Roshd CHU, Casablanca, Morocco, [3]Biochemistry and immunology Laboratory, Faculty of Sciences, Rabat, Morocco, [4]Ophtalmology departement, Casablanca, Morocco

Background/ Introduction

Cardiovascular disease mainly related to atherosclerosis present the leading cause of death around the world. It is known that genetic and environmental factors play an important role, but pathogens like *Chlamydophila pneumoniae* (*C. pneumoniae*) can be involved in the development of these diseases.

Objectives

The main objective of our study is to evaluate the association between *C. pneumoniae* infection and cardiovascular diseases in Moroccan patients by case/control study and molecular characterization of the detected strains.

Method

A total of 252 subjects, 137 cardiovascular diseases patients and 115 controls, were enrolled. Clinical data were recorded and blood was sampled, in parallel 37 atherosclerotic plaques were obtained from patients subjected to surgery. *C. pneumoniae* DNA detection in peripheral blood mononuclear cells (PBMCs) and atherosclerotic plaques was performed by nested PCR. The same method was conducted to amplify a fragment of ompA gene and amplicons were sequenced for strains molecular characterization. The sequences were aligned using BioEdit and phylogenetic tree was constructed by MEGA6 software. The data were statistically analyzed by Epi Info, P value <0.05 was considerate significant.

Results

PCR results showed 58% positive cases in PBMCs and 86% in atherosclerotic plaques. However, positivity in control subjects was lower with 21.5% in PBMCs, a significant statistical difference was revealed between cases and controls (p <0.001). The alignment and analysis of *C. pneumoniae* sequences from 55 PBMCs and 28 atheroma plaques showed that majority presented 98% homology with human *C. pneumoniae* reference strains. However, different single nucleotide polymorphisms were revealed at different positions. The phylogenetic comparison with *C. pneumoniae* strains retrieved from GenBank showed an identity with human once. Furthermore, some of our strains were clustered with animal strains.

Conclusions

Our case/control study confirmed the involvement of *C. pneumoniae* in cardiovascular diseases (atherosclerosis) development in Moroccan patients and the phylogenetic study confirmed the inter-human transmission and let suggesting the zoonotic one.

14.30-14.45: Characterization of the in vitro effect of penicillin on *Chlamydia suis*

Cory A. Leonard, Martin Levkut, Nicole Borel
University of Zurich, Zurich, Zurich, Switzerland

Background/ Introduction

Chlamydia suis, the primary chlamydial agent infecting pigs and subject to heavy antibiotic pressures *in vivo*, is the only chlamydial species with known acquired antibiotic resistance. Penicillin, a Beta-lactam antibiotic, primarily targets Gram-positive bacteria. It has been reported to induce a non-infectious stress response in several animal- and human-infecting *Chlamydia*e.

Objectives

This study aimed to characterize the *in vitro* effect of penicillin (Pen) on the *C. suis* reference strain S45, with the long term objective of studying Pen treatment effects on *C. suis* field strains.

Method

C. suis-infected LLC-MK2 cells (monkey kidney epithelial cell line) were exposed to low (1 unit/ml) or high (500 units/ml) concentrations of Pen immediately following inoculation until inclusion maturity at 39 hours post infection (hpi). To evaluate recovery from the antibiotic, media was exchanged at 39 hpi to continue or discontinue exposure for 24 or 48 hours. At 39, 63 and 87 hpi, host cell numbers, inclusion numbers and inclusion morphology were determined by immunofluorescence microscopy and titration by sub-passage was used to demonstrate infectious bacteria production.

Results

At 39 hpi, Pen-exposed infected cells showed similar inclusion numbers as those mock-exposed. Pen-exposed *Chlamydia*e contained aberrant bacterial forms within relatively small inclusions and exhibited reduced infectivity compared to mock-exposed controls. At 63 hpi, and more so at 87 hpi, Infectious bacteria production recovered upon discontinuation of 1 unit/ml Pen exposure, but not upon discontinuation of 500 U/ml Pen exposure. At 63 and 87 hpi, *Chlamydia*-induced cell death occurred in mock-exposed controls, while cell survival was improved in Pen-exposed cells. Similar results were observed in the presence or absence of the eukaryotic protein translation inhibitor cycloheximide.

Conclusions

Exposure of *C. suis*-infected cells to low-concentration Pen induced the viable but non-infectious chlamydial stress response, while high-concentration Pen exposure killed this chlamydial species/strain. Similar investigations of field strains may reveal variation in Pen susceptibility, ultimately helping determine how Pen treatment may affect *C. suis* in pigs *in vivo*.

14.45-15.00: Recombination shapes the evolution of *Chlamydia suis*: a swine pathogen with evidence for zoonotic transmission

Hanna Marti[1], Sandeep J. Joseph[2], Xavier Didelot[3], Santiago Castillo-Ramirez[4], Timothy D. Read[2], Deborah Dean[1,5]
[1]UCSF Benioff Children's Hospital Oakland Research Institute, Oakland, California, USA, [2]Emory University School of Medicine, Atlanta, Georgia, USA, [3]Imperial College London, London, England, UK, [4]Universidad Nacional Autónoma de México, Cuernavaca, Morelos, Mexico, [5]UCSF and UC Berkeley Departments of Bioengineering, Berkeley, California, USA

Background/ Introduction

Close phylogenetic relatives of *Chlamydia trachomatis* pose a zoonotic threat, especially tetracycline resistant *Chlamydia suis* strains that have acquired a tetracycline transposon via horizontal gene transfer (HGT), and have been found to infect the conjunctiva, nares, pharynx and stool of Belgian pig farmers and the conjunctiva of Asian trachoma patients.

Objectives

To perform comparative genomics of *C. suis* strains with other publically available *Chlamydia* species genomes and identify their genomic organization, mechanisms of evolution and potential for transmission of the tetracycline transposon to closely related species, especially *C. trachomatis*.

Method

Eleven *C. suis* strains from various anatomical sites and *C. pecorum* strain 1710S isolated from a swine abortion were genome sequenced using GS-FLX and/or Illumina. These and publically available *Chlamydia* genomes were analyzed. MAUVE was used for whole-genome alignments. Phylogenetic reconstructions utilized maximum likelihood and coalescent-based ClonalFrame, the latter of which was applied to analyze the nature and frequency of homologous recombination. Population structure analysis was performed using ChromoPainter and fineSTRUCTURE. The influence of positive selection and demography were compared to *C. trachomatis* and *C. muridarum*. BEAST estimated dates of the Last Common Ancestors and historical population sizes.

Results

C. suis has the highest rate of fixed recombination of any *Chlamydia* species. Unlike *C. trachomatis*, *C. suis* clades did not resolve along disease/anatomical demarcations. Admixture occurred between strains of different clades and with *C. muridarum* but there was no evidence for non-laboratory-induced exchange with other *Chlamydia*. The tetracycline resistance transposon was likely acquired from Betaproteobacteria through a single HGT event in the 1950s, after tetracycline was introduced into pig feed, and likely spread throughout *C. suis* strains by multiple recombination events. Selective pressure from tetracycline along with balancing selection may be responsible for recent bottlenecks in *C. suis* populations.

Conclusions

C. suis is a rapidly evolving pathogen with the ability to acquire and, in most cases, retain the tetracycline transposon. The high homology with *C. trachomatis,* and reports of zoonotic infections suggest that it may be an emerging pathogen with potential for transferring drug resistance to *C. trachomatis*.

15.00-15.15: Characterising the global population framework for *Chlamydia pecorum*, a veterinary pathogen of domesticated animals and wildlife

Adam Polkinghorne[1], Helena Seth-Smith[2], Nathan Bachmann[1], Martina Jelocnik[1], Nicole Borel[3], Peter Timms[1], Nicholas Thomson[4]

[1]University of the Sunshine Coast, Sippy Downs, QLD, Australia, [2]Functional Genomics Centre Zurich, Zurich, Switzerland, [3]University of Zurich, Zurich, Switzerland, [4]Wellcome Trust Sanger Institute, Hinxton, UK

Background/ Introduction

Chlamydia pecorum is a veterinary pathogen with a wide host range. Livestock infections cause underestimated losses to producers. Wildlife infections also occur with the koala a well-recognised host. Sympatry of these host populations raises questions over the role of cross-host transmission in the epidemiology and evolution of *C. pecorum*.

Objectives

The aim of this study is to establish a global population framework for *C. pecorum*, to enable further insight into the origin, evolution and adaptation of this pathogen to the different hosts that it infects.

Method

Large scale genome sequencing was performed on *C. pecorum* isolates and clinical samples (approximately 100) from livestock (sheep, cattle, pigs, goats) and koalas from Europe, USA and Australia. Custom *C. pecorum* Agilent Sure-select probes were used to hybridise chlamydial DNA from host cell contaminants. Sequencing was performed on Illumina platforms. Sequences were compared to existing (n=15) *C. pecorum* genome sequences available from Genbank.

Phylogenetic analysis was performed using kSNP. Recombination analysis was performed using Gubbins. Evolutionary analysis including estimates of the most recent common ancestor were calculated using BEAST. Evidence for mixed infections was detected using Hapflow.

Results

Culture-independent genomics was successful in capturing sufficient *C. pecorum* DNA to assemble near full-length genome sequences for the majority of clinical samples and cultured isolates. Comparative *pecorum* genomics analysis revealed considerable intra-strain diversity with >10,000 SNP differences present between them most distantly related strains. Phylogenetic analysis revealed evidence for (a) European livestock strains that are ancestral to Australian livestock strains; (b) clades containing closely related 'pathogenic' *C. pecorum* subtypes and (c) koala isolates within different clades of European and Australian livestock. These relationships are supported by evidence of recombination between strains from different hosts.

Conclusions

This work contributes a significant new body of data to understand the global relationships between *C. pecorum* infections of domesticated animals and wildlife. Molecular evidence from this study provides further evidence for cross-host transmission of these veterinary pathogen between livestock species and for potential 'spill-over' to wildlife as well.

15.45–16.15

KEYNOTE: GILBERT GREUB

Waddlia chondrophila

Gilbert Greub, Institute of Microbiology of the University of Lausanne, Lausanne, Switzerland

Waddlia chondrophila was isolated from a bovine foetus in 1990 in USA. Initially considered as a rickettsia, it was reclassified within the *Chlamydiales* order/Waddliaceae family in 1999. In 2002, another isolate was recovered from a stillborn calf in Germany. The role of Waddlia in bovine abortion was then supported by a serological study and by the documented presence of Waddlia DNA in bovine placenta in the setting of abortions.

In humans, the role of *Waddlia* was suspected as an agent of miscarriage based on two serological studies and based on the presence of *Waddlia* in placenta documented by specific PCR and immunohistochemistry. Presence of anti-waddlia antibodies was also associated to tubal factor infertility. Moreover, Waddlia might also play a role in bronchiolitis, a hypothesis further supported by a mice model of lung infection and by the replication of *Waddlia* in pneumocytes.

Given its likely pathogenic role towards humans and bovines, this *Chlamydia*-related bacterium has been actively studied and nowadays, given (i) its ability to grow in a large variety of cells including amoebae and mammalian cells, (ii) its short doubling time, and (iii) its relatively large cells, it is also used as a model organism to study the *Chlamydiales* biology.

The genome analysis of *Waddlia*, which is more than twice larger than the genome of *C. trachomatis*, is encoding a T3SS that is likely functional since T3SS inhibitors completely inhibited waddlial growth. Genome analysis also showed the relatively impressive metabolic capacities of *Waddlia*, which contrarily to *C trachomatis* is able to synthesize.

Genome analysis also allowed us to identify a functional catalase that produces water and oxygen from hydrogen peroxide. Catalase is a major virulence factor that may partially explain why Waddlia successfully grows in amoebae, in macrophages and in other phagocytic cells. Waddlia also escape early the endocytic pathway and is growing in vacuoles expressing endoplasmic reticulum proteins. When we studied the intracellular traffic of *Waddlia*, we also confirmed its tight association with mitochondria, likely a source of ATP and lipids. Host ATP may be imported thank to an ATP-ADP translocase, an energy parasitism enzyme also present in the other *Chlamydiales*.

Availability of the genome allowed an extended study of its transcription regulatory network, as well as proteomic analysis of its immunogenic proteins and adhesins.

We also extensively studied the cell division of Waddlia, demonstrating the importance of the protein RodZ in controlling the septal localisation of MreB at the septum. MreB is an actin homologue that polymerizes and triggers the binary fission of Waddlia. The peptidoglycan layer is then remodeled by amidases such as NlpD and AmiH and the outer membrane is pulled in during division by the Tol-Pal protein. The fact that *Waddlia* is susceptible to Phosphomycin (contrarily to *C. trachomatis* which is resistant) allowed us to better study the peptidoglycan of *Waddlia* since Phosphomycin is targeting MurA, the first enzyme of the peptidoglycan biosynthetic pathway. Thus, alike penicillin derivatives, phosphomycin induce the formation of aberrant bodies, a possible persistence form.

Altogether *Waddlia chondrophila* thus represents a fascinating model organism to better understand chlamydial biology and given its emerging role as a pathogen merits to be further studied.

16.15-16.30: Marine *Chlamydiae* are motile - evidence from single cell genomes

Astrid Collingro[1], Marc Mußmann[1], Stephan Köstlbacher[1], Steven J. Hallam[2], Ramunas Stepanauskas[3], Matthias Horn[1]

[1]*Division of Microbial Ecology, University of Vienna, Vienna, Austria,* [2]*Department of Microbiology and Immunology, University of British Columbia, Vancouver, Canada,* [3]*Bigelow Laboratory for Ocean Sciences, East Boothbay, USA*

Background/ Introduction

Beyond human and animal pathogenic *Chlamydiaceae*, there is an enourmous diversity of *Chlamydiae* comprising at least 180 additional families. Members of many of these chlamydial families are of marine origin and are not represented by cultured isolates so far.

Objectives

In order to gain insights into the biology of these yet uncultured *Chlamydiae*, and to understand their genomic diversity and similarity to known *Chlamydiae*, we recovered and analysed three chlamydial single-cell amplified genome (SAG) sequences from marine habitats.

Method

Single microbial cells from water samples from the Saanich Inlet (CAN) and Northern Sea sediment (GER), respectively, were sorted by high-speed fluorescence-activated cell sorting (FACS). Genomic DNA of these cells was amplified by multiple displacement amplification (MDA), and chlamydial SAGs were identified by 16S rRNA gene sequencing. Three chlamydial SAGs were subsequently sequenced on MiSeq and NextSeq (Illumina) instruments. Sequence reads were quality checked, assembled with SPAdes, and annotated with ConsPred. Phylogenetic analyses were performed with MrBayes or RAxML.

Results

For each SAG approximately 41-50% of the genome could be reconstructed, indicating genomes sizes of 2.2-2.6 Mbp. The affiliation of the SAGs to deeply branching *Chlamydiae* of marine origin was confirmed by phylogenetic analysis of 16S rRNA and additional marker genes. Predicted metabolic capabilities are consistent with those reported for other *Chlamydiae*. The presence of type III secretion genes, ATP/ADP-translocases, CPAF and other *Chlamydia*-specific genes are pointing towards an intracellular life style of these microbes. Interestingly, all three SAGs harbor genes for chemotaxis and assembly of flagella. Phylogenetic analysis of flagellar genes suggests a common chlamydial origin of this trait.

Conclusions

Analysis of the first SAGs of marine *Chlamydiae* suggests an intracellular life style by employing characteristic mechanisms for host interaction known from other *Chlamydiae*. In addition they have the genetic repertoire for chemotaxis and motility, which they might use to trace or attach to their hosts.

16.30-16.45: Lausannevirus and *Estrella lausannensis* evolutionary dynamics

Linda Mueller[1], Trestan Pillonel[1,2], Claire Bertelli[1,2], Nicolas Salamin[2,3], Gilbert Greub[1,2]
[1]Institute of Microbiology,Lausanne University Hospital and University of Lausanne, Lausanne, Switzerland, [2]SIB Swiss Institute of Bioinformatics, Lausanne, Switzerland, [3]Department of Ecology and Evolution, University of Lausanne, Lausanne, Switzerland

Background/ Introduction

Amoebae-resisting microorganisms (ARMs) raised a great interest during the last decade. Among them, *Chlamydiales* and large DNA viruses. Given the suspected higher plasticity of viral genomes and possible genes exchanges with bacteria when present in the same amoebal host, to describe their evolutionary dynamics is of major interest.

Objectives

This work aimed at investigating mutation rates of two recently discovered ARMs: *Estrella lausannensis* (~2.8 Mb), a member of the *Chlamydiales* order and Lausannevirus (~346 kb), belonging to the Nucleocytoplasmic Large DNA viruses (NCLDVs). Both microorganisms were isolated from water samples by *Acanthamoeba castellanii* co-culture.

Method

We co-cultured both ARMs together in *A. castellanii* for 1 year (144 passages). During this time period, we split our culture in two lineages each 3 months, in order to obtain 8 different subcultures at the end of the year. All subcultures were sequenced using MiSeq Illumina (paired end reads, 2x150 bp) and Single Nucleotide Polymorphism (SNP) as well as Insertion/Deletion (INDEL) calling were performed on the sequences of both, Lausannevirus and *E. lausannensis*. Quantitative real-time PCR allowed the quantification of viral and bacterial abundance of each subculture.

Results

SNP/INDEL calling revealed a striking viral stability (2-7 mutations/culture/year), as well as an expected low mutation appearance in *Estrella lausannensis* (4-10 mutations/culture/year). Interestingly, 15% of bacterial mutations were fixed while no viral mutations were, suggesting the presence of more than one population among the same viral subculture. Remarkably, mutations in *Estrella lausannensis* were mainly located in a gene encoding for a phospoenolpyruvate-protein phospotransferase (PtsI), implicated in sugar metabolism and conserved among the *Chlamydiales* order. Despite none of the known active sites of PtsI exhibit mutations, possible alterations of its activity are now investigated in vitro.

Conclusions

Both microorganisms exhibited stable genomes and more non-synonymous than synonymous mutations. Moreover, we detected no lateral gene transfer between *E. lausannensis* and Lausannevirus during one year of co-culture. Currently, we are investigating the activity of the different *E. lausannensis* PtsI variants to assess the impact of observed mutations.

16.45-17.00: Culture-independent genomics of a novel chlamydial pathogen of fish provides insight into the evolution of pathogenicity in the *Chlamydiae*

Alyce Taylor-Brown[1], Weihong Qi[2], Nathan L Bachmann[1], Andrew Bridle[3], Terry Miller[4], Barbara Nowak[3], Helena Seth-Smith[2,5], Lloyd Vaughan[5], Adam Polkinghorne[1]
[1]*Centre for Animal Health Innovation, Faculty of Science, Health, Engineering and Education, University of the Sunshine Coast, Sippy Downs, Australia,* [2]*Functional Genomics Centre, University of Zurich, Zurich, Switzerland,* [3]*Institute of Marine and Antarctic Studies, University of Tasmania, Newnham, Australia,* [4]*School of Marine and Tropical Biology, James Cook University, Smithfield, Australia,* [5]*Institute of Veterinary Pathology, University of Zurich, Zurich, Switzerland*

Background/ Introduction

Several recently described *Chlamydiales* families that are associated with epitheliocystis in fish may also derive from the evolutionary ancestors of the family *Chlamydiaceae*. Due to the lack of culture systems, little is otherwise known about the biology of these *Chlamydia*-like organisms (CLOs).

Objectives

We sought to characterise a novel uncultured chlamydial species (*Candidatus*. Simili*Chlamydia epinepheli*) from cultured Orange-spotted grouper (*Epinephelus coioides*) from North Queensland to gain insight into the evolution and pathogenicity of the *Chlamydiae*.

Method

Gills fixed in formalin were processed for histology and *in situ* hybridisation using *Chlamydiales*-specific probes. Gills stored in ethanol were processed for DNA extraction, PCR and sequencing. Genomic DNA extracted from gills was enriched for microbial DNA by methylated host DNA depletion and whole genome amplification was conducted prior to shotgun sequencing on an Illumina MiSeq. The resulting reads were pre-processed and de novo assembled using SPAdes, and genomes were analysed using a series of bioinformatics tools including metagenomics binning software (MEGAN and MaxBin) for reconstruction of genome drafts. Automated and manual annotation was conducted using Prokka, RAST and Artemis.

Results

Basophilic inclusions were present in the gills of 22/31 fish. Presence of the chlamydial pathogen in the cysts was confirmed by *in situ* hybridisation. 16S rRNA gene sequencing revealed this species to be a novel member of the *Ca.* Parili*Chlamydia*ceae. *De novo* metagenome assembly and binning resulted in 78,820 contigs grouped into 7 bins, the chlamydial bin representing approximately 75% of the genome. Genomics analysis revealed that this novel CLO possesses an intact Type Three Secretion system and several chlamydial virulence factors such as CPAF. *Ca.* Simili*Chlamydia epinepheli* thus forms the most ancient branch of the *Chlamydiae* sequenced to date.

Conclusions

We have identified a novel uncultured pathogen of fish in the order *Chlamydiales*, prevalent in successive cohorts of cultured grouper. This study contributes the first genomic information for a CLO described in fish, and provides insight into the unique biology and pathogenicity of this phylum.

17.00-17.15: Sequencing the obligate intracellular *RhabdoChlamydia heleveticae* within its tick host *Ixodes ricinus*

Trestan Pillonel[1], Claire Bertelli[1,2], Sébastien Aeby[1], Marie De-Barsy[1], Nicolas Jacquier[1], Carole Kebbi-Beghdadi[1], Linda Mueller[1], Ludovic Pilloux[1], Manon Vouga[1], Gilbert Greub[1,3]
[1]*Center for Research on Intracellular Bacteria, Institute of Microbiology, University Hospital Center and University of Lausanne, Lausanne, Vaud, Switzerland,* [2]*Swiss Institute of Bioinformatics, Lausanne, Vaud, Switzerland,* [3]*Service of Infectious Diseases, University Hospital Center, Lausanne, Vaud, Switzerland*

Background/ Introduction

The *RhabdoChlamydiaceae* is one of the most widely distributed family of the order *Chlamydiales*. A recent study of the prevalence of *Chlamydiae* in ticks in Switzerland reported the presence of *RhabdoChlamydia* 16S ribosomal sequences in >2% of the 8534 analyzed pools of ticks. Nevertheless, *RhabdoChlamydia* remains uncultivated and poorly studied.

Objectives

In order to investigate the evolution and biology of *Chlamydiae* in ticks, we sequenced the genome of one strain directly from a pool of ticks presenting a high concentration of bacterial DNA with >97% of 16S rRNA identity to *RhaboChlamydia crassificans*.

Method

The genome was sequenced using the MiSeq system with paired-end 150 bp reads. Over 24 million reads were obtained, containing approximately 40% of *Ixodes ricinus* sequences that were filtered out by mapping to the available draft genome of *Ixodes scapularis* and *Ixodes ricinus*. The assembly was done using Edena and Velvet. The annotation was done using Prokka. Domains were annotated using InterProScan. Predicted coding sequences were compared to the NCBI non-redundant and COG databases using BLASTp. Comparative analyses were done with 31 proteomes of *Chlamydiales* strains, 1 *Verrucomicrobia* and 2 *Planctomycetes*. Proteins were grouped into orthologous groups using orthoMCL.

Results

The genome could be assembled into 38 contigs and one plasmid. Pairwise comparisons of 16S ribosomal sequences indicate that its closest described relative is *R. porcellonis* with 98.98% of sequence identity. The *RhabdoChlamydia* sp. exhibits a smaller genome (1.7Mbp) as compared to other *Chlamydia*-related bacteria, with reduced metabolic capabilities and numerous parasitic transporters. It shares approximately 700 protein families with the five *Chlamydia*-related families, and 580 (~40% of its proteome) with *C. trachomatis*. Only 60% of the proteins exhibited an NCBI nr best hit within the *Chlamydiae* phylum. 19% of the proteins presented no significant hits at all.

Conclusions

This project reports the first genome of a *RhabdoChlamydiaceae* species. This obligate intracellular bacteria is frequent in *Ixodes* ticks, vectors of multiple human diseases. It exhibits a significantly smaller genome as compared to other *Chlamydia*-related species, reduced metabolic capabilities and numerous transporters reflecting its parasitic life-style.

THURSDAY MORNING, 8TH SEPTEMBER

SESSION 7:

Trachoma

Chairs:
Robin Bailey & Phil Giffard

08.30 – 09.00

KEYNOTE: DAVID MABEY

Will trachoma be eliminated by 2020?

David Mabey. London School of Hygiene and Tropical Medicine.

Background In 1998 the World Health Assembly passed a resolution to eliminate trachoma as a public health problem by the year 2020. The target was to reduce the prevalence of active, follicular trachoma (TF) in children aged 1-9 years to less than 5%, and the prevalence of potentially blinding late stage trachoma (trichiasis) to less than 1 per 1000 in every district in the world through the SAFE strategy: Surgery for trichiasis, Antibiotic (azithromycin) mass drug administration (MDA) to treat ocular *Chlamydia trachomatis* infection, and Facial cleanliness and Environmental improvement to reduce eye to eye transmission of *C. trachomatis (Ct)*. Are we going to achieve these ambitious targets by 2020?

Impressive progress has been made since 1998. The 500 millionth dose of donated azithromycin was given in Ethiopia in 2015, the estimated number of people with active trachoma has fallen from 150 million in 1995 to 21 million in 2011, and nine countries have met the WHO elimination targets. The Global Trachoma Mapping Project – the largest disease mapping project ever undertaken – was completed in 2015; more than 2 million people were examined in 29 countries, and prevalence data are now available for every district in which trachoma has been or has been suspected to be endemic. This means that resources can be targeted to where they are needed – typically poor populations living in remote, rural locations.

Recent research findings to support trachoma elimination. An estimated 7.2 million people still need surgery for trichiasis, but which operation should they have? Until 2016 the WHO recommended bilamellar tarsal rotation (BLTR) for the correction of trichiasis, although high rates of recurrence were reported after this operation. In 2016 a randomised controlled trial in Ethiopia showed that a different operation, posterior lamellar tarsal rotation (PLTR), led to significantly lower recurrence rates than BLTR (13% vs 22%) [1]. As a result of this study the WHO now recommends PLTR as the operation of choice.

In many communities the prevalence of active trachoma remains above 10% in children even though the prevalence of ocular *Ct* infection is close to zero following repeated rounds of MDA. This observation has raised a number of questions: Can other bacteria cause TF in trachoma-endemic populations? Are people with TF in the absence of *Ct* infection at risk of developing conjunctival scarring, which causes the blinding sequelae of trachoma? How should trachoma control programmes decide when to stop MDA, and what is the most effective strategy for post-elimination surveillance?

Can other bacteria cause trachoma? A study of the conjunctival microbiome in Gambian subjects, using deep sequencing of the 16S rRNA gene, found a reduced diversity of bacterial species, and a greater abundance of *Corynebacterium* and *Streptococcus* species in subjects with scarring trachoma than in controls with normal eyes [2]. Ocular swabs from children with active, follicular trachoma are more likely than those with normal eyes to be culture positive for *Streptococcus pneumoniae* and *Haemophilus influenzae* [3]. These bacteria are not known to cause follicular conjunctivitis outside trachoma endemic communities, raising the possibility that Ct infection may lead to changes in the conjunctival epithelium which persist after Ct infection has resolved.

Does Ct infection cause epigenetic changes in the epithelium? Transcriptome arrays comparing conjunctival gene expression at various stages of trachomatous disease have found that many thousands of genes are differentially regulated in the conjunctival epithelium. A data mining approach identified microRNAs that were enriched for targets within lists of differentially regulated genes, in particular those involved in epithelial-mesenchymal transition (EMT), evidence of which has been found in Ct infected epithelial cells in fallopian tube tissue [4,5]. MicroRNA (miRNA) 155 has been shown to be upregulated in children with active trachoma, and miRNA 184 to be down-regulated [6]. Fibroblasts cultured from patients with scarring trachoma showed increased matrix remodelling properties compared to those from subjects with normal eyes and a pro-fibrotic and pro-inflammatory gene expression profile, with increased expression of IL-6 [7].

What drives the scarring process in trachoma? Two cohorts of individuals with established conjunctival scarring due to trachoma were examined every six months for two years, and conjunctival swabs were taken to study gene expression and test for Ct infection by PCR. [8] Progressive scarring was seen in 135/585 (23%) subjects in Ethiopia, and 173/577 (30%) in Tanzania, although Ct infection was found in only 4 subjects at baseline and one subject at 12 months. There was a strong relationship between progressive scarring and the number and severity of inflammatory episodes. Increased expression of S100A7, IL1B, IL17A, CXCL5, CTGF, CEACAM5 and CD83 was seen during episodes of inflammation. A genome-wide association study of 1090 cases of scarring trachoma and 1531 controls identified polymorphisms in genes involved in cell cycle and immune response pathways that were associated with scarring [9]. An important role for the innate immune system is supported by recent immunohistochemical studies of scarring trachoma [10,11]. A placebo controlled trial of doxycycline, which has anti-inflammatory as well as anti-bacterial activity, is in progress in patients undergoing trichiasis surgery in Ethiopia to see if this will reduce the rate of recurrence.

How should we decide when to stop mass drug administration? A study in The Gambia suggested that it may be more cost effective to use a molecular test for ocular Ct infection to decide when to stop MDA than to follow WHO guidelines [12], but the cost of these tests is prohibitive for most national programmes. Serological testing of dry blood spots for antibodies to the Ct-specific pgp3 antigen has been suggested as an alternative method of confirming that transmission has been interrupted. Changes in age-specific seroprevalence have been shown to correlate with elimination of ocular Ct infection in some Tanzanian communities [13,14], but further validation of this method is needed in different populations.

Remaining Challenges: Why has the SAFE strategy had little impact in some communities?

In some of the most severely affected populations, eg. in Ethiopia, the prevalence of active trachoma remains stubbornly high in spite of repeated rounds of MDA with azithromycin, in some cases given every 6 months. Clinically significant macrolide resistance has not been found in Ct, although there is some evidence that people with higher Ct bacterial loads are more likely to be Ct positive after treatment with azithromycin. It may be that two doses given one week apart would be more effective in eliminating ocular Ct infection in communities with high bacterial loads. The evidence base in support of the F and E components of the SAFE strategy is weak, although modelling studies suggest that interventions to interrupt transmission will be essential if we are to achieve the elimination targets in severely affected communities [15]. Further studies are needed to identify exactly how ocular Ct is transmitted, and which behavioural or environmental interventions are effective in reducing transmission.

References:
1. Habtamu E et al. Lancet Global Health 2016; 4: e175-184
2. Zhou Y et al. Genome Medicine 2014; 6 : 99
3. Burr SE et al. PloS NTDs 2013 ; 7 : e2347
4. Derrick T et al. Mediators of Inflammation 2015, article ID 791847
5. Kessler M et al. Am J Pathol 2012; 180: 186.
6. Derrick T et al. BMC Infectious Diseases 2016; 16: 60
7. Kechagia Z et al. Scientific Reports 2016. In press.
8. Burton MJ et al. PloS NTDs 2016 ; 9: e0003763.
9. Roberts CH et al. Scientific Reports 2015; 5: 17447.
10. Hu VH et al, PLoS NTDs 2016. In press
11. Derrick T et al. PLoS NTDs 2016. In press.
12. Harding-Esch et al. PloS NTDs 2015 ;9: e0003670
13. Martin DL et al. PloS NTDs 2015; 9: e0003555
14. West SK et al. PLoS NTDs 2016; 10 : e0004352
15. Gambir M et al. Ophthalmic Epidemiology 2015 ; 22: 394

09.00-09.15: Identifying miRNA biomarkers for progression of scarring trachoma

Tamsyn Derrick[1,2], Athumani Ramadhani[1,2], Karim Mtengai[2], Patrick Massae[2], Matthew Burton[1], Martin Holland[1]

[1]London School of Hygiene and Tropical Medicine, London, UK, [2]Kilimanjaro Christian Medical Centre, Moshi, Tanzania

Background/ Introduction

100 million people are currently at risk of trachoma. A significant proportion of these will develop scarring trachoma and trichiasis. We previously showed that miR-147b and miR-1285 were upregulated in Gambian adults with inflammatory scarring trachoma and miR-155 and miR-184 expression correlated with *trachomatous inflammation-intense* in children from Guinea Bissau.

Objectives

To determine whether the single or combined expression of miR-147b, miR-1285, miR-155 and miR-184 are able to identify individuals with increased risk of incident or progressive scarring trachoma over a 4 year period.

Method

Total RNA and DNA were extracted from conjunctival swab samples taken from 506 children between the ages of 6 and 10 living in northern Tanzania that were enrolled in a 4 year longitudinal study. *C. trachomatis* infection was diagnosed by droplet digital PCR. Expression of miR-147b, miR-1285, miR-155 and miR-184 and the endogenous control U6 were tested in all 506 baseline samples by qPCR. The same individuals were assessed for incidence and progression of conjunctival scarring by comparison of photographs taken at enrollment and 4 years later.

Results

The contribution of miRNA expression level, *C. trachomatis* infection status and clinical phenotype at baseline to incident and progressive scarring was tested using multivariate logistic regression. The ability of these 4 miRNA to classify individuals with progressive scarring trachoma over a four-year period versus non-progressors was evaluated.

Conclusions

A miRNA signature that could identify individuals at risk of scarring trachoma and trichiasis before the onset of clinical signs might enable therapeutic intervention. They may also serve as a correlate of protection from sequelae and provide a hypothesis for mechanistic investigations in vitro.

09.15-09.30: *Chlamydia trachomatis* from Australian Aboriginal people with trachoma are polyphyletic composed of multiple distinctive lineages

Patiyan Andersson[1], Simon R. Harris[2], Helena M.B. Seth-Smith[2,3], James Hadfield[2], Colette O'Neill[4], Lesley T. Cutcliffe[4], Fiona P. Douglas[1], Valerie L. Asche[1], John D. Mathews[1,5], Susan I. Hutton[1], Derek S. Sarovich[1], Steven Y.C. Tong[1], Ian N. Clarke[4], Nicholas R. Thomson[2,6], Philip M. Giffard[1]
[1](1) Menzies School of Health Research, Darwin, Australia, [2](2) The Wellcome Trust Sanger Institute, Cambridge, UK, [3](3) University of Zurich, Zurich, Switzerland, [4](4) University Medical School, Southampton General Hospital, Southampton, UK, [5](5) School of Population and Global Health, University of Melbourne, Melbourne, Australia, [6](6) London School of Hygiene and Tropical Medicine, London, Australia

Background/ Introduction

Current data on *Chlamydia trachomatis* phylogeny shows that there is only a single trachoma-causing clade, which is distinct from the lineages causing urogenital and lymphogranuloma venerum diseases.

Objectives

To describe the first genome sequences of ocular *C. trachomatis* from young children with signs consistent with trachoma in a trachoma endemic region of northern Australia.

Method

Twelve isolates collected and initially cultured in the late 1980s, were revived and propagated in cell culture, and subjected to whole genome sequencing. The original MOMP serotyping designated them as B (n=5), Ba (n=2) and C (n=5). The isolates were phylogenetically compared with genome sequences of 53 *C. trachomatis* reference strains representative of the diversity of the species. A genome wide association study was carried out to identify loci putatively associated with ocular tropism.

Results

The Australian trachoma isolates form two lineages that both fall outside the classical trachoma lineage, instead being placed within urogenital clades of the *C. trachomatis* phylogenetic tree. The isolates appear to be recombinants with urogenital *C. trachomatis* genome backbones in which loci that encode immunodominant surface proteins (*ompA* and *pmpEFGH*) have been replaced by those characteristic of classical ocular isolates. No strains from the classic trachoma lineage were found, and the variant lineages observed in this study seem to be the dominant strains causing trachoma in the region.

Conclusions

The results indicate that ocular tropism is functionally associated with some sequence variants of *ompA* and *pmpEFGH*. These observations suggest that the presence of residual trachoma strains following trachoma eradication efforts could provide potential for trachoma-associated gene variants to be transferred to prevalent urogenital strains, and facilitate trachoma reemergence.

09.30-09.45: Anti-chlamydial serology in the Solomon Islands where active trachoma is common but trichiasis is scarce

Robert Butcher[1], Oliver Sokana[2], Kelvin Jack[2], Richard T Le Mesurier[3], Anthony W Solomon[1], David C Mabey[1], Chrissy h Roberts[1]
[1]London School of Hygiene & Tropical Medicine, London, UK, [2]Solomon Islands Ministry of Health and Medical Services, Honiara, Solomon Islands, [3]University of Melbourne, Melbourne, Australia

Background/ Introduction

In the Solomon Islands, the prevalence of trachomatous inflammation – follicular (TF) suggests trachoma warrants intervention (26.1% in those aged 1-9 years), but the prevalence of trichiasis suggests it does not (<0.1% in all ages). The prevalence of ocular *Chlamydia trachomatis* infection appears to be low (1.3%).

Objectives

We set out to use molecular diagnostic tests to further clarify whether the prevalent follicular conjunctivitis in the Solomon Islands is associated with ocular *Ct* infection to help guide policy makers on the likely value of expensive further rounds of azithromycin MDA.

Method

Six months following the first round of MDA, we randomly selected households from 13 villages in the Solomon Islands that had high baseline prevalence of active trachoma (>10% of total surveyed village population). All residents of selected households over the age of 1 year were examined for evidence of trachoma according to the WHO simplified grading scheme. Dried blood spots were collected from all participants. Anti-pgp3 ELISA was conducted on each dried blood spot to assess exposure to *Ct*. A bimodal mixture model was used to identify positive and negative populations and the threshold for seropositivity.

Results

The prevalence of TF in children aged 1-9 years was 14.2% according to clinical grade. The prevalence of trachomatous scarring in those aged 18 years and over was 2.4%. The overall prevalence of seropositivity in those aged 1-9 years was 20.9%. Seropositivity was not associated with TF in the 1-9 years age group; 22.2% of TF cases and 20.6% of those without TF had evidence of pgp3 exposure (chi-squared p = 0.818). 77.8% of TF cases did not have antibodies to pgp3 in their blood.

Conclusions

Pgp3 seroprevalence here is similar to published seroprevalence from areas with <5% childhood TF. TF appears to be nonspecific for *Ct* infection and may be a poor tool to guide MDA in the Solomon Islands. Infection testing may be important to avoid unnecessary antibiotic exposure in other programs.

09.45-10.00: Association between Natural Killer (NK) cell receptor-ligand subsets and scarring trachoma in the context of *Chlamydia trachomatis* (Ct) infection

Adriana Goncalves[1], Pateh Makalo[2], Hassan Joof[2], Sarah Burr[2], Sophie Moore[2], Tamsyn Derrick[1], Joanna Houghton[1], Christine D Palmer[1], Sandra Molina[1], David C W Mabey[1], Robin L Bailey[1], Martin R Goodier[1], Chrissy h Roberts[1], Martin J Holland[1,2]
[1]*London School of Hygiene and Tropical Medicine, London, UK,* [2]*Medical Research Council Unit, Fajara, Gambia*

Background/ Introduction

Repeated ocular *Chlamydia trachomatis* (Ct) infection causes blinding trachoma. Natural Killer (NK) cells have been implied in the resolution of Ct infection as they are a primary source of IFN-γ that increases with age. Different NK cell receptors and ligands have also been implicated in the pathology of the disease.

Objectives

We investigated the role of NK cells and NK cell receptors on the immunopathology of trachomatous disease. The function and phenotype of different NK cell receptors and NK cell subsets was investigated in cases with scarring trachoma (TS) and healthy controls in the context of Ct infection.

Method

Blood and buccal swabs were collected from 93 Gambians (40 TS cases and 53 controls). Peripheral blood mononuclear cells (PBMCs) were isolated by density gradient centrifugation and genomic DNA was obtained from buccal swabs by standard salting procedures. Upon overnight stimulation of PBMCs with Ct elementary bodies (EB) in the presence or absence of cytokines (IL-12, IL-18); CD3-CD56+ NK cells were analyzed by flow cytometry for functional markers (IFN-γ, CD107a and CD25) and a number of NK cell receptors (CD16, NKG2C), maturation (CD57) and different KIR receptors (KIR2DL1, KIR2DS1, KIR2DL2 and KIR2DL3). Individuals were genotyped for NKG2C, KIR and HLA-C1/2.

Results

NK cells were the main source of early IFN-γ in response to Ct. Preliminary results have confirmed the association between HLA-C2, KIR2DL3 allele and scarring trachoma. Even though, we observed no general differences in IFN-γ and CD107a production between cases and controls, our research has shown that the frequency and function of KIR expressing NK cells within the different HLA-C genotypes varies depending on specific KIR/HLA pairings. NK cell functions are governed by the repertoire of receptor-ligand combinations on NK cells, possibly affecting how NK cells respond to Ct infection in cases and controls.

Conclusions

Although the global function of NK cells did not differ between TS cases and healthy controls, we observed different proportions of NK cell subtypes that express different repertoires of KIR receptors as a function of the respective KIR-ligand genotype. These receptor-ligand combinations were shown to be associated with scarring trachoma.

THURSDAY MORNING, 8TH SEPTEMBER

SESSION 8:

Epidemiology

Chairs:

Peter Marsh & Judit Deák

10.30–11.00

KEYNOTE: JANE HOCKING

Chlamydia control– where to from here? Results from the Australian *Chlamydia* Control Effectiveness Pilot (ACCEPt)

Jane S Hocking. Centre for Epidemiology and Biostatistics, Melbourne School of Population Health, University of Melbourne, Victoria, Australia.

Introduction

Chlamydia trachomatis is the most commonly reported sexually transmitted infection in Australia; diagnosis rates have risen dramatically from 74 per 100,000 in 1999 to 367 per 100,000 in 2014 (over 80,000 cases in 2014). As over 80% of infections are asymptomatic, screening is the main way to detect cases. However, there is considerable debate about the effectiveness of *Chlamydia* screening. In response to this concern, the Australian Government funded the Australian *Chlamydia* Control Effectiveness Pilot (ACCEPt), a clinical trial of *Chlamydia* testing in general practice. This paper will present the final results of the ACCEPt trial and explore what the ACCEPt results mean for the future of *Chlamydia* control.

Aims of ACCEPt

To assess the feasibility, acceptability, efficacy and cost-effectiveness of an organised programme of annual *Chlamydia* testing in general practice.

Methods

Study design and rationale

ACCEPt was conducted as a cluster randomised controlled trial (RCT) design (Australian Clinical Trial Register, ACTRN1260000297022). An intervention to support increased *Chlamydia* testing was allocated at the geographical area level (rural towns) and all general practice clinics within each town were recruited. The fundamental premise of this trial was that increased levels of testing could be achieved by providing support, and that once levels of *Chlamydia* testing were sufficiently increased, the prevalence of *Chlamydia* would fall. The trial was up to four year's duration and commenced in late 2010.

Participants

GPs working in general practices located in selected towns were enrolled in the trial and men and women aged 16 to 29 years who had ever been sexually active were eligible to be tested.

Intervention and control

GPs or other health care providers, where appropriate, were requested to offer an annual *Chlamydia* test to all eligible 16 to 29 year old patients when they presented for a consultation for any reason. Clinics received a multifaceted support package designed to facilitate testing. Clinics in the control group were asked to continue their usual practice.

Outcomes

The primary outcome was *Chlamydia* prevalence measured among a consecutive sample of eligible patients aged 16 to 29 years attending all participating clinics conducted prior to randomisation and repeated again at the conclusion of the trial. The change in *Chlamydia* prevalence between the two surveys was measured to determine whether increased *Chlamydia* testing led to a reduction in *Chlamydia* transmission in the underlying population. Secondary outcomes measured included annual *Chlamydia* testing and re-testing rates, annual *Chlamydia* positivity and re-infection rates and pelvic inflammatory disease (PID) diagnoses.

Sample size and statistical methods

A total sample size of 54 geographical areas (27 in each group) was required to detect a difference in prevalence between the groups of 2% at the end of the study with 80% power (4% in control and 2% in intervention group) and assuming a design effect of 2. Primary analyses were conducted according to the intention to treat principle. Formal statistical comparisons were based on generalised mixed models that accounted for cluster (town), practice and participant variability.

Results

Recruitment was completed in December 2011 with 143 clinics recruited in 54 rural towns across 4 Australian states. Over 90% of clinics approached agreed to participate and over 1,200 general practitioners and 150 practice nurses were recruited. Only one clinic (control group) withdrew from the trial.

About 3,800 men and women aged 16 to 29 years participated in each prevalence survey with similar response rates of about 70% for each survey. About 72% of participants were female. The prevalence dropped significantly in the intervention group from 5.0% (95%CI: 4.0%, 6.2%) to 3.4% (95%CI: 2.7%, 4.3%; OR=0.7; 95%CI: 0.5, 0.9). The prevalence declined but not significantly in the control group from 4.5% (95%CI: 3.6%, 5.6%) to 3.4% (95%CI: 2.6%, 4.5%; OR=0.8; 95%CI: 0.5, 1.1). The treatment effect was OR=0.8 (95%CI: 0.5, 1.5), showing a 20% greater reduction in prevalence in the intervention group compared with the control group, although this was non-significant.

During the intervention period, over 41,000 *Chlamydia* tests were conducted in the intervention group compared with about 27,000 in the control group. Annual *Chlamydia* testing rates increased from 8.1% to 20.0% per year in the intervention group compared with a smaller increase from 8.1% to 12.7% per year in the control group.

Analyses of *Chlamydia* re-testing rates, re-infections and PID diagnosis rates are ongoing and will be presented.

Discussion

Australia is the only country to have evaluated multiple rounds of opportunistic *Chlamydia* screening in a pragmatic randomised controlled trial, despite the existence of longstanding recommendations and widespread screening in many countries. Analyses to date show that the ACCEPt intervention increased *Chlamydia* testing uptake among 16 to 29 year olds in general practice, but it did not have a measurable effect on the estimated prevalence of *Chlamydia* in the population, when compared with existing practice. Further ongoing analyses will investigate whether the intervention had an impact on PID. A cost-effectiveness analysis will be undertaken and the results used to make recommendations to the Australian Government about future *Chlamydia* testing policy.

11.00-11.15: The Netherlands *Chlamydia* Cohort Study (NECCST): risks of long-term complications after *Chlamydia trachomatis* infection in women, intermediate outcomes

Bernice M Hoenderboom[1,2], Aloysia AM van Oeffelen[1], Birgit HB van Benthem[1], Jan EAM van Bergen[3,4], Sander Ouburg[2], Servaas A Morré[2], Ingrid VF van den Broek[1]
[1]Centre for Infectious Disease Control, National Institute for Public Health and the Environment, Bilthoven, The Netherlands, [2]Laboratory of Immunogenetics, Department of Medical Microbiology and Infection Control, VU University Medical Center, Amsterdam, The Netherlands, [3]Department of General Practice, Division Clinical Methods and Public Health, Academic Medical Center, Amsterdam, The Netherlands, [4]STI AIDS Netherlands (SOA AIDS Nederland), Amsterdam, The Netherlands

Background/ Introduction

The Netherlands *Chlamydia* Cohort Study (NECCST) follows a cohort of women of reproductive age prospectively for ≥10 years to investigate *Chlamydia trachomatis* (Ct) disease progression and the role of host-genetic-biomarkers. NECCST is a continuation of the *Chlamydia* Screening Implementation (CSI, 2008-2011) which invited 300,000 young adults for annual Ct testing.

Objectives

The aim of this study is to assess the risk of long-term complications after *Chlamydia* infection in women with and without a Ct-history. Here we describe intermediate results over a period of 4-7 years after CSI-enrolment.

Method

From October 2015 - June 2016, CSI women (N=14,685) who consented to be approached for future research are invited for NECCST. From respondents, questionnaire data and blood samples for Ct Immunoglobulin G (IgG) measurement are obtained. Ct-history is based on CSI test outcomes, self-reported infections and Ct-IgG presence. Pregnancies and the following long-term complications: Pelvic Inflammatory Disease (PID), ectopic pregnancy and female subfertility, are determined by self-reporting. Subfertility will be checked in medical registers end 2016. Here, preliminary data from NECCST were combined with CSI-data and analysed. Risks were compared between women with/without a Ct-history using chi-squared tests.

Results

Currently, of 4,126 invited women, 1,594 (38.6%) responded including 432 (27.1%) with previous Ct-infections, a 9% increase in Ct-history from CSI to NECCST. Median age was 31.8 and 32.3 years in women with/without Ct-history. Fifty women (3.1%) reported PID, 5.1% and 2.4% in women with/without Ct-history, respectively (p=0.01). In total, 717 (45.0%) women reported ≥1pregnancies and 99 (6.4%) subfertility: 7.4% versus 6.0% in women with/without Ct-history (p=0.30). Of women reporting ≥1pregnancies, 12 (1.7%) reported ectopic pregnancy, 2.8% versus 1.2% in women with/without Ct-history (p=0.13). In total, 135 (8.5%) women reported ≥1complications, 10.0% and 7.9% in women with/without Ct-history, respectively (p=0.19).

Conclusions

Crude preliminary results of the first subset of respondents after 4 to 7 years follow-up suggests risk differences in the incidence of complications between women with/without Ct-history. In September, the first data collection round of NECCST will be completed and more robust results can be presented (expected response 45%=6,600).

11.15-11.30: Epidemiology of the new variant of *Chlamydia trachomatis* (nvCT) in Sweden ten years after its discovery: What has happened?

Jenny Dahlberg[1], Ronza Hadad[2], Karin Elfving[3], Inger Larsson[4], Jenny Isaksson[1], Hans Fredlund[2], Magnus Unemo[2], Björn Herrmann[1]
[1]*Uppsala University, Uppsala, Sweden,* [2]*Örebro University Hospital, Örebro, Sweden,* [3]*Falu Lasarett, Falun, Sweden,* [4]*Sunderby Hospital, Luleå, Sweden*

Background/ Introduction

In 2006 a new variant of *Chlamydia trachomatis* (nvCT) was discovered in Sweden. It has a plasmid deletion that resulted in false negative test results using Abbott m2000 (Abbott) and COBAS Amplicor/TaqMan48 (Roche). The proportion of nvCT was initially up to 65% in counties using Abbott/Roche test systems.

Objectives

To analyse the nvCT prevalence in two counties (Dalarna and Örebro) that used Roche tests in 2006 and thereafter changed to tests able to detect nvCT. The nvCT was also followed in two counties (Norrbotten and Uppsala) that used ProbeTec (BectonDickinson (BD)), which always has been able to detect nvCT.

Method

CT-positive samples were collected in 2007, 2008, 2009, 2011 and 2015. The proportion of nvCT was determined by using a PCR that discriminated nvCT from wild type CT (Herrmann et al, Sex Transm Dis 2012,39:648-650). Genotyping of *ompA* and 5 MLST genes was performed as previously described (http://mlstdb.bmc.uu.se/).

Results

Altogehter, 5019 samples were analysed, ranging from 107 to 374 per year from each county. The proportion of nvCT significantly decreased in counties using Roche tests (Dalarna: 2007, 65% (122/188); 2015, 6.2% (18/292); Örebro: 2007, 48% (106/219); 2015, 6.7% (25/374) (p<0.001)). In counties using BD tests a significant overall decrease was seen for the study period, but starting from a lower level (Uppsala: 2007, 24% (60/253); 2015, 5.2% (18/344); Norrbotten: 2007, 9% (106/219); 2015, 5.3% (19/361) (p<0.124)).
Nine nvCT cases from 2015 were identical in the MLST genes and in *ompA*. They were also identical with 74 cases from 2006-2007.

Conclusions

The nvCT prevalence has decreased significantly and possibly converged into a steady state of 5-7% irrespectively of initial county rates.
Genotyping indicates that nvCT is clonal and genetically stable.

THURSDAY MORNING, 8TH SEPTEMBER

SESSION 9:

Serology

Chairs:

Servaas Morré & Patrick Horner

11.30-11.38: Estimates of trachoma prevalence using serology are sensitive to analysis methods

Stephanie J Migchelsen[1], Diana Martin[2], Gretchen Cooley[2], Sarah Gwyn[2], Peter Paul Rubangakene[3], Patrick Turyaguma[3], Khamphoua Southisombath[4], Hassan Joof[5], Pateh Makalo[5], Neal Alexander[1], Susan Lewallen[6], Paul Courtright[6], Chrissy h Roberts[1], David Mabey[1]

[1]London School of Hygiene and Tropical Medicine, London, UK, [2]Centres for Disease Control and Prevention, Atlanta, GA, USA, [3]ENVISION Programme, RTI International, Kampala, Uganda, [4]Ministry of Health, Vientiane, People's Democratic Republic of Lao, [5]MRC Unit, Fajara, Gambia, [6]Kiliminjaro Centre for Community Ophthalmology, Cape Town, South Africa

Background/ Introduction

Ocular infection with *Chlamydia trachomatis* (Ct) causes trachoma, the leading infectious cause of blindness. With increasing focus on eliminating trachoma as a public health problem, countries are seeking confirmation of trachoma-free-status. Surveys show poor correlation between clinical signs and infection, particularly in low-endemic communities. Serology may be an alternative indicator.

Objectives

Recent studies have used serological tests to indicate cumulative exposure to Ct infection in trachoma endemic populations. Our study aimed to evaluate the use of serology as an alternative indicator for trachoma surveillance by detecting antibodies against Pgp3, an immunodominant Ct antigen. Different methods for the classification threshold were explored.

Method

Clinical examinations were carried out as part of international trachoma surveys in three countries (Laos, Uganda, The Gambia). Dried blood spots were collected from participants and were tested for antibodies to Pgp3 using an enzyme-linked immunosorbant assay (ELISA). Classification thresholds were set using Receiver operating characteristics (ROC)-curves, fixed mixture models (FMM), and visual inspection of the inflection point. ELISA results were compared to clinical findings. Age-specific seroprevalence curves were generated using the different thresholding approaches.

Results

The prevalence of clinical trachoma was low in all three countries and lower than the seroprevalence of anti-*Ct* antibodies.

The fixed mixture model (FMM) determined identical classification thresholds (0.55 optical density (OD) units) in all four population samples. Visual inspection of the inflection point produced threshold values and estimated seroprevalence similar to those set by FMM. A ROC curve based on standards provided by the Centres for Disease Control and Prevention resulted in a higher threshold (0.755) and a significantly lower estimated seroprevalence of anti-*Ct* antibodies. Age groups were insufficiently sized for precision estimates.

Conclusions

For serology to be used as an alternative marker for trachoma transmission, standardisation of assays is required including universal reference standards for comparison between studies as well as standardised analysis methods. Estimates of seroprevalence are highly sensitive to the analysis method chosen, especially when the overall prevalence is low.

11.38-11.46: Seroprevalence of antibodies to a urogenital derivative of *Chlamydia trachomatis* plasmid-encoded Pgp3 in 15-year-old children in England

Catherine E Winstanley[1], Ian N. Clarke[1], Ezra Linley[2], Peter Marsh[3]
[1]University of Southampton, Southampton, Hampshire, UK, [2]Public Health England, Manchester Royal Infirmary, Manchester, Greater Manchester, UK, [3]Public Health England, Southampton General Hospital, Southampton, Hampshire, UK

Background/ Introduction

No systematic investigation of the seroprevalence of *C. trachomatis* in the under 16s population in England has been conducted, despite evidence of chlamydial diagnoses and increasingly earlier sexual debut. As patients under 16 are not actively recruited for screening, this data will provide insight into the need for screening children.

Objectives

We aimed to determine the seroprevalence of anti-Pgp3 antibodies in male and female 15-year-old children in England with a recently improved and validated sensitive and specific indirect ELISA using a urogenital derivative of *C. trachomatis* Pgp3.

Method

We used an indirect ELISA incorporating recombinant Pgp3 derived from urogenital *C. trachomatis* serovar E (pSW2) expressed as a fusion protein with an N-terminal glutathione s-transferase (GST) tag to detect antibodies in patient sera. 708 anonymised and unlinked serum samples collected from 15-year-old male and female children from England were blinded and tested. Sera that returned an OD value above the 0.652 cut-off were considered positive for anti-Pgp3 antibodies. Sera that reacted to Pgp3 were also assayed against GST as a negative control.

Results

Overall seroprevalence of serum samples sourced from genitourinary medicine (GUM) clinics was 24.32% (95% CI; 16.68-33.38%). Seroprevalence of serum samples collected from non-GUM clinic or unknown sources were 8.55% (95% CI; 5.50-12.55%) and 7.34% (95% CI; 4.76-10.72%) for females and males, respectively. All sera assayed against the GST negative control returned background-corrected OD values below 0.498. One serum sample returned an OD value of 0.753 against GST and was not used in any seroprevalence analyses.

Conclusions

The seroprevalence of anti-Pgp3 antibodies is an indicator of current and prior *C. trachomatis* exposure. Our data show that the seroprevalence in 15-year-olds in England is similar to 16-24-year-olds, the group targeted by the National *Chlamydia* Screening Programme.

11.46-11.54: Exploring the impact of previous *Chlamydia* diagnoses on Pgp3 antibody response to infection

Paula B Blomquist[1,2], Gillian Wills[3], Daphne Kounali[4,5], Kevin Dunbar[1,2], Myra McClure[3], Tony E Ades[4,5], Kate Soldan[1,2], Paddy J Horner[4,5], Sarah Woodhall[1,2]
[1]*Public Health England, London, UK,* [2]*NIHR Health Protection Research Unit in Blood borne and Sexually Transmitted Infections at UCL, London, UK,* [3]*Imperial College London, London, UK,* [4]*NIHR Health Protection Research Unit in the Evaluation of Interventions at University of Bristol, London, UK,* [5]*University of Bristol, London, UK,* [6]*University Hospitals Bristol NHS Trust, London, UK*

Background/ Introduction

Surveys measuring the seroprevalence of *Chlamydia trachomatis* (CT) antibodies are a promising means of estimating *Chlamydia* incidence to evaluate *Chlamydia* control programmes when combined with other data. However, the relationship between CT antibody response and history of CT infection needs to be defined to interpret findings from serological studies.

Objectives

This study aims to investigate the potential of two enzyme-linked immunosorbent assays (ELISA) targeted at the CT-specific antigen, Pgp3, as an epidemiological tool to evaluate *Chlamydia* screening. This interim analysis quantifies the relationship between history of known *Chlamydia* infection and the Pgp3 antibody response among samples tested to-date.

Method

We used a national surveillance system, the genitourinary medicine clinic activity dataset (GUMCAD), to identify serum samples leftover from routine HIV/syphilis testing. Eligible samples were from 16-44 year-old GUM-attending women with at least one known *Chlamydia* diagnosis and a *Chlamydia* test on the date the blood sample was taken. Samples were obtained from diagnostic laboratories and tested anonymously using an indirect (sensitivity=73.8%) and a double-antigen Pgp3 ELISA (sensitivity=82.9%). Pgp3 seropositivity is presented for samples from women with a same-day CT positive test ("CT+ves") and from those with a same-day CT negative test and at least one previous CT diagnosis ("follow-ups").

Results

This interim analysis included 425 samples (287 CT+ves; 138 follow-ups). Point estimates of Pgp3 seropositivity were lower in follow-ups compared to CT+ves using the indirect (56.5% vs 63.4%) but not the double-antigen assay (68.8% vs 68.3%). Among CT+ves, seropositivity was higher in samples from women with at least one previous GUMCAD-recorded *Chlamydia* diagnosis versus those with none (indirect:76.9% vs 62.8%; double-antigen:92.3% vs 67.2%). However this result should be interpreted with caution given the small number of CT+ves with a previous diagnosis (n=13). Testing of additional serum samples with varying histories of *Chlamydia* is ongoing, results of which will be presented.

Conclusions

Pgp3 seropositivity may be higher in women with repeat CT and may decrease with time. Seropositivity was lower than expected among CT+ves, which may arise from clinical diagnoses occurring soon after CT acquisition, prior to seroconversion. Final results will inform a multi-parameter evidence synthesis model of CT incidence in England.

11.54-12.02: Does immune response to *Chlamydia trachomatis* predict tubal factor infertility, a prospective study

Päivi Joki-Korpela[1], Tiina Rantsi[1], Hanna Öhman[2], Mirja Puolakkainen[3], Aini Bloigu[2], Jorma Paavonen[1], Heljä-Marja Surcel[2], Aila Tiitinen[1]

[1]Department of Obstetrics and Gynecology, University of Helsinki, Helsinki, Finland, [2]The National Institute for Health and Welfare, Oulu, Finland, [3]Haartman Institute Department of Virology, University of Helsinki, Helsinki, Finland

Background/ Introduction

Subfertility is a major health problem requiring costly evaluation and management. The association of tubal factor infertility (TFI) and chlamydial infection has been confirmed in several studies. Laparoscopy is a golden standard when detecting TFI. However, it is invasive, costly and can cause complications to patients.

Objectives

Non-invasive methods would be needed to identify TFI for effective and economical planning of the treatment. In order to develop simple, noninvasive screening test that could reliably predict those positive with TFI we evaluated the role of *Chlamydia trachomatis* infection in subfertile patients.

Method

Blood samples were collected from 228 couples referred for infertility investigations to Department of Obstetrics and Gynecology, Helsinki University Hospital during July 2007-December 2010. Follow-up was done until the first successful pregnancy or until June 2014.

A possible history of past *C.trachomatis* infection was studied by analyzing *C.trachomatis* IgG (anti-CTR), IgA and chlamydial heat shock protein 60 (CHSP60)-specific antibodies as well as lymphocyte proliferative reactivity against chlamydial elementary body and recombinant CHSP60 antigens.

Results

Altogether 160 (70,2%) women were examined for tubal patency either by hysterosalpingosonography or by laparoscopy. TFI was found in 26 out of 160 patients. IVF treatment was needed more often for the TFI cases (46,2%) than for the subjects with patent tubes (39,0%). Life birth rate was lower among the TFI cases (53,8%) than in the subjects with patent tubes (79,1%; $p<0.016$). Anti-CTR antibodies were found in 20,6% and anti-HSP60 antibodies in 13,8% of the subjects. Prevalence of anti-CTR (33,3%) or anti-CHSP60 (31,8%) antibodies was three fold higher among the TFI cases than among the subjects with patent tubes ($p<0.03$).

Conclusions

Anti-CTR and anti-HSP60 antibodies were detected more frequently in TFI patients than in subjects with patent tubes. However, these tests are not sensitive enough to be used clinically to predict tubal status.

12.15-12.30: The ECDC *Chlamydia* control in Europe Guidance 2015 - advancing *Chlamydia* prevention and control in the European Union/European Economic Area (EU/EEA)

Otilia Mårdh, Gianfranco Spiteri, Andrew Amato-Gauci
European Centre for Disease Prevention and Control (ECDC), Stockholm, Sweden

Background/ Introduction

Chlamydia trachomatis is the most frequently reported sexually transmitted infection (STI) in the EU/EEA, with 396,128 cases reported in 2014, 63% among 15-24 year-olds. National rates ranged from below 1 to 549 diagnoses per 100,000 population, reflecting differences in control activities intensity and surveillance across the Member States.

Objectives

The European Centre for Disease Prevention and Control (ECDC) *Chlamydia* control in Europe guidance 2015 is an update of the 2009 edition and aims at supporting policy makers and national programme coordinators in EU/EEA countries to develop, implement and improve their *Chlamydia* control activities.

Method

ECDC convened a technical group to critically review the scientific evidence on the epidemiology and natural history of *Chlamydia* and on the clinical impact and cost-effectiveness of screening programmes. This evidence was supplemented by a mapping of *Chlamydia* control policies through a survey of Member States in 2012 and a qualitative assessment of the 2009 guidance impact on *Chlamydia* policy changes. An expert panel consultation in 2014 provided further insight about the use of the first guidance edition, discussed the evidence review and survey findings and made suggestions for guidance revision.

Results

Evidence was found that widespread testing can reduce the risk of pelvic inflammatory disease within one year after testing (RR= 0.64 [95%CI 0.44-0.9]) but not the prevalence of infection. The 2009 guidance has been used for policy changes by 11/25 countries. The minimum level for *Chlamydia* prevention and control activities recommended by 2015 guidance includes: a national strategy/plan for STIs control, primary STIs prevention activities, evidence-based case management guidelines (with partner notification), surveillance of diagnosed cases and evaluation plan for the strategy. Widespread opportunistic testing or a screening programme is recommended if resources exist and adequate monitoring and evaluation implemented.

Conclusions

Although the evidence-base for *Chlamydia* control policies has advanced since 2009, future research is needed on the natural history of infection and the impact of interventions at population level. ECDC's guidance policy options should be considered by the Member States according to their specific epidemiological, healthcare and resource environments.

THURSDAY AFTERNOON, 8TH SEPTEMBER

SESSION 10:

Diagnostics

Chairs:

Julius Schachter & Barbara Van Der Pol

13.30–14.00

Keynote: Angelika Stary

Chlamydia Diagnosis:

The more we test, the more we find

Angelika Stary. Outpatients Centre for STD Diagnosis, Vienna, Austria

Since most of the persons infected with *Chlamydia trachomatis* (*C. trachomatis*) are not aware of their infection, which can lead to serious complications, the identification of infected individuals and an appropriate treatment is of upmost importance. Recommendations for the laboratory-based detection of *C. trachomatis* are regularly renewed by the CDC, which provide an overview on available tests, an update on standard procedures for sampling and processing specimens, and advise for the interpretation of test results for laboratory reporting. Furthermore, European guidelines for the management of *Chlamydia* infections have been established and published in 2016 by the International Union against Sexually Transmitted Infections (IUSTI) in Europe, and are also regularly updated. They focus on all different aspects concerning *Chlamydia* and provide a summary of laboratory procedures.

Indications for *Chlamydia* diagnosis include not only patients with clinical symptoms which might be caused by *C. trachomatis*, but also a large number of core group persons diagnosed with other STIs, sexual contacts of persons with an STI, termination of pregnancy or any intrauterine intervention, and, finally, the large number of individuals with sexual risk behaviour.

Chlamydia culture is not anymore the goldstandard technology and has been substituted by nucleic acied amplification tests (NAATs), identifying *Chlamydia* specific DNA or RNA with superior sensitivity and specificity. There are several validated, quality-assured, and FDA-approved NAATs recommended for *Chlamydia* diagnosis using invasive and non-invasive specimen types. These include Aptima assays, Abbott technologies, BD ProbeTec DNA assays, the Cobas technologies and Xpert assays and are listed in the MMWR recommendations 2014 of the CDC. In this overview there are also data summarized on evaluated specimen types and on transport and storage conditions. Non-FDA-approved technologies are offered internationally in an increasing number, and should be validated at least against one approved NAAT. Positive, negative, and inhibition controls as well as participation in an appropriate EQA system are needed for quality assurance. Simply quoting sensitivity and specificity data from package inserts or published studies is not enough to exclude variables which might influence the evaluation.

The sensitivity range of FDA-approved NAATs is above 90% or higher, the specificity is usually above 98%. However, it is important to consider, that all diagnostic NAATs can generate inaccurate results with certain false positive or false negative results mostly as a consequence of incorrect sampling, transport, and test procedure. Although it is unlikely that environmental or cross contamination of *C.trachomatis* may lead to a significant number of false positive results, the participation for laboratories on a regular quality control evaluation should be included in the standard regulations for quality assurance and improve confidence in the results.

Rapid point of care tests (POCT) have been developed in order to provide an easy and quick test result with treatment recommendations at the first visit of the patient. Few technologies are already FDA-approved and sensitivities range between 25% and 65%. They may be cost-effective for those individuals who are not willing or able to wait for longer than 40 minutes, which is a key element for the recommendation of a POCT, despite a lower sensitivity than NAATs. Considering the evaluation results when compared to FDA-approved NAATs, their recommendation is limited and there is still room for improvement. "Assured" POCT have yet to become available.

Stability of *C. trachomatis* in the specimen types is an important issue if they are not processed in the same site of collection. It has been shown by CA. Gaydos and T. Quinn that *Chlamydia* remains detectable on dry swabs at 4°C for more than 30 days at lowest concentrations which confirms that NAATs are an appropriate technology for trachoma diagnosis in areas where this infection is endemic and samples may need to be shipped.

The number of different urogenital specimen types recommended for *Chlamydia* testing has increased over the last decades and the high performance pattern for all different swabs has been proven in many studies in Europe and the USA. In case of clinical symptoms, women should be examined and an endocervical sample should be taken for *Chlamydia* testing. For screening purposes, vulvovaginal swabs have proven to provide similar or even better results when compared to cervical smears, even if selfcollected. Alternatively, first-void urine (FVU) can be recommended in women, if no other specimens are available and NAATs are used for testing. In men, FVU is the recommended first choice specimen type for urogenital *Chlamydia* diagnosis and has substituted urethral swabs. Even penile swabs have shown a similar high senstitivity when carefully provided and tested by NAATs. Pharyngeal and rectal specimens are recommended routinely for MSM in addition to urine, but have not yet been lisenced for NAATs. In many studies these assays have proven to perform with a higher sensitivity and specificity when compared with other test procedures and therefore are recommended as the first choice technology. In MSM with receptive rectal intercourse, identification of LGV by genotyping of positive samples after rectal screening by NAATs should follow the identification of *C. trachomatis*, irrespective of the presence of clinical symptoms.

The question, whether a test of cure (TOC) should be recommended, has been discussed over a longer period of time and is not routinely suggested. Only in case of persisting symptoms, the use of a second- or third-line treatment, non-compliance to therapy or suspected re-exposure of infection, as well as for extragenital treatment, a TOC is recommended. Further considerations were discussed over several years, whether positive specimens should be routinely retested and confirmed by NAAT with a different target to be amplified. This additional test procedure is no longer recommended, since the retest has shown an overall >90% concurrence with the initial test for *C. trachomatis*. Also pooling of specimens was considered as an attempt to reduce the higher material costs. There has been evidence that up to 10 unrine specimens can be cost-effective without any loss of sensitivity and specificity with a saving of 40-60'% dependend on the positivity rate of the examined persons. However, the additional time needed for the performance of the pooling protocol as well as the potential risk for cross-contamination by the extensive handling of samples must be considered. A further advantage of NAATs is the combined diagnosis of gonococcal infections with the same specimen type and a high performance pattern also for these organisms in most of the NAATs.

In summary, there is no doubt that the development of molecular technologies had an impact on the improvement of *Chlamydia* diagnosis of genital as well as extragenital infections. Comparison studies have demonstrated a high performance pattern with reliable results in a short period of time. With these technologies it is possible to develop large scale screening programmes in asymptomatic individuals who are regarded as high risk persons in order to reduce the infection rate of *C. trachomatis* and minimize longterm sequalae in the future.

14.00-14.10: What explains anorectal *Chlamydia* detection in women: implications for test and treatment strategies

Janneke C.M. Heijne[1], Geneviève A.F.S. Van Liere[2,3], Christian J.P.A. Hoebe[2,3], Johannes A. Bogaards[1], Birgit H.B. Van Benthem[1], Nicole H.T.M. Dukers-Muijrers[2,3]
[1]Centre for Infectious Diseases Control, National Institute for Public Health and the Environment, Bilthoven, The Netherlands, [2]Department of Sexual Health, Infectious Diseases and Environmental Health, South Limburg Public Health Service, Geleen, The Netherlands, [3]Department of Medical Microbiology, School of Public Health and Primary Care (CAPHRI), Maastricht University Medical Center (MUMC+), Maastricht, The Netherlands

Background/ Introduction

Anorectal *Chlamydia trachomatis* (*Chlamydia*) infections are common in women irrespective of recent anal intercourse. However, anorectal *Chlamydia* testing in women is often done on indication of recent anal intercourse or symptoms, hence many anorectal infections go unnoticed. Furthermore, standard treatment for urogenital infections (azithromycin) shows reduced effectiveness for anorectal *Chlamydia*.

Objectives

To explore the role of anorectal infections in *Chlamydia* transmission and to estimate the impact of interventions aimed at improved detection or treatment of anorectal infections.

Method

We developed a pair compartmental model of heterosexuals aged 15-29 years attending STI clinics, in which women can be susceptible to or infected with *Chlamydia* urogenitally and/or anorectally, and men urogenitally. Transmission probabilities per vaginal and anal sex act, together with an autoinoculation probability, were estimated by fitting to anatomic site-specific prevalence data (14% urogenital and 11% anorectal prevalence). We investigated the 10-year reduction in *Chlamydia* prevalence from routine universal anorectal testing and/or universal doxycycline use, relative to continued standard of care (anorectal testing on indication and treating urogenital infections with azithromycin and detected anorectal infections with doxycycline).

Results

The transmission probability per anal sex act was 5.8% (IQR: 3.0%-8.3%), per vaginal sex act 2.0% (IQR: 1.7%-2.2%), and the daily autoinoculation probability when infected at one location was 0.7% (IQR: 0.5%-1.0%). At the urogenital site, most infections were caused by vaginal intercourse, whereas at the anorectal site most were caused by autoinoculation. Treating universally with doxycycline instead of azithromycin resulted in a relative decrease in prevalence of 4.3% (IQR: 3.5%-5.3%) and routine universal anorectal testing in 8.7% (IQR: 7.6%-9.7%) compared to continuation of the standard of care. In absolute terms, these reductions were small.

Conclusions

Autoinoculation between anatomic sites in women seems likely and could be important for *Chlamydia* transmission. Change to routine universal anorectal testing or doxycycline as the standard treatment for *Chlamydia* in women is not expected to substantially reduce *Chlamydia* population prevalence. Therefore, re-evaluating the standard of care is not (yet) indicated.

14.10-14.20: V-PCR as a novel approach to evaluate *Chlamydia trachomatis* viability

Kevin J.H Janssen[1], Christian J.P.A Hoebe[1,2], Mayk Lucchesi[1], Lisanne Eppings[1,2], Nicole H.T.M Dukers-Muijrers[1,2], Petra F.G Wolffs[1]
[1]*Department of Medical Microbiology, School of Public Health and Primary Care (CAPHRI), Maastricht University Medical Center (MUMC+), Maastricht, Limburg, The Netherlands,* [2]*Department of Sexual Health, Infectious Diseases, and Environmental Health, South Limburg Public Health Service (GGD), Geleen, Limburg, The Netherlands*

Background/ Introduction

Although widely used, NAATs are known to amplify the available target DNA without discriminating between DNA originating from viable or non-viable CT. Recent studies have demonstrated that CT positivity could be detected up to 8 weeks post treatment. Until today the true clinical implications of such results are still unexplored.

Objectives

This study aimed to evaluate and implement viability PCR (v-PCR) to discriminate viable from non-viable CT.

Method

Aliquots of CT culture were subjected to heat-treatment at 95°C for 15 minutes resulting in a decrease of inclusion forming (IFU) units to zero. Heat inactivated CT culture was mixed with the untreated viable CT culture in defined ratios representing 0%, 0.1%, 1%, 10%, 50%, and 100% viability, respectively. Ratios were spiked in different media, namely 2SP transport medium, urine, and MEM culture medium. Two different serotypes of CT were used to conduct experiments, namely serotype D and serotype LGV II. The DNA intercalating dye propidium monoazide (PMA) was used as sample pretreatment prior to DNA purification following quantitative-PCR (qPCR).

Results

Conform expectations, the DNA yields of all ratios were comparable without PMA treatment, as equal amounts of DNA were present. In contrast, when applying v-PCR, increasing proportions of viable CT culture led to a substantial increase in DNA yield, i.e. decrease in Ct values in qPCR. As expected, PMA treatment almost completely inhibited amplification of DNA from heat-inactivated CT (i.e. a signal reduction of 99.9%). Additionally, PMA treatment of the 100% viable sample showed no significant reduction of amplifiable DNA, indicating that all DNA from viable CT was amplifiable.

Conclusions

v-PCR showed to be a fast and sensitive method for assessing CT viability without the need of labor intensive, difficult to perform, and insensitive culture methods. Future work will focus on the assessment of the viability of CT in clinical samples by the vPCR method.

14.20-14.30: The Danish *Chlamydia* Study: Analysis of longitudinal trends in *Chlamydia* testing and diagnosed incidence in men

Katy ME Turner[1], Bethan Davies[3], Maria Frolund[4], Helen Ward[3], Thomas Benfield[2], Margaret May[1], Inge Panum[2], Henrik Westh[2]
[1]University of Bristol, Bristol, UK, [2]Hvridovre Hospital, Copenhagen, Denmark, [3]Imperial College London, London, UK, [4]Staten Serum Institut, Copenhagen, Denmark

Background/ Introduction

The **Danish *Chlamydia* Study** is a retrospective case-control study constructed from linked administrative health data from the Danish National Board of Health and the purpose-generated dataset of *Chlamydia* laboratory test records. We analyse the epidemiological trends in *Chlamydia* testing and *Chlamydia* diagnoses in Denmark from 1991 to 2011.

Objectives

To describe combining and linking individual level patient records from national Danish administrative, health and purposive-generated datasets to generate further analysis of the impact of *Chlamydia* screening on reproductive outcomes. We focus particularly on *Chlamydia* testing and diagnosis in men.

Method

The study design is secondary data linkage and analysis using a retrospective population based case-control cohort. In Denmark, we collated linked, individual level data on all *Chlamydia* testing and hospital admissions data (population level) in men >=15. We compared testing and diagnosis in men compared with women in Denmark.

Results

The Danish *Chlamydia* Study includes records of 326,430 men; 65,286 cases and 261,144 controls (201,013 never tested). There were 291,530 *Chlamydia* tests recorded, of which 85,004 (29%) were positive. At first recorded test, 14.8% (52,784/356,407) men were *Chlamydia* positive, of whom 11.0% were retested in 60 to 180 days, 23.7% (1,371/2,744) of those were also infected at the second test. Tested men were about twice as likely as women to be infected at first test and about half as likely to test again after their first test (whether negative or positive).

Conclusions

The **Danish *Chlamydia* Study** is a rich database resource. In Denmark, despite sustained high levels of *Chlamydia* testing in women there has been limited impact on positivity. The high positivity in tested men suggests substantial undiagnosed infection which could hamper *Chlamydia* control efforts at the population level.

14.30-14.40: High proportion of anorectal *Chlamydia trachomatis* in STI clinic women after routine universal urogenital and anorectal screening

Geneviève AFS van Liere[1,2], Nicole HTM Dukers-Muijrers[1,2], Luuk Levels[3], Christian JPA Hoebe[1,2]
[1]*Public Health Service South Limburg, Department of Sexual Health, Infectious Diseases and Environmental Health, Geleen, The Netherlands,* [2]*Department of Medical Microbiology, School of Public Health and Primary Care, Maastricht University Medical Center (MUMC+), Maastricht, The Netherlands,* [3]*Public Health Service North Limburg, Department of Sexual Health, Infectious Diseases and Environmental Health, Venlo, The Netherlands*

Background/ Introduction

Selective symptom- and sexual history-based testing is used to manage anorectal *Chlamydia trachomatis* (CT) and *Neisseria gonorrhoeae* (NG) infections in women. Little is known about the differences between CT and NG regarding prevalence and risk factors for infection using routine universal anorectal testing in women.

Objectives

This study informs the optimal control strategy for anorectal CT and NG infections by using the largest cohort of women routinely universally tested for anorectal CT and NG up to date.

Method

All women (n=1012) aged 16 years and older attending our STI-clinic between January-December 2015 were offered routine universal testing for anorectal and urogenital *Chlamydia trachomatis* and *Neisseria gonorrhoeae*. Specimens were tested using nucleic acid amplification tests. Of women, 94% (n=953) participated in the study. Data were collected on demographics, sexual behaviour and symptoms. CT and NG positivity was calculated by dividing the number of positive tests by the total number of tests, multiplied by 100. Univariable and multivariable logistic regression analyses were used to identify factors associated with anorectal CT and NG.

Results

Anal sex was reported by 19.8% (n=174) of women, anal symptoms were reported by 1.6% (n=15). Urogenital CT positivity was 11.0% (n=105), anorectal CT positivity was 13.4% (n=128). Age ≤21 years was the only factor associated with anorectal CT infections (OR 2.1, 95% CI 1.3-3.4). Self-report of anal sex or anal symptoms were not associated with anorectal CT. Urogenital NG positivity was 1.5% (n=14), anorectal NG positivity was 1.3% (n=12). Self-report of anal sex and anal symptoms were independently associated with anorectal NG infections (OR 3.5, 95% CI 1.03-11.8 and OR 16.2, 95% CI 3.1-86.4, respectively).

Conclusions

Anorectal testing in women who did not report anal sex or symptoms is feasible and highly acceptable. Selective testing on indication of symptoms and sexual history is an appropriate control strategy for anorectal NG infections, but not for anorectal CT infections in women visiting the STI clinic.

15.40-15.55: A critical review on current knowledge on pelvic inflammatory disease (PID) with special reference to chlamydial infections

Per-Anders Mårdh
Lund University, Lund, Sweden

Background/ Introduction

There is still a number of white spots in the understanding of PID and its role in sub-fertility, infertility and poor-obstetrics outcomes.
Failures of antibiotic therapy of PID are common. Studies on drugs kinetics and their distribution in endometrial and tubal tissue, including in previously damaged mucosal surfaces, are scanty.

Objectives

To discuss the need to identify the entire microbiota of the upper female genital tract in PID, both in acute and chronic cases.

Method

A summary of current gaps in the knowledge on PID with focus on *Chlamydia* infections.

Results

Failure of NAAT to identify chronic *Chlamydia trachomatis* infections in fallopian tubes should be recognised. Individual pattern of persistence in antibody production hampers epidemiological serological studies. There are still difficulties to diagnose endometritis in clinical practice and thereby to establish its role in fertility problems. In a *Chlamydia*-infected endometrium there are obstacles for egg nidation. Studies on infertility and contribution of various PID etiological agents have so far not met the needed follow-up periods. Influence of various assisted reproduction techniques allowing women to conceive should be included in such studies, same for the impact of male factor in infertile couples.

Conclusions

Studies are still needed to recognise which agents may cause PID and how to best treat these infections to avoid complications, such as chronic pelvic pain, ectopic pregnancy and fertility problems.

15.55-16.10: The Oncogenic Potential of *Chlamydia* Infection

Allen Tsang
Wake Forest School of Medicine, Winston-Salem, USA

Background/ Introduction

We have been applying an innovative approach that relies on combining advanced technologies capable of measuring thousands of individual modifications in infected cells with computational methods to ultimately identify patterns that are consistent with transformation of a normal cell into a tumor-like state.

Objectives

To reveal key molecular signatures induced by *Chlamydia* in normal epithelial cells.

A. To determine transient and persistent changes in DNA methylation, protein abundance, phosphorylation and protein oxidation using state-of-the-art mass spectrometry.

B. To identify molecular signatures of infection with by integrating proteomics and epigenetics data using new computational methods.

Method

To investigate redox processes associated with chlamydial infection, we have used a chemical probe Biotin-1,3-cyclopentanedione that contains a biotin tag, for tracking protein oxidation in cells. This has been applied together with quantitative mass spectrometry and network analysis tools to recognize specific host proteins that are target of *Chlamydia*-induced ROS. The oncogenic signatures generated from this study will guide future recognition of *Chlamydia*-induced cancers, which will be important for development of preventive and therapeutic approaches.

Results

Using quantitative mass spectrometry and computational tools, we recognized the changes in protein expression induced by chlamydial infection. Some of the targeted proteins are involved in the proliferation, infiltration and migration of tumor cells. Additionally, chlamydial infection manipulates the host sources of reactive oxygen species (ROS) and uses these as signaling molecules for *Chlamydia*'s survival and development in the host cell.

Conclusions

We used a systematic approach to evaluate the Oncogenic Potential of *Chlamydia* Infection. Since infectious agents can be cleared from the organism with time and/or treatment. Therefore, we focused on the "footprints" left by infectious agents regardless if these are still present in the infected cancer tissue.

CLINICAL RESEARCH DAY

Chairs:

Aura Andreasen

Sarah Woodhall

Kevin Dunbar

Patrick Horner

Katy Turner

Charlotte Gaydos

Ned Hook

Jan van Bergen

10.00 – 10.30

ALISON QUAYLE:

Immunity and immunoevasion: understanding the host-*Chlamydia* relationship and its consequence to infection outcomes and our hope for a vaccine.

Alison Qualye, PhD. Department of Microbiology, Immunology and Parasitology, Louisiana State University Health Sciences Center, New Orleans, Louisiana 70112, United States of America.

Chlamydia trachomatis is an obligate intracellular bacterium with a unique developmental cycle. Serovars D through K are tropic for the columnar epithelial cells of the urogenital tract. The endocervix is the most common site of infection in women, but organisms can ascend into the uterus and Fallopian tubes where they may cause pelvic inflammatory disease and the longer-term sequelae of tubal infertility and ectopic pregnancy. How and why untreated chlamydial infections can be asymptomatic for substantial periods of time, some infections progress to cause significant pathology and others spontaneously resolve without antibiotic treatment is not understood, but, collectively, they suggest that the local, genital immune response to this pathogen is only variably protective and effective. In this talk we will review the elements of immunity that contribute to a local, genital immune response and the current paradigms on immunity and immunopathogenesis of chlamydial infection. We will also review the strategies that *C. trachomatis* uses to survive in the genial tract by exploiting, adapting to, or evading, certain genital immune and environmental conditions. A particular emphasis will be placed on the role of interferon gamma as a key mediator in the resolution of chlamydial infection, and its compromise by endogenous factors that modulate the genital milieu, and, in particular, bacterial vaginosis (BV). Finally, we will discuss the application of this information to improve the prospect for an effective vaccine, and for developing targeted therapies to enhance the functionality of the local immune response.

10.30 – 11.00

MALCOLM PRICE:

The natural history of *Chlamydia trachomatis* infection in women: a multi-parameter evidence synthesis

Malcolm J Price[1], AE Ades[2], Kate Soldan[3], Nicky J Welton[2], John Macleod[2], Ian Simms[3], Daniela DeAngelis[3,4], Katherine ME Turner[2] and Patrick J Horner[2,5]

[1]Institute of Applied Health Research, University of Birmingham, Birmingham, UK; [2]School of Social and Community Medicine, University of Bristol, Bristol, UK; [3]Public Health England (formerly Health Protection Agency), Colindale, London, UK; [4]Medical Research Council Biostatistics Unit, Cambridge, UK; [5]Bristol Sexual Health Centre, University Hospital Bristol NHS Foundation Trust, Bristol, UK

Background and objectives: The evidence base supporting the National *Chlamydia* Screening Programme, initiated in 2003, has been questioned repeatedly, with little consensus on modelling assumptions, parameter values or evidence sources to be used in cost-effectiveness analyses. The purpose of this project was to assemble all available evidence on the prevalence and incidence of *Chlamydia trachomatis* (CT) in the UK and its sequelae, pelvic inflammatory disease (PID), ectopic pregnancy (EP) and tubal factor infertility (TFI) to review the evidence base in its entirety, assess its consistency and, if possible, arrive at a coherent set of estimates consistent with all the evidence.

Methods: Evidence was identified using 'high-yield' strategies. Bayesian Multi-Parameter Evidence Synthesis models were constructed for separate subparts of the clinical and population epidemiology of CT. These were: duration of asymptomatic CT; incidence, prevalence and duration of CT considered together; the risk of PID following CT infection; the incidence of PID and the proportion of PID attributable to CT; the cumulative incidence of PID, of repeat episodes and the prevalence of previous salpingitis; the relation between salpingitis and EP; the relation between salpingitis and TFI; and the relation between CT and TFI from serological case–control studies. Under each of these headings, multiple sources of evidence were assembled and their interpretation was reviewed. We assessed the consistency of estimates derived from alternative evidence sources. Where appropriate, different types of data sources were statistically combined to derive coherent estimates. Where evidence was inconsistent, evidence sources were re-interpreted and new estimates derived on a post-hoc basis. Where models and interpretations were based on post-hoc reasoning, this was highlighted, and any conclusions were considered as tentative and requiring further confirmation.

Results: An internally coherent set of estimates was generated, consistent with a multifaceted evidence base including: prospective and retrospective epidemiological studies, fertility surveys, routine UK statistics on PID and EP, and data on CT incidence, prevalence and duration. Among the key findings were that the risk of PID (symptomatic or asymptomatic) following an untreated CT infection is 17.1% [95% credible interval (CrI) 6% to 29%] and the risk of salpingitis is 7.3% (95% CrI 2.2% to 14.0%). In women aged 16–24 years, screened at annual intervals, at best, 61% (95% CrI 55% to 67%) of CT-related PID and 22% (95% CrI 7% to 43%) of all PID could be directly prevented. For women aged 16–44 years, the proportions of PID, EP and TFI that are attributable to CT are estimated to be 20% (95% CrI 6% to 38%), 4.9% (95% CrI 1.2% to 12%) and 29% (95% CrI 9% to 56%), respectively. The prevalence of TFI in the UK in women at the end of their reproductive lives is 1.1%: this is consistent with all PID carrying a relatively high risk of reproductive damage, whether diagnosed or not. Every 1000 CT infections in women aged 16–44 years, on average, gives rise to approximately 171 episodes of PID and 73 of salpingitis, 2.0 EPs and 5.1 women with TFI at age 44 years.

Conclusions and research recommendations: The study establishes a set of interpretations of the major studies and study designs, under which a coherent set of estimates were generated. CT is a significant cause of PID and TFI. CT screening is of benefit to the individual, but detection and treatment of incident infection may be more beneficial. Women with lower abdominal pain need better advice on when to seek early medical attention to avoid risk of reproductive damage. The study provides new insights into the reproductive risks of PID and the role of CT. Further research is required on the proportions of PID, EP and TFI attributable to CT to confirm predictions made in this report, and to improve the precision of key estimates. The cost-effectiveness of *Chlamydia* screening should be re-evaluated using the findings of this report.

11.30 – 12.00

JANET WILSON:

Should we be taking multiple specimens from women and if so how?

Dr Janet Wilson. Consultant in Sexual Health & HIV, Leeds Teaching Hospitals NHS Trust, UK

Chlamydia is the most common bacterial STI in the UK. The majority of infections in women are asymptomatic but it is associated with serious complications such as pelvic inflammatory disease (leading to infertility) and adverse outcomes in pregnancy and neonates. Community screening in asymptomatic women using urogenital samples is now widespread. The optimum sample for urogenital screening /testing is the vulvo-vaginal swab and the evidence for this will be evaluated briefly.

As well as infecting the urogenital tract, *Chlamydia* can also infect the rectum and pharynx (extra-genital sites), usually with no symptoms. In some women *Chlamydia* infection will be found in both the urogenital tract and at extra-genital sites, but in others it will be present at extra-genital sites only, so if all anatomical sites are not tested some infections will be missed. The few small studies looking at extra-genital *Chlamydia* infections in women suggest the prevalence may be as high as in men who have sex with men. There is also concern that the most commonly used treatment for *Chlamydia*, azithromycin 1g single oral dose, may not have good efficacy for treating rectal *Chlamydia* leaving persistent rectal infection which may be a reservoir for reinfection of the urogenital *Chlamydia* tract.

If community screening were to include sampling from extra-genital sites, women would need to perform these samples themselves. However there has been only one published study of self-taken rectal samples in women and none assessing self-taken pharyngeal samples. The results of a new study comparing self-taken extra-genital samples with clinician-taken samples will be presented. BASHH, European and CDC guidelines suggest the sexual history should be used to guide whether rectal and pharyngeal samples should be taken. Associations between having receptive anal sex and rectal *Chlamydia* infection will be presented.

Even if samples taken from the rectum and pharynx, as well as the routine urogenital area, identify additional cases of *Chlamydia* the diagnostic cost is trebled making it unaffordable for most NHS services. Could all samples from one person (VVS, rectum and pharynx) be pooled and analysed together? This would mean that the laboratory cost is the same as currently, (assuming the sensitivity and specificity of the pooled tests is the same as if the samples are analysed individually), making it cost-effective to screen women from all potential sites of infection. The results of a new study comparing self-taken VVS and extra-genital samples analysed separately and as a pooled sample will be presented.

The use of self-taken pooled samples could improve testing for *Chlamydia* in all women. Infections from all sites could be identified without an increase in the cost of the diagnostic tests. This will prevent the false reassurance of negative VVS community screening where extra-genital infections are being missed, without increasing the cost. There will be benefits to the individuals but also to public health in that more infections will be diagnosed resulting in treatment and partner notification thus reducing onward transmission.

12.00 – 12.30

HENRY DE VRIES:

The enigma of lymphogranuloma venereum spread in men who have sex with men: does ano–oral transmission play a role?

Henry John C. de Vries, PhD, MD.

STI Outpatient Clinic and †Public Health Service Amsterdam, Public Health Laboratory, Cluster of Infectious Diseases Amsterdam, the Netherlands;

Department of Dermatology, Academic Medical Centre, University of Amsterdam, Amsterdam, the Netherlands.

Lymphogranuloma venereum (LGV) proctitis caused by the *C. trachomatis* strain L2b is endemic among men who have sex with men (MSM) in Western society. The first cases were found in Rotterdam dating back in 2003.[1,2] Let alone a few reported cases in women, LGV caused by the L2b strain is a focused epidemic exclusively found in MSM.[3] Most reports arise from European nations. In the United Kingdom (UK), national data show a sharp increase in diagnoses of LGV since 2012.[4] The majority of cases live in London, with high rates of co-infection with HIV and other sexually transmitted infections.

LGV is known for two main specific clinical presentations, the "classical" inguinal syndrome and the anorectal syndrome. The anorectal syndrome is characterised by severe proctitis symptoms like anal cramps (tenismus), pain, bloody discharge, and constipation due to edema of the mucosal lining and underlying tissue. These symptoms seem important to identify LGV proctitis as reaffirmed earlier in a UK study concluding that tenesmus alone or in combination with constipation made a diagnosis of LGV in MSM presenting with rectal symptoms likely.[5]

Before 2003, LGV was primarily seen in tropical regions and was characterized by a typical clinical presentation of a destructive infection of the external genitalia with an extensive inflammatory response leading to the formation of suppurating inguinal bubo's and systemic symptoms like fever, arthritis and malaise. This "classical" presentation is also known as inguinal LGV. In contrast to the "classical" presentation, the largest majority of MSM with LGV in the current Western epidemic presents with a severe proctitis and/or proctocolitis.[6] To explain the asymmetric distribution of anorectal and inguinal LGV infections, tissue tropism (with a higher affinity of LGV serovars to rectal mucosa compared with urethral epithelia) has been suggested, but so far not yet confirmed.[7-9] Thus, the majority of reported infections in MSM are found in the anorectal canal and not urogenital. How a man with LGV proctitis transmits the infection to his partner who subsequently also develops an anorectal infection remains a conundrum, and leaves the mode of transmission within the MSM network unclear. In the early days of the epidemic sharing toys or fisting practices have been suggested as transmission modes[10], but subsequently dismissed.[11]

For long, there was the false assumption that LGV infections were symptomatic in the majority of cases.[12] This in contrast to an earlier prospective study from Amsterdam showing that about a quarter of the anorectal LGV cases did not present with symptoms when screened systematically[13]; this ratio has not changed significantly since.[6] A recent prospective study performed in the UK now affirms the Amsterdam finding of a considerable proportion of asymptomatic LGV cases (27%) in a large nationwide cohort.[14] From a patient perspective the detection of asymptomatic LGV cases seems obvious; many asymptomatic patients are possibly pre-symptomatic and early detection can prevent considerable morbidity and irreversible damage on the longer run. Yet from a public health perspective it is of utmost importance to prevent the ongoing "silent" transmission in the population.

Given the increasing trend, the LGV endemic is clearly not under control. Therefore, directed screening must be intensified. Apart from the focus on the 25% asymptomatic anorectal infections, LGV infections at other locations, (e.g. urethral and pharyngeal) are possibly of importance within the transmission network. A few years ago we reported in this journal that in 341 MSM with anorectal LGV, 2.1% had concurrent urethral LGV, and among their partners 6.8% had urethral LGV infections.[15] In the accompanying editorial in the same issue, Ward and Ronn questioned whether non-rectal LGV can account for substantial "reservoirs" that need targeted screening to get this epidemic under control.[16] Prospective studies are required to see if routine screening of non-rectal LGV in MSM is needed and cost-effective.

A daring explanation for persistent *C. trachomatis* infections in women was suggested recently by Rank and Yeruva in an article called "An Alternative Scenario to Explain Rectal Positivity in *Chlamydia*-Infected Individuals".[17] They bring forward that *Chlamydia*e in virtually every natural animal host reside naturally in the gastro-intestinal tract and are transmitted via the fecal–oral route. They can persist in the gastro-intestinal tract for long periods of time in the absence of apparent inflammation and pathology.[18] Igietseme et al. proved back in 2001 that mice infected orally with the mouse *Chlamydia*, *C. muridarum*, become infected in the lower intestinal tract and are unable to clear the infection.[19] This paradigm could possibly account as an explanation for the unanswered findings in the current LGV epidemic in MSM. Ano-genital transmission of L2b *C. trachomatis* could occur between men, but oral infection may also occur via ano-oral sex or mechanical transmission (figure). Oral infection may result in clinical or subclinical pharyngitis, and the organisms may pass through the gastro-intestinal tract to the large intestine and rectum. Here, L2b strains could either induce symptomatic LGV proctitis or induce an asymptomatic infection; in both cases contributing to the ongoing transmission. Whether this theory proves right in the human situation is to be seen, and its contributing factor to the LGV epidemic in MSM remains to be addressed in future research.

References:

1   Nieuwenhuis, R. F., *Sex Transm.Infect.* **79**, 453-455 (2003).
2   de Vrieze,N.H *Expert Rev Anti Infect Ther* **12**, 697-704 (2014).
3   Heiligenberg, M. *BMC Res Notes* **7**, 355 (2014).
4   Childs, T. *Euro Surveill* **20**, 30076 (2015).
5   Pallawela, S. N. *Sex Transm Infect* **90**, 269-274 (2014).
6   de Vrieze, N. H., *Sex Transm Infect* **89**, 548-552 (2013).
7   Bax, C. J. *Sex Transm Infect* **87**, 503-507 (2011).
8   Jeffrey, B. M. *Infect Immun* **78**, 2544-2553 (2010).
9   Versteeg, B. *BMC Infect Dis* **14**, 464 (2014).
10   Nieuwenhuis, R. F. *Clin.Infect.Dis.* **39**, 996-1003 (2004).
11   Van der Bij, A. K. *et al. Clin.Infect.Dis.* **42**, 186-194 (2006).
12   Ward, H. *et al. Sex Transm.Infect.* **85**, 173-175 (2009).
13   de Vries, H. J. *Sex Transm.Dis.* **35**, 203-208 (2008).
14   Saxon, C. *Emerg Infect Dis* **22**, 112-116 (2016).
15   de Vrieze, N. H. *Sex Transm Dis* **40**, 607-608 (2013).
16   Ward, H. *Sex Transm Dis* **40**, 609-610 (2013).
17   Rank, R. G. *Clin Infect Dis* **60**, 1585-1586 (2015).
18   Rank, R. G. *Infect Immun* **82**, 1362-1371 (2014).
19   Igietseme, J. U. *Infect Immun* **69**, 1832-1840 (2001).

12.30 – 13.00

NICOLA LOW:

Chlamydia control programmes – what should we do?

Nicola Low, Reader in epidemiology and public health, Department of Social and Preventive Medicine, University of Bern, Bern, CH-3012, Switzerland.

It is strange that we need to ask the question, "what should we do?" with *Chlamydia* control programmes 20 years after the publication of the first randomised controlled trial of an intervention to detect and treat asymptomatic *Chlamydia* infection in young women. But maybe it's because *Chlamydia trachomatis* infections (*Chlamydia*) are still the most commonly reported sexually transmitted infection (STI) in the UK, Europe, USA and other high income countries after more than 20 years of *Chlamydia* control efforts.

Chlamydia control strategies have emphasised the expansion of efforts to test and treat as many asymptomatic young adults as possible. The rationale is that treating asymptomatic infections will reduce *Chlamydia* transmission and that reducing *Chlamydia* transmission will reduce damaging reproductive tract complications, particularly in women.

What has happened to *Chlamydia* over time?

The prevalence of *C. trachomatis* in samples of the general population detected has not changed much since we started measuring it in urine samples using nucleic acid amplification tests. In Britain, the prevalence of *Chlamydia* aged 18 to 24 years was the same in 2010-11 (women 3·2%, 95% confidence interval, CI 2·2 to 4·6; men 2.6%, 1.7 to 4.0%) as it was a decade earlier (women 3.1%, 95% CI 1.8 to 5.2%; men 2.9%, 1.3 to 6.3%), according to the National Surveys of Sexual Attitudes and Lifestyles. Prevalence thus appeared stable (although we do not know what happened in between), despite a national campaign in England that claimed that widespread opportunistic testing amongst under 25 year olds would reduce *Chlamydia* transmission. In the USA National Health and Nutrition Examination Surveys, *Chlamydia* prevalence in women in the general population aged 15-24 years, who were the target age group for opportunistic testing, was 4.1% (95% CI 2.4 to 6.8%) in 1999–2000 and 3.8% (2.4 to 6.0%) in 2007–2008 with fluctuations in the years between that are compatible with sampling variation. Estimates of *Chlamydia* point prevalence in national population-based samples appear to be similar in countries that do not have recommendations about widespread opportunistic *Chlamydia* (France, Slovenia, Croatia).

What has happened to pelvic inflammatory disease (PID), ectopic pregnancy and infertility over time?

I have not found any source of data about consistently monitored trends of *Chlamydia*-associated PID, ectopic pregnancy or infertility. This is disturbing because preventing these conditions is the main clinical endpoint of *Chlamydia* control. Surveillance based on hospital statistics show reductions in all cause PID, e.g. in the USA and Canada. But these reductions were most dramatic when *Chlamydia* testing was only starting in the late 1980s and early 1990s and they coincide with reductions in STI that many attribute to the response to the HIV epidemic. Interestingly, the same trends also occurred in countries like Australia that had not introduced any *Chlamydia* control efforts at that time.

What could *Chlamydia* control efforts achieve?

Here, the evidence from mathematical modelling studies, clinical trials and observational epidemiological studies diverge. All mathematical modelling studies to date predict that a programme of repeated *Chlamydia* testing and treatment will reduce the prevalence of *Chlamydia* infection in a hypothetical population over time. Models differ widely in the magnitude of the predicted reductions, depending on model structure and their assumptions about *C. trachomatis* dynamics and sexual network characteristics. Several modelling studies predict dramatic reductions in *Chlamydia* prevalence at moderate levels of test uptake, in contrast to the patterns observed in repeated cross-sectional studies.

Two cluster-controlled trials have looked at the effects of *Chlamydia* testing strategies on prevalence in the general population. In both, there was no difference between intervention and control groups in the proportion of positive *Chlamydia* tests (in the Netherlands) or estimated prevalence in unselected general practice patients (in Australia) after two to three years, but *Chlamydia* test uptake was not very high in either trial.

Four randomised controlled trials looked at the effects on PID incidence of a single offer of a *Chlamydia* screening test. The trials overall suggest that PID incidence was lower in intervention and control groups but effects were smaller in the two trials at low risk of bias (relative risk 0.80, 95% CI 0.55 to 1.17) than in those at high or unclear risk of bias (relative risk 0.42, 95% CI 0.22 to 0.83).

The clinical diagnosis of PID is both insensitive and non-specific and most PID is not caused by *C. trachomatis*. As a result, only a small fraction of all-cause PID could be prevented (up to 14%), even under optimistic scenarios (population at high risk of *Chlamydia* and all *Chlamydia*-associated PID prevented).

What should we do?

We have done plenty of testing and amassed plenty of research evidence over the past 20 years. But research findings do not give a coherent picture about what we are doing. We don't know whether *Chlamydia* testing recommendations simply increase the relative proportions of reinfection or repeated infections, compared with maintaining a stable level of prevalent infections over time. It is still not clear whether the degree of reduction in reported diagnoses of all-cause PID is compatible with the expected impact of *Chlamydia* testing over time or, if not, what other factors might have contributed. We do not know whether the women who undergo opportunistic *Chlamydia* testing are those who would have developed tubal infertility. We do know that it is extremely difficult to stop screening programmes once they have started. It is time to stop promoting widespread age-based *Chlamydia* testing without a better understanding of its effects on *Chlamydia* transmission and complications. In the meantime, there is plenty of work to do to improve standards of clinical care to ensure appropriate treatment, partner notification and follow up of people who have been diagnosed with *Chlamydia* infection.

14.00 – 14.30

PAULA BARAITSER:

How can we make best use of the Internet in order to improve the cost effectiveness of STI services?

Paula Baraitser. Senior Lecturer, Kings Centre for Global Health, Kings College London, UK.

Online sexual health services are an increasingly popular delivery modality for sexually transmitted infection (STI) testing. They provide 24 hour access with self sampling kits sent in the post, text message results, online partner notification, online clinical support, postal treatment and rapid referral to services as required. In increasingly resource constrained clinical environments they offer a potentially cost effective solution to increasing access to STI testing.   However online services vary in cost and quality and their contribution to sexual health improvement depends on accessibility for high-risk populations; the user interface and product design; the quality of remote clinical support and the interface with clinical services. This presentation uses the evaluation of an innovative online sexual health service, SH24 (www.sh24.org) to explore the contribution of online services to cost effective sexual health improvement.

14.30 – 15.00

JANNEKE HEIJNE:

How could a *Chlamydia* vaccine impact on patient care? A mathematical modelling study

Janneke Heijne. National Institute for Public Health and the Environment (RIVM), The Netherlands.

Chlamydia trachomatis (*Chlamydia*) has proven to be difficult to control. Even in countries with longstanding screening recommendations or programmes, *Chlamydia* prevalence in the targeted populations has hardly declined in the last decade. In the long term, an effective vaccine might be the most successful intervention to decrease *Chlamydia* prevalence. A *Chlamydia* vaccine has not yet been developed but the prospects are increasingly promising. It is therefore important to evaluate the potential impact of different *Chlamydia* vaccine strategies on population prevalence.

Mathematical modelling is a tool for estimating the theoretical impact of interventions in a population. It makes it possible to compare the effectiveness of different intervention strategies in the same hypothetical population thereby identifying optimal strategies, something that is often not possible or too costly in real life. The optimal vaccination strategy however, might differ depending on the type of protection after vaccination. A vaccine providing full protection for a proportion of the vaccinated population and leaving the remainder fully susceptible (all-or-nothing vaccine) might have a different optimal strategy than vaccines that provide the same level of partial protection for all vaccinated individuals.

Very few modelling studies looked at the impact of *Chlamydia* vaccination on prevalence in humans. Two studies looked at the impact of a fully protective vaccine for 10 years: one found elimination to be possible (1) and the other one that vaccination could be cost-effective (2). However, full protection is not likely since animal models have shown that sterilizing immunity is difficult to achieve making it more likely that a future vaccine will provide partial protection. One study investigated partial vaccine protection and found that this could also strongly reduce *Chlamydia* population prevalence (3). However, the assumed vaccination uptake in this model (100% in young females or 50% in both sexes) is not very realistic, as the coverage of current HPV vaccination campaigns in western countries ranges between 30% to 90% in young females.

We used mathematical modelling to focus on more realistic vaccination scenarios that aim to reduce both population prevalence and long-term complications such as pelvic inflammatory disease (PID). We developed a deterministic SIR (susceptible, infected, recovered) model of heterosexuals. The model includes sexual activity classes that differ in the number of new partners and the duration of partnerships, informed by sexual behavioural data from UK and The Netherlands. We investigated the impact of vaccinating before sexual debut (by entry in the model) and targeted vaccination towards high-risk individuals.

Preliminary results show that the impact of vaccination strategies on reducing *Chlamydia* prevalence and PID is highly dependent on the characteristics of future vaccines; large reductions are observed when the vaccine reduced the duration of infection or decreased susceptibility to infection. Current efforts in vaccine development should be accompanied by mathematical models to investigate the optimal strategies.

References: 1. Brunham RC et al. J Infect Dis. 2005;192(10):1836-44; 2. Owusu-Edusei K et al. Emerg Infect Dis. 2015;21(6):960-8; 3. Gray RT et al. J Infect Dis. 2009;199(11):1680-8.

15.30 – 16.00

Barbara Van Der Pol:

Developments on *Chlamydia* diagnostics – what will you be doing in three year's time?

Barbara Van Der Pol, PhD, MPH. University of Alabama at Birmingham School of Medicine.

Diagnostic methods for detection of infectious diseases have undergone a technological explosion in the last two decades. At the forefront of much of this advancement has been detection of *Chlamydia trachomatis*. Difficulties associated with growing this organism such as adequate endocervical sampling; painful urethral sample collection; cold-chain transport; extremely limited storage time above $-80^{\circ}C$; and, tissue culture facilities and technical skill requirements. As a result of these barriers to routine screening, developing technologies were quickly applied to detection of the sexually transmitted pathogen.

Non-culture assays for *Chlamydia*, which were developed in the late 1980's, were quickly replaced by nucleic acid-based tests which included DNA-probe assays as well as nucleic acid amplification tests (NAATs). The advantages of NAATs overcame many of the obstacles historically associated with detection of chlamydial infections and also included very high sensitivity regardless of the viability of the organisms; the ability to bundle *Chlamydia* and *Neisseria gonorrhoeae* testing; capacity for accurate screening among asymptomatic populations; and, utilization of less invasive and patient-obtained samples such as urine and vaginal swab specimens.

Current NAATs have achieved sufficiently high analytical sensitivity based on limit of detection studies that we no longer need to pursue methods that would increase that characteristic of testing. Newer generation NAATs have succeeded in migrating assays to highly automated instruments with platforms with throughput that allows efficient and cost-rational screening in centralized reference laboratories. Further, next-gen NAATs are expanding the STI menu by adding detection of *Trichomonas vaginalis and Mycoplasma genitalium* that can be performed from the sample collected for *Chlamydia*/gonorrhea testing.

The emphasis now is on development of more rapid, easier to use and less expensive diagnostic tools for use in both clinical and non-clinical settings. Currently, the best time to results available for *Chlamydia* screening is a 90 minute assay. In some settings, this is an acceptable wait time, but in the majority of settings the assay time to results needs to be 30 minutes or less in order to be effectively used for test-and-treat programs. Further, none of the assays available today are suitable for use by non-technical staff in a non-laboratory setting. These advances of shorter and simpler NAATs are just around the corner, some may even have CE-mark approval by the time of this meeting. Improvements are also being realized in reducing costs by development of both NAATs and non-amplified rapid, point-of-care assays that utilize new technologies. This session will describe some of the new technologies that are likely to be available in the near future and may substantially change how we offer STI screening in upcoming years.

16.00 – 16.30

WILL GEISLER:

Azithromycin (1g) should remain the treatment of choice for *Chlamydia.*

Debate

WM Geisler. Departments of Medicine and Epidemiology, Division of Infectious Diseases, University of Alabama at Birmingham.

Azithromycin 1g should remain the preferred treatment for *Chlamydia*. The single dose administration allows for directly observed therapy for patients and simplifies patient delivered partner therapy, which helps to ensure adherence of treatment for patients and their partners. Treatment adherence is a concern with the 7-day doxycycline regimen for *Chlamydia* treatment, and studies have demonstrated that nonadherence with doxycycline is associated with an increased frequency of *Chlamydia* treatment failure. Azithromycin has been demonstrated to be highly efficacious for urogenital *Chlamydia* treatment (97%) based on findings from a meta-analysis of 12 randomized clinical trials and a recently published randomized clinical trial that controlled for limitations of earlier urogenital *Chlamydia* treatment trials. There has been concern raised about the efficacy of azithromycin 1g for rectal *Chlamydia* treatment based on findings from several observational studies, however the quality of evidence from these studies is very poor and there has never been a randomized clinical trial for rectal *Chlamydia* treatment. Azithromycin 1g remains a first line recommended treatment for urogenital and rectal *Chlamydia* in the Centers for Disease Control and Prevention Sexually Transmitted Diseases Treatment Guidelines, 2015.

16.30 – 17.00

TARIQ SADIQ:

Azithromycin (1g) should not remain the treatment of choice for *Chlamydia*. Debate

Tariq Sadiq. St George's University of London.

The serious reproductive health sequelae of *Chlamydia trachomatis* infection demands highly effective treatment and is underlined by the introduction of national programmes of opportunistic testing and treating. Single dose (1g) of azithromycin, an azalide antibiotic with favorable pharmacokinetics, ease of administration, low toxicity and high efficacy has been in use for over two decades for *Chlamydia* treatment and control programs. However, this strategy threatens the management and control of other serious STIs, acquired through common means of sexual exposure with *Chlamydia*, challenging clinical and public health providers to maintain the highest standards of antibiotic stewardship. Widespread use of single dose azithromycin, associated strongly with emergence and spread of 23srRNA macrolide resistant mutations, poses significant risks through increasing prevalence of resistance in circulating strains of *Neisseria gonorrhoeae*, *Mycoplasma genitalium* and *Treponema pallidum*. Furthermore, the effectiveness of single dose treatment for *Chlamydia* is increasingly being questioned. The argument for maintaining single dose azithromycin for a ubiquitous condition as genital *Chlamydia* infection thus risks breaching basic biomedical cautionary principles of not doing harm to patients or the public and, until we have clearer data towards the contrary, azithromycin (1g) should *not* remain the treatment of choice for *Chlamydia*.

POSTER SESSION A

A1 Influence of female sex hormones on the gene expression of in vitro cultured *Chlamydia abortus*

Daniel Álvarez, Antonio Murcia-Belmonte, Antonio J. Buendía, Nieves Ortega, M. Carmen Gallego, Laura Del Río, Jesús Salinas, M. Rosa Caro
Universidad de Murcia, Murcia, Murcia, Spain

Background/ Introduction

The recrudescence of *Chlamydia abortus* (CA) at certain moments of pregnancy and oestrous cycle in sheep suggests that female sex hormones might play an important role on the immunopathology of ovine enzootic abortion (OEA). However, further studies about this subject are needed.

Objectives

The aim of this study was to investigate the influence of reproductive hormones estradiol and progesterone on the cycle of CA by analysing the expression of genes in *in vitro* cultured CA treated with these hormones.

Method

Macrophage like cells (RAW 264.7) were cultured under 3 different conditions: i) addition of estradiol, ii) addition of progesterone and iii) no hormones supplementation, as control. Cell monolayers were then infected with CA strain AB7 and samples of the cultures were taken at 48 and 72 hours post-infection. RNA was extracted and purified with a commercial kit and its quality was measured by spectrophotometry. A set of 20 target genes of CA were selected for this study to analyse their transcriptional response patterns. This analysis was carried out by qRT-PCR followed by relative quantification.

Results

The fold changes relative to the reference gene (*16S rRNA*) showed that there was no difference in gene expression between hormone treated and non-treated groups (every studied gene was regulated less than 2-fold). Our results showed that the cycle of CA was not affected by sex hormones. This could be explained by a lack of responsiveness to hormones of the cell line used or by non-adequate hormone concentrations established. Additional results with specific chlamydial host cell lines, such as LE (originated from ovine endometrium) and AH-1 (ovine trophoblast), treated with higher doses of hormones, are being analyzed in our laboratory.

Conclusions

The treatment of macrophage cells with reproductive hormones such as progesterone and estradiol did not alter the transcriptional response pattern of CA. The results in progress with the lines LE and AH-1 will be communicated in the 8th Meeting of the ESCR in Oxford, September 2016.

A2 *Chlamydia trachomatis* (CT) seroprevalence in American inner city children and adolescents - implications for vaccine development

Natalie Banniettis[1], Sirisha Thumu[2], Aviva Szigeti[1], Kobkul Chotikanatis[1], Margaret Hammerschlag[1], Stephan Kohlhoff[1]

[1]State University of New York Downstate Medical Center, Brooklyn, New York, USA, [2]NYU Lutheran Medical Center, Brooklyn, New York, USA

Background/ Introduction

Prevention of CT infection is an ideal application for a vaccine program which should optimally be administered before sexual debut. However, there are limited epidemiologic studies of CT infection in an unselected pediatric population since universal screening and treatment of pregnant women was implemented in the U.S. in 1993.

Objectives

To determine current seroepidemiology of CT infection in children in a U.S. inner city population.

Method

Anonymized serum samples were obtained from children in 2 hospitals in Brooklyn, New York from 2013-2015. CT IgG was determined using EIA. The following age strata were used: <9, 9-10, 11-12, 13-14, 15-16, 17-18, 19-20 y. Infants less than 1 y of age were excluded from the final analysis as their antibody titers reflect placental transmission of maternal anti-CT IgG.

Results

1002 sera were included in the final analysis. Mean age was 14.0 y and median 16 y. 67% were females. CT antibody was first detected at 12 y and 14 y for females and males, respectively. The prevalence of anti-CT antibody in children >9 y was 8.5% (73/859), was higher in females than in males (10.7% vs 5.2%, respectively, $p=0.004$) and increased with age. Among females, peak seropositivity occurred at 17 y of age (10/51, 19.6%). A significant effect of age and gender on CT serological status was noted.

Conclusions

The prevalence of antibody was higher and appeared earlier in females, mirroring national surveillance trends based on NAATs. The delay in male antibody detection may be due to later exposure and/or anatomical and physiological factors between the sexes. These data are critical in informing potential CT vaccine strategies.

A3 Serum influences the uptake of *Chlamydia trachomatis* in human monocytes

Robert Winther, Thomas Guldbæk Poulsen, Mads Lausen, Svend Birkelund
Department of Health Science and Technology, Aalborg, Denmark

Background/ Introduction

Upon genital *Chlamydia trachomatis* infection inflammation will develop in which monocytes will infiltrate the tissue and make contact with *C. trachomatis*. Monocytes are important for elimination of microorganisms and for antigen presentation but little is known about these processes in chlamydial infections.

Objectives

In the present study we investigated the uptake of *C. trachomatis* in monocyte derived macrophages without centrifugation, identified components important for the uptake and determined the compartment in which *C. trachomatis* was localized after uptake.

Method

Peripheral blood mononuclear cells (PBMC) were obtained from a *C. trachomatis* sero-negative person. PBMC were seated on 8 wells Permanoxâ chamber slides in RPMI1640 with 10% heat inactivated FCS. Non- adherent cells were washed away after 2 hrs. Serovar D was added in RPMI1640 with 10% human serum or human heat inactivated serum. After 4 hrs. cells were fixed and stained with *C. trachomatis* MAb32.3 against chlamydial major outer membrane protein. Cell nuclei were stained with DAPI. For double staining rabbit anti *C. trachomatis* was used in combination with anti Lysosomal-associated membrane protein 1 (LAMP1).

Results

Monocytes were infected with *C. trachomatis* D in presence of human serum or human heat inactivated serum. After four hrs cells were fixed and stained, the number of *Chlamydia* per cell was counted. In presence of heat inactivated serum few cells with few *Chlamydia* were observed in contrary to serum where many cells harboured high number of *Chlamydia*.

To investigate the endocytic pathway a double staining for *Chlamydia* and the lysosomal marker LAMP1 was made. *C. trachomatis* D showed co-localization with LAMP1. No inclusions were observed after 30 hrs.

Conclusions

The study showed that *C. trachomatis* uptake by monocytes are dependent on a heat-labile factor in human serum. The most likely heat-labile factor is complement, important for uptake of microorganisms into monocytes. The uptake leads the *Chlamydia*e to the lysosomal pathway, in agreement with no inclusions were observed.

A4 Pelvic Inflammatory Disease: Involving patients and public in guiding healthcare professionals on how to present changes in the evidence base

Paula Blomquist*[1,2], Sarah Cochrane*[3], Sarah Woodhall[1, 2 ,4], Paddy Horner[3, 4 ,5]

*These authors contributed equally to this work

[1]Public Health England, London, UK, [2]National Institute for Health Research (NIHR) Health Protection Research Unit in Blood Borne and Sexually Transmitted Infections at UCL, London, UK, [3]University Hospitals Bristol NHS Foundation Trust, Bristol, UK, [4]NIHR Health Protection Research Unit in the Evaluation of Interventions at University of Bristol, Bristol, UK, [5]University of Bristol, Bristol, UK

Background/ Introduction

A recent multi-parameter evidence synthesis of the natural history of *Chlamydia* provides new information on risk of chronic sequelae following diagnosis of Pelvic Inflammatory Disease (PID). Patient public involvement (PPI) is increasingly important in research/service development, and offers a means to determine how best to apply new evidence in practice.

Objectives

To organise a PPI group exploring best integration of new evidence on PID in electronic patient records (EPR) and conversations with patients. This informs local service delivery and guides an NIHR-funded study aiming to pilot PID sub-codes in EPR, improving surveillance data. We report on the most successful recruitment method.

Method

Initially posters and flyers within clinic were trialled for a 2-week period to recruit female patients aged 18-30 years. The second method involved distributing survey-style invitations to all female attendees in a 1-week period; firstly asking if they believe patients should be involved in NHS service planning, and asking to provide contact details if they would like to be involved. All interested patients were asked by telephone or email to partake in an evening focus group at the clinic, reviewing information leaflets on PID with varying levels of detail. Patients were reimbursed for their time.

Results

The first method received no responses. Using the second method, 62 surveys were completed. 56 (90.3%) agreed patient involvement is important and 22 (35.5%) said they would be interested in being involved. 24 patients provided their contact details, however, 9 of these were outside of the target age range. 4 (57%) of 7 participants who confirmed, attended the meeting. Background understanding of PID varied between the patients and was linked to personal experiences. All patients confirmed they would prefer the information leaflet with the most detail, including percentage risk of future complications.

Conclusions

Focused survey-style invitations improved PPI group recruitment. Most survey respondents agreed public involvement is important: fewer wished to participate. The small PPI group favoured detailed sequelae information, which guides clinical practice and protocol development for piloting PID sub-codes. We will utilise this PPI recruitment method in the future.

A5 Structure-function characterisation of *Chlamydia pneumoniae* Major Outer Membrane Protein (MOMP)

Amy E Danson[1,2], Isabel de Moraes[2,3], Martin Walsh[2], Sheila MacIntyre[1], Kim A Watson[1]
[1]University of Reading, Reading, Berkshire, UK, [2]Diamond Light Source (DLS), Didcot, Oxfordshire, UK, [3]Membrane Protein Laboratory (MPL), DLS/Imperial College London, Didcot, Oxfordshire, UK

Background/ Introduction

Major outer membrane proteins (MOMPs) are structurally and immunologically dominant proteins in the *Chlamydia* outer membrane (OM). Both the surface exposure and abundance of MOMP suggests a possible role in *Chlamydia*-host interactions, highlighting MOMP as a possible vaccine target. The proposed beta-barrel structure also indicates a role in ligand transport.

Objectives

Currently, there is very little literature surrounding structure-function characterisation of *Chlamydia* MOMPs due to difficulties in producing recombinant protein in a folded, active state. This research is focussed on using X-ray crystallography to solve MOMP's structure and ligand assays to assess functionality.

Method

Synchrotron radiation circular dichroism (SRCD) and Fourier transform infrared radiation (FTIR) spectroscopy data have been used to provide a more detailed insight into MOMP's structure-function properties. Preliminary electrophysiology has been performed to assess its role as a porin. Functional assays are in progress to assess MOMP's potential activity as a fatty acid transporter, due to its structural resemblance to the transporter FadL of *E. coli*. Course grained molecular dynamics (MD) simulations have been used to model MOMP's organisation within the OM, with aims to extend to atomistic modelling of ligand transport. X-ray crystallography has revealed a low resolution crystal structure.

Results

SRCD and FTIR spectroscopic data revealed that MOMP is predominantly a beta-sheet protein. MOMP's thermal stability is increased in the presence of FAs, as shown by SRCD spectroscopy. Channel activity of MOMP is suggestive of a monomeric state with slow but discernible porin activity. A 4Å resolution crystal structure, from non-optimised crystals, revealed a beta-barrel structure with an occluded pore. Preliminary results from MD simulations have shown that two MOMPs modelled in a DPPE/DOPG bilayer will form stable clusters.

Conclusions
MOMP is a beta-barrel protein with an occluded pore, which displays some channel activity. MOMP may have a role in FA binding and transport due to observed thermal stabilisation in the presence of FAs and its resemblance to FadL.

A6 Activity of synthetic peptides against *Chlamydia spp.*

Manuela Donati[1], Giovanna Cenacchi[2], Edoardo Vecchio Nepita[1], Valentina Papa[2], Nicole Borel[3], Simone Magnino[4], Roberta Biondi[1], Aurora Levi[1], Octavio Franco[5]
[1]*DIMES, Microbiology, University of Bologna, Bologna, Italy,* [2]*DIBINEM, Pathology, University of Bologna, Bologna, Italy,* [3]*Institute of Veterinary Pathology, Vetsuisse Faculty, University of Zurich, Zurich, Switzerland,* [4]*IZSLER, National Reference Laboratory for Animal Chamydioses, Pavia, Italy,* [5]*Centre of Proteomics and Biochemistry, Catholic University of Brasilia, Brasilia, Brazil*

Background/ Introduction

chlamydial infections are primarily treated with tetracycline and macrolides. Despite the *in vitro* activity of these drugs, persistent *Chlamydia* infections have been reported and a stable tetracycline-resistance associated with *tet*(C) genomic islands integrated into the chlamydial chromosome has been described for *C. suis* strains isolated from pigs.

Objectives

The formulation of synthetic peptides with antimicrobial activity has become extremely attractive. The *in vitro* antimicrobial activity of the synthetic mastoparan (wasp generated peptide), clavanins (α-helical peptides from the marine tunicate *Styela clava*) and Pa-Map (alanine-rich peptide from the polar fish *Pleuronectes americanus*) against antibiotic-resistant bacteria has been reported.

Method

The synthetic peptides mastoparan L (ML) and MO (MMO), clavanin (C) and MO (CMO), *Pa*-MAP 1.5 and 1.9, were diluted two-fold from 80 to 1.25 micrograms/mL, tested against *Chlamydia* elementary bodies, calculating the lowest peptide concentration required to achieve more than 50% reduction of chlamydial inclusions compared to untreated controls. Tests were carried out on 36 isolates of eight *Chlamydia* species, namely 18 *C. trachomatis* (D, E, F, G, H, I, J, K, L2 serovars), five *C. pneumoniae*, five *C. psittaci*, two *C. abortus*, two *C. pecorum*, one *C. avium*, two *C. suis* isolates and the *C. muridarum* strain Nigg.

Results

CMO reduced ≥50% the inclusion numbers of all 36 *Chlamydia* isolates at a concentration of 10 micrograms/mL. ML was active against *C. trachomatis*, *C. pneumoniae*, *C. muridarum* and *C. suis* at 10 micrograms/mL but did not exert any inhibitory effect on the other *Chlamydia* species tested, even at 80 micrograms/mL. At the concentration of 80 micrograms/mL the peptides MMO, C and *Pa*-MAP 1.5 and 1.9 were ineffective against all isolates. The electron microscopy investigation on *Chlamydia* elementary bodies treated with CMO or ML showed a membrane vacuolar degeneration, particularly evident in CMO-treated elementary bodies.

Conclusions

Clavanin MO was the most active peptide against all *Chlamydia* strains tested, causing changes in the membrane morphology. Mastoparan L was active against *C. trachomatis*, *C. pneumoniae*, *C. muridarum*, *C. suis*. Further studies are needed to consider these peptides potential and promising compounds in the treatment of persistent chlamydial infections.

A7 A VCG-based *Chlamydia abortus* subunit vaccine induces cross protective immunity against challenge

Francis O. Eko[1], Roshan Pais[1], Raedeen Russell[1], Qing He[1], Yusuf Omosun[1], Carolyn M. Black[2], Joseph U. Igietseme[1,2]
[1]*Morehouse School of Medicine, Atlanta, GA, USA*, [2]*Centers for Disease Control (CDC), Atlanta, GA, USA*

Background/ Introduction

Chlamydia abortus (Cab) is the causative agent of ovine enzootic abortion (OEA) and poses a zoonotic risk to pregnant women. Although current live attenuated 1B vaccines are efficacious they cause disease in vaccinated animals and inactivated vaccines are only marginally protective, underlining the need for new effective safer vaccines.

Objectives

We compared the immunomodulatory functions of *Vibrio cholerae* ghosts (VCG) with CpG/FL adjuvants in enhancing MHC II and costimulatory molecules on DCs, boost innate immune responses and improve the cross protective immunity of a Cab subunit vaccine candidate against heterologous challenge in a mouse model of genital infection.

Method

Groups of mice were immunized intranasally 3 times, 2 wk apart with lyophilized rVCG expressing the polymorphic membrane protein 18D (rVCG-Pmp18D) or glycoprotein D from HSV-2 (rVCG-gD2) control or rPmp18D+CpG/FL (Fms-like tyrosine kinase 3 Ligand; Flt3L) in 20 ml of PBS/mouse and challenged intravaginally with 10^6 IFU of live Cab 3 weeks after the last immunization. Following cervicovaginal swabbing and isolation of *Chlamydia*e in tissue culture, the level of protection was assessed based on the number of mice with positive vaginal cultures, length of vaginal bacterial shedding, and number of IFUs recovered after challenge with a heterologous Cab strain.

Results

Delivery of rPmp18D with VCG was more effective than with CpG+FL in up-regulating the expression of molecules critically involved in T cell activation and differentiation, including MHC II, CD40, CD80, and CD86, activation of TLRs and NLRP3 inflammasome engagement, and secretion of IL-1-beta and TNF-alpha. Compared to CpG+FL, rVCG-delivered Pmp18D elicited more robust antigen-specific humoral and cellular immune responses in mice. Based on the predefined protective criteria following challenge with the heterologous *C. abortus* strain B577, vaccine delivery with VCG induced superior protective immunity than delivery with a combination of CpG1826 and FL, a nasal DC-targeting adjuvant.

Conclusions

These results demonstrate that the ability of VCG to induce innate/adaptive immune responses and enhance the cross protective immunity of a Cab subunit vaccine is superior to CpG+FL. Thus, VCG is a suitable delivery vehicle and adjuvant to target antigens to DCs for boosting protective immunity against microbial infections.

A8 High prevalence of *Chlamydia trachomatis* infection among pregnant women under 21 years-old in Buenos Aires, Argentina

Andrea Carolina Entrocassi[1], Valeria Paula Gualtieri[1], Dolores Parisi[2], Mabel Rizzo[3], Graciela Baptista[4], María Lucía Gallo Vaulet[1], Natalia Malen Goria[1], Antonio Parisi[5], Sonia Quiruelas[5], Marcelo Rodriguez Fermepin[1]

[1]*Universidad de Buenos Aires, Unidad de Estudios de Chlamydiae y otras infecciones del tracto genital, Cátedra de Microbiología Clínica, Facultad de Farmacia y Bioquímica., Ciudad de Buenos Aires, Buenos Aires, Argentina,* [2]*"Hospital Materno Infantil", Tigre, Buenos Aires, Argentina,* [3]*General Hospital "Dr. Pedro Penna", Bahía Blanca, Buenos Aires, Argentina,* [4]*Health Care Center "San Isidro Labrador", San Isidro, Buenos Aires, Argentina,* [5]*Ministerio de Salud de la Provincia de Buenos Aires, La Plata, Buenos Aires, Argentina*

Background/ Introduction

The frequency of *Chlamydia trachomatis* infection has been extensively studied in many different populations. Prevalence values are wide distributed depending on population demographics and risk related features. Most studies focused on pregnant adolescents show prevalence values of 8% to 12%, but this group was not yet studied in our Country.

Objectives

Given that we have previously reported a significant association between neonatal conjunctivitis by *Chlamydia trachomatis* and young age of neonate mothers, the aim of this study was to determine the frequency of *C. trachomatis* infection among pregnant women under 21 years-old in Buenos Aires province, Argentina.

Method

A multicentric study supported by the Health Ministry of Buenos Aires was carried out involving four hospitals at four different cities. The Universidad de Buenos Aires university hospital was the training node of the network. From May 2013 to August 2014, *Chlamydia trachomatis* detection was offered to every asymptomatic pregnant woman aged 14 to 21 years-old attending each participating hospital for routine pregnancy control. Detection of *C. trachomatis* on first void urine samples was performed by Real-Time PCR targeting the cryptic plasmid. Positive samples were confirmed at the university hospital by *ompA* nested PCR and then genotyped by PCR-RFLP.

Results

Seven hundred and eighty one adolescent pregnant women were enrolled during the study. *C. trachomatis* was detected on 22.5 % (176/781) of the analyzed samples, and was confirmed by *ompA* nested PCR. Genotyping was successful on 87% of the positive samples, showing that genotype E as the most frequently detected (39.5%) followed by F (17.8%), D (15.8%) and I/Ia (7.9%). Two samples were characterized as mixed infections (J+D and E+H).

Conclusions

The *C. trachomatis* prevalence found in this study was unusually high, even for a group always described as a high risk population. These results point out the need to focus the attention of health care institutions on young pregnant women, specially because of further consequences on fertility and neonatal health.

A9 *Chlamydia trachomatis* detection and genovar distribution in clinical urogenital and blood specimens in patients in Saratov, Russia: a case-control study

Valentina A. Feodorova[1,2], Edgar S. Sultanakhmedov[3], Yury V. Saltykov[1,2], Sergey S. Zaitsev[1], Tatiana I. Polyanina[1], Sergey R. Utz[3], Charlotte A. Gaydos[4], Thomas C. Quinn[4,5], Vladimir L. Motin[6]
[1]*Saratov Scientific and Research Veterinary Institute, Federal Agency for Scientific Organizations, Saratov, Russia,* [2]*Saratov State Agrarian University, Saratov, Russia,* [3]*Saratov State Medical University, Saratov, Russia,* [4]*Johns Hopkins University School of Medicine, Baltimore, MD, USA,* [5]*National Institute of Allergy and Infectious Diseases, Baltimore, MD, USA,* [6]*University of Texas Medical Branch, Galveston, TX, USA*

Background/ Introduction

Depending on sexual behavior, *C. trachomatis* (CT) can be found in the urogenital or pharyngeal sites of infected patients. Serum specimens obtained from patients with genital chlamydial infection could contain elementary bodies of CT as documented by culture, immunogold electron microscopy and TaqMan PCR.

Objectives

This prospective study to investigate: (i) whether CT DNA could be detected in blood samples of infected patients compared with their genital sites, and (ii) to describe CT genovar distribution in a case-control study of attendees with asymptomatic genital *Chlamydia* infection in Saratov Clinic of Skin and Venereal Diseases, Russia.

Method

For detection of CT, clinical specimens from genital sites (urethra and cervix) and blood were collected from heterosexual married couples and individuals, Saratov Region (n=22). CT DNA isolated using the DNeasy Blood and Tissue Kit (QIAGEN, Hilden, Germany) was amplified by several commercial end-point and duplex TaqMan PCRs followed by sequencing and *ompA*-genovar typing. In parallel, each CT-positive blood and genital specimen was tested by slide technique and direct immunofluorescent test with CT A-L serovar-specific monoclonal antibodies.

Results

Overall, blood samples were 77.3% and 95.5% positive by PCR to either cryptic plasmid or chromosomal targets, respectively. Only 63.6% and 86.4% positive reactions were registered with genital samples in the same PCRs. The CT genovar distribution in blood samples among single-infected patients (66.7%) was 60% E (E1&E2), 10% F and 30% G, and co-infection by E1+F /E1+G+J/E1+G/F+G in 33.3% of multi-infected patients. Genital samples demonstrated 59.1% of single infection as CT genovars: 7.7% D, 84.6% E (E1, E2, E6), 7.7% G. Genital co-infection was found in 4.5% cases as E1+G.

Conclusions

Detection of CT in blood samples could aid in the efficiency of the laboratory diagnostics for *Chlamydia* infection especially in asymptomatic *Chlamydia* patients with negative genital probes. This assay can be utilized to further investigate the frequency and mechanisms of CT single and mix-infection.

A10 Genital *Chlamydia trachomatis* ompA types and genovar distribution in clinical specimens of *Chlamydia* patients in multi-ethnic Region, Saratov, Russia

Valentina A. Feodorova[1,2], Svetlana S. Konnova[1], Yury V. Saltykov[1,2], Sergey S. Zaitsev[1], Edgar S. Sultanakhmedov[4], Tatiana I. Polyanina[1], Ivan V. Druzhkin[3], Sergey R. Utz[4], Edward A. Fedotov[3], Charlotte A. Gaydos[5], Thomas C. Quinn[5,6], Vladimir L. Motin[7]
[1]*Saratov Scientific and Research Veterinary Institute, Federal Agency for Scientific Organizations, Saratov, Russia,* [2]*Saratov State Agrarian University, Saratov, Russia,* [3]*Medical Diagnostic Di-Center, Saratov Region, Engels city, Russia,* [4]*Saratov State Medical University, Saratov, Russia,* [5]*Johns Hopkins University School of Medicine, Baltimore, MD, USA,* [6]*National Institute of Allergy and Infectious Diseases, Baltimore, MD, USA,* [7]*University of Texas Medical Branch, Galveston, TX, USA*

Background/ Introduction

C. trachomatis (CT) typing is important for global epidemiology, study of trends in transmission and evolutionary strategy of this pathogen. The typing helps to recognize co-infection of *Chlamydia* patients with two or more CT variants to improve national and trans-national surveillance programs and global STI surveillance systems.

Objectives

The main goal was to learn about the prevalence and genovar distribution of genital chlamydial infections among random heterosexual chlamydial patients in multi-ethnic Region located at South-East of European part of Russia with respect to their gender, age, nationality and place of residence.

Method

Clinical samples (cervical or urethral swabs) from a random cohort of patients (n = 856) who addressed to seven different diagnostic laboratories in the Saratov Region for suspected chlamydial infection were screened for the presence of CT. Total DNA was extracted directly from clinical specimen by using the DNeasy Blood and Tissue Kit (Qiagen) and analyzed routinely by commercial end-point and a duplex TaqMan PCRs. The genovars of CT were determined by standard *ompA*-typing of CT-positive samples. Additionally CT-positive clinical samples were tested with monoclonal antibodies specific to CT serovars A-L.

Results

Positive PCR reaction was detected in 61 samples (7.1%); among then were men (n=12, 19.7%), women (n=42, 68.8%), and anonyms (n=7, 11.5%) of the age ranging in 19-45 years (26.4±5.4), and included 12 different ethnic groups characteristic for this Region. The genovars were distributed as 41.9% of E (E1, E2, E6), 21.6% of G (G1, G2, G3, G5), 13.5% of F1, 9.5% of K, 6.8% of D (D1, Da2), 4.1% of J1, and 2.7% of H&H2. Moreover, 82% of CT-positive patients were infected with a single genovar CT, while 18% demonstrated co-infection with either two or three genovars.

Conclusions

The most prevalent in both single-infected and multi-infected patients for any age and gender groups were genovars E, G and F; Slavic and non-Slavic populations had the prevalence of E, G, D and E, G, K, respectively; urban and rural populations had E, G, F and E, K prevalence, respectively.

A11 Implication of the novel Swedish variant of *Chlamydia trachomatis* (nvCT) in human infertility in couple, Saratov Region, Russia

Valentina A. Feodorova[1,2], Edgar S. Sultanakhmedov[3], Yury V. Saltykov[1,2], Sergey S. Zaitsev[1], Tatiana I. Polyanina[1], Sergey R. Utz[3], Michael J. Corbel[4], Charlotte A. Gaydos[5], Thomas C. Quinn[5,6], Vladimir L. Motin[7]
[1]*Saratov Scientific and Research Veterinary Institute, Federal Agency for Scientific Organizations, Saratov, Russia,* [2]*Saratov State Agrarian University, Saratov, Russia,* [3]*Saratov State Medical University, Saratov, Russia,* [4]*The National Institute for Biological Standards and Control (NIBSC), Potters Bar, UK,* [5]*Johns Hopkins University School of Medicine, Baltimore, MD, USA,* [6]*National Institute of Allergy and Infectious Diseases, Baltimore, MD, USA,* [7]*University of Texas Medical Branch, Galveston, TX, USA*

Background/ Introduction

Infertility is a global challenge. Asymptomatic chlamydial genital infection caused by the wild type of *Chlamydia trachomatis* (wtCT) is the most commonly identified agent of human infertility. Contribution of the novel 'Swedish' variant of C. trachomatis (nvCT) bearing a 377 bp deletion has been less studied.

Objectives

This study investigated whether the novel 'Swedish' variant (nvCT) may be a possible cause of infertility in a heterosexual married couple from Saratov Region, who during 6 years experienced multiple unsuccessful attempts at pregnancy by natural fertilization and in vitro fertilization (IVF) procedures.

Method

Clinical specimens were collected from both genital (urethra and cervix) and extra-genital sites (pharynx, conjunctive, blood) of a couple, female and male partners, 25 and 28 years old, ethnic Dagestanians, with nether somatic and endocrinal pathology nor clinical manifestations of chlamydial genital infection. The presence of either wtCT or nvCT strains in each sample was determined by PCR, followed by sequencing and *ompA*-genovar typing. Clinical samples were also tested with *Chlamydia* monoclonal antibodies to CT serovars A-L. Serological study for both partners, semen analysis for male, and hormonal status for female were performed in dynamics for two years of observation.

Results

The female samples contained exclusively DNA of nvCT. After antibiotic therapy, DNA of wtCT of genovars E and D were detected in specimens from female conjunctiva and oropharynx. The male samples showed co-infection of nvCT and wtCT. Identical SNP within the variable region 4 of the *ompA* gene confirmed the identity of wtCT strains found in both partners. Only the female demonstrated positive anti-chlamydial IgG titer of 1:160 at both initial screen and during re-examination. The sperm characteristics of the male partner, including motility (immotile spermatozoa was 51.1% versus 21.6%) and vitality (46% versus 68%) declined progressively over two years.

Conclusions

Infertility in this couple was probably caused by chronic asymptomatic and persistent infection with the *C. trachomatis* nvCT variant. This initial nvCT-associated infection was later complicated by co-infection with wtCT variants of different genovars (as D, E1, E2).

A12 Validating a trachomatous trichiasis specific survey design

Rebecca M. Flueckiger[1], Tansy Edwards[1], David Mabey[1], George Kabona[3], Jeremiah Ngondi[2], Mwingira Upendo[3], Charles Opondo[1], Rachel Pullan[1]
[1]*London School of Hygiene & Tropical Medicine, London, UK,* [2]*ENVISION, RTI International, Washington DC, USA,* [3]*NTD Control Program, Ministry of Health and Social Welfare Tanzania, Dar Es Salaam, Tanzania*

Background/ Introduction

Obtaining precise prevalence data helps programmes plan surgical services, monitor progress, and assess whether elimination goals have been accomplished. A trachomatous trichiasis (TT) survey will be piloted in three countries representing different phases of trachoma elimination and geographic contexts to test the precision and cost effectiveness of the survey design.

Objectives

To validate the survey design, which measures TT in the 40-years-and-older population with precision appropriate for meeting the WHO elimination target of <0.1% in the total population and to weigh the relative gain in precision from this design against the associated increase in cost.

Method

The survey is powered to estimate prevalence within 40-years-and-older populations (sample size: 1,529). To create a sample suitable for simulations we will over-sample, increasing cluster count from 40 to 60. Individuals 40-years-and-older in half the clusters and all individuals in the remaining half will be examined. An electronic data collection system will be used allowing for time-stamps.

Cluster-level prevalence will be calculated and plotted to explore distribution. Time-cost associated with different cluster makeups and fuel costs based on travel time between clusters will be determined, allowing us to calculate the cost associated with additional clusters required by the 40-year-and-older design.

Results

Results from this project are expected to be completed July 2016 and will be presented in September.

Conclusions

Conclusions will be available upon completion of this project and will be presented in September.

A13 *Chlamydia trachomatis* infection prevalence and serovar distribution in a high-density urban area in the North of Italy

Claudio Foschi[1], Paola Nardini[1], Nicoletta Banzola[2], Antonietta D'Antuono[2], Monica Compri[1], Roberto Cevenini[1], Antonella Marangoni[1]
[1]Microbiology, DIMES, University of Bologna, Bologna, Italy, [2]Dermatology, DIMES, University of Bologna, Bologna, Italy

Background/ Introduction

Chlamydia trachomatis (CT) is the causative agent of the most common bacterial sexually transmitted infection (STI) worldwide. CT molecular typing plays a fundamental role in finding association between serovars and epidemiological characteristics and can be crucial for therapeutic appropriateness.

Objectives

The aim of this study was to assess CT infection prevalence and serovar distribution in a high density urban area in the North of Italy, by comparing different groups of subjects divided on the basis of care providers they referred to

Method

From January 2011 to May 2014, data about all the urogenital and extra-genital samples (anorectal and/or pharyngeal swabs) submitted to the Microbiology of St. Orsola Hospital in Bologna for CT detection were collected.

The specimens were obtained from three different groups of patients: subjects attending the STI Outpatients Clinic of the Hospital, patients attending gynecological clinics or people referring to general practitioners. All the samples were processed by a real-time PCR assay (Versant CT/GC DNA 1.0; Siemens) and in case of positivity, molecular genotyping based on RFLP analysis was performed. A $P < 0.05$ was considered statistically significant.

Results

Overall CT infection prevalence was 8.1% with significant differences between sub-groups (P<0.01), but stable during the study period. STI Clinic was mainly responsible for CT diagnosis, whereas the lowest prevalence was detected in gynecological clinics, despite a high number of tests performed.

Extra-genital samples were almost exclusively collected from males at the STI Clinic. Interestingly, 4.4% of CT positive cases would have been missed if extra-genital sites had not been tested.

CT serovar distribution was influenced by gender, age, anatomic site (P<0.01) and care providers (P=0.01). L2 serovar was detected only in extra-genital samples from males at the STI Clinic.

Conclusions

First, significant differences in the contribution of CT testing and diagnosis between care providers were noticed. Secondly, extra-genital testing need to be encouraged, especially outside the STI Clinic. Finally, CT typing is crucial for the appropriate management in specific settings, such as LGV in extra-genital samples of high-risk populations.

A14 The Novel *Chlamydia pneumoniae* molecule interacts with Huntingtin-interacting protein 14

Izumi Yanatori, Kazunobu Ouchi, Fumio Kishi
Kawasaki Medical School, Kurashiki, Japan

Background/ Introduction

It is known that several intracellular pathogens inhibit phagosome maturation and modulate host vesicle trafficking pathways by translocating effectors. chlamydial and corresponding host cell factors that control the intracellular trafficking are not well known yet.

Objectives

To identify novel *C. pneumoniae* molecules which disturb the vesicle transport system, we screened 455 ORFs without any known functions by using a yeast expression system. We focused on one of the candidate molecules, CPj0783, and investigated CPj0783 function in this study.

Method

We performed two kinds of screening; (1) A mis-sorting assay in yeast cells to find out *C. pneumoniae* effector proteins that modulate host vesicle trafficking pathway, (2) Genomic screening for *C. pneumoniae*-specific antigens using serum samples from *C. pneumoniae* infected patients. Based on the results obtained from these screenings, we chose one of the candidate molecules, CPj0783. To identify the interacting host protein, we performed the yeast two-hybrid screening and then confirmed the protein-protein interaction by GST pull-down assay and coimmunoprecipitation assay.

Results

We found 10 *C. pneumoniae* candidate genes involved in aberrant vesicular trafficking in host cells. One of the candidate genes, CPj0783, was recognized by antibodies from *C. pneumoniae*-infected patients. The expression of CPj0783 was detected at mid to late-cycle time points and increased during the inclusion maturation. It was revealed by yeast two-hybrid screening that CPj0783 interacted with Huntingtin-interacting protein 14 (HIP14). The specific interaction between CPj0783 and HIP14 was demonstrated by an *in vivo* co-immunoprecipitation assay and an *in vitro* GST pull-down assay. It was also demonstrated that HIP14 was localized in the Golgi apparatus and colocalized with CPj0783.

Conclusions

CPj0783 disturbs the vesicle transport system in yeast. In mammalian cells CPj0783 interacts with HIP14 that is involved in palmitoylation-dependent vesicular trafficking. CPj0783 may cause abnormal vesicle-mediated transport by interacting with HIP14.

A15 Analysis of home-self-collection urogenital samples for the detection of *Chlamydia trachomatis* and *Neisseria gonorrhoeae* compared to in-clinic-self-collected specimens

Charlotte Gaydos[1], Mathilda Barnes[1], Perry Barnes[1], Laura Dize[1], Hongyu Chen[2], Lars Mouritson[2]
[1]Johns Hopkins University, Baltimore, Maryland, USA, [2]Sorenson Genomics, LLC, Salt Lake City, Utah, USA

Background/ Introduction

Self-collection of urogenital samples, such as vaginal swabs by women and urine by men, is acceptable to patients. Home-collection of such samples is not yet highly acceptable.

Objectives

This study aimed to compare accuracy and acceptability of clinic self-collection vs. home self-collection of vaginal swabs for women and urine from men for the detection of *Chlamydia* (CT) and gonorrhea (NG).

Method

A total of 211 subjects were enrolled in the IRB approved Phase IIa study and were asked to provide two analyzable paired specimens: one that was self-collected in the clinic (reference) and one provided from home self-collection and mailed to the Identigene laboratory for testing. Women self-collected vaginal swabs and men collected urine specimens. A satisfaction home-collection survey questionnaire was completed (N=152) and returned with the mailed home-collection kit. All samples were tested by a nucleic acid amplification test (NAAT) (Aptima Combo2, Hologic) for CT and NG.

Results

Of 211 patients, 55% were female, 97% were Black, 42% were ages 18-25 years, and 73% were symptomatic. For clinic-collected tests, CT prevalence was 9%; NG prevalence was 5%. Patients returned 155 (73.5%) kits. Of 83 female kits, overall agreement for CT was 95.2% and 98.8% for NG. For 72 male kits, agreement was 100% for CT and 98.6% for NG. Agreement for both was 98.1% (304/310). Of 152 returned surveys, most responses were considered favorable; most respondents took <20 min to read instructions and collect sample; and indicated they would be very likely to recommend the home-collection kit.

Conclusions

It appeared that women and men were accepting of collecting urogenital specimens at home and the overall positive and negative test agreement was comparable to paired samples self-collected in the clinic.

A16 Efficacy of azithromycin for treatment of anogenital *Chlamydia trachomatis* infections in prepubertal children

Kendra K. Ham[1], Michelle I. Amaya[1], Carrie E. Busch[1], Margaret R. Hammerschlag[2]
[1]*Medical University of South Carolina, Charleston, SC, USA,* [2]*SUNY Downstate Medical Center, Brooklyn, NY, USA*

Background/ Introduction

The American Academy of Pediatrics (AAP) Redbook guidelines recommend that children between the ages of 6 months to 8 years and less than 45 kilograms be treated for anogenital *Chlamydia* infections with erythromycin base or ethylsuccinate. Some medical providers prescribe azithromycin as a more palatable alternative with shorter duration.

Objectives

We aimed to determine what most providers are prescribing for children in this age group with anogenital *Chlamydia* infections, with particular interest in treatment successes and failures. We also aimed to evaluate the treatment successes and failures at our own institution (Medical University of South Carolina) as a comparison.

Method

REDCap data software was used to develop a survey to assess the self-reported practices of specialists who treat children in this age group, specifically to analyze the drug treatment choices and history of treatment failures. The survey was sent to two professional Child Abuse Pediatric societies, including the Ray E. Helfer Society and the AAP Section on Child Abuse and Neglect (SOCAN). Descriptive statistics were performed on the data exported from the survey, along with comparative analysis on the results of the two groups. A retrospective chart review was performed at our institution, and descriptive statistics used for analysis.

Results

The survey response rate was 12.8% and 14.8% for Helfer and SOCAN, respectively. The treatment preference was similar in both groups, with 60% of Helfer and 68% of the SOCAN preferring azithromycin 20 mg/kg for one dose. Ten percent of Helfer responders and 7.1% of SOCAN responders have observed treatment failures. Of the providers who observed treatment failures with erythromycin, failures occurred in 33.3%, in both groups. A total of 16 charts were reviewed retrospectively, and 7 were included for analysis. All 7 patients were prescribed azithromycin, varying dosages and duration. Seventy-one percent exhibited successful treatment with azithromycin.

Conclusions

While the majority of providers prefer azithromycin to erythromycin, both treatments have been observed to result in treatment failures. Clear preference and efficacy for azithromycin use were reported, but results are limited by low response rate and low prevalence of prepubertal anogenital *Chlamydia trachomatis* infections.

A17 Performance of a prototype *Chlamydia* and gonorrhoea recombinase polymerase amplification point-of-care test in three sexual health clinics

Emma M. Harding-Esch[1,2], Sebastian S. Fuller[1,2], Christine Chow[2], Mark A. Harrison[2], Mathew J. Parker[3], Olaf Piepenburg[3], David G. Brooks[3], Catherine L. Hall[2], Marcus J. Pond[2], Phillip E. Hay[4], Rajul R. Patel[5], Johanna Turpitt[5], Nicola R. Fearnley[6], Paula Sharratt[6], Kevin J. Dunbar[1], Catherine M. Lowndes[1], S Tariq Sadiq[2,1]
[1]Public Health England, Colindale, London, UK, [2]Applied Diagnostic Research & Evaluation Unit, St George's, University of London, London, UK, [3]TwistDx Limited, Cambridge, UK, [4]Courtyard Clinic, St George's University Hospitals NHS Foundation Trust, London, UK, [5]Department of Sexual Health, University of Southampton, Southampton, UK, [6]Bradford Teaching Hospitals NHS Foundation Trust, Bradford, UK

Background/ Introduction

Providing rapid and accurate sexually transmitted infection (STI) diagnostics that meet World Health Organisation (WHO) ASSURED criteria will reduce transmissions and improve treatment efficacy by reducing time to treatment and eliminating the need for unnecessary empirical treatment of contacts.

Objectives

We performed a prospective, multi-centre study to provide preliminary data on a 15-minute turnaround time recombinase polymerase amplification (RPA)-based assay for male and female urogenital samples, to inform decision-making about further development of the assay.

Method

Patients (symptomatic and asymptomatic) at three participating NHS sexual health clinics in England were invited to participate. Consenting females provided an additional self-collected vaginal swab (SCVS) and an aliquot of first-catch urine (FCU). An additional aliquot of urine from routine FCU was retained from consenting males. Samples were sent to TwistDx for processing by staff blinded to clinical results. RPA results were compared to routine clinic CT/NG Nucleic Acid Amplification Test (NAAT) results; discrepancies were resolved using Cepheid CT/NG GeneXpert. The study was conducted within the eSTI2 Consortium's (www.esti2.co.uk) Diagnostic Evaluations workstream, and approved by a UK Research Ethics Committee.

Results

414 males and 442 females consented. Both RPA and clinic NAAT results were available for 392 males and 395 females. For male and female FCU and SCVS: CT prevalence was 8.9%, 7.3% and 7.1%; NG prevalence was 3.1%, 0.8% and 0.8% (only three female NG cases), respectively.

Specificity and positive predictive value (PPV) were 100% for all sample types except male CT FCU (99.7% specificity, 97.1% PPV). Sensitivity for CT was 94.3% for male FCU and 100% in female FCU, surprisingly higher than for SCVS (96.4%). NG sensitivity was 100% for all FCU. 2/3 NG positive SCVS were correctly identified.

Conclusions

This prototype assay fulfils several WHO ASSURED criteria: accuracy, rapidity, and thermo-stability. The higher sensitivity in female FCU than SCVS warrants further investigation. The results, particularly rapidity without loss of performance, suggest that once further developed and commercialised, this test has potential to positively impact clinical practice and public health.

A18 A role for apoptosis-associated speck-like protein containing a C-terminal caspase recruitment domain (ASC) in host immunity against chlamydial infection

Qing He[1], Danielle N. McKeithen[1], Khamia Ryans[1], Tankya Simoneaux[1], Godwin A. Ananaba[2], Francis Eko[1], Carolyn M. Black[3], Uriel Blas-Machado[4], Joseph U. Igietseme[3]
[1]Morehouse School of Medicine, Atlanta, GA, USA, [2]Clark Atlanta University, Atlanta, GA, USA, [3]Centers for Disease Control & Prevention (CDC), Atlanta, GA, USA, [4]University of Georgia, Athens, GA, USA

Background/ Introduction

Emerging reports indicated that ASC shapes immune responses through dendritic cells and lymphocytes. However, the ability of ASC to regulate mucosal immune responses against chronic *Chlamydia* infection is unknown. Knowledge of the immunoregulatory function of ASC in mucosal immunity against *Chlamydia* will provide novel insight into effective vaccine design strategies.

Objectives

To investigate the role of ASC in modulating innate and adaptive immune responses against chronic genital *Chlamydia* infection

Method

We investigated chlamydial infectivity, the development of pathologies in the genital tract (GT), fertility, and the recruitment and activation of dendritic cells, macrophages and T cells in the GT of *C. trachomatis*-infected wild type (WT) and ASC knockout (KO) mice.

Results

chlamydial infectivity in ASC KO mice was significantly higher ($p<0.05$) compared to WT mice. Also, the ASC KO mice had severe alterations in the structure of the GT as an indication of greater pathologies, as compared to WT mice. Furthermore, IL-1β and IL-18 production, as well as immune cell activation and *Chlamydia*-specific Th1 response were down regulated in the GT of infected ASC KO mice, indicating that the absence of ASC impairs the host innate and adaptive immunity.

Conclusions

These results revealed that ASC may play an important protective role in the mucosal immunity against genital chlamydial infection.

A19 Azithromycin treatment failure in women diagnosed with genital *Chlamydia* infection

Jane Hocking[1], Lenka Vodstrcil[1,4], Willa Huston[2], Peter Timms[3], Marcus Chen[4], Catriona Bradshaw[4], Karen Worthington[4], Amba Lawrence[8], Ruthy McIvor[5], Sam Phillips[7], Sepehr Tabrizi[6,7]
[1]*University of Melbourne, Melbourne, Australia,* [2]*University of Technology Sydney, Sydney, Australia,* [3]*University of Sunshine Coast, Sippy Downs, Australia,* [4]*Melbourne Sexual Health Centre, Carlton, Australia,* [5]*Sydney Sexual Health Centre, Sydney, Australia,* [6]*Murdoch Children's Research Institute, Parkville, Australia,* [7]*The Royal Children's and The Royal Women's Hospitals, Parkville, Australia,* [8]*Queensland University of Technology, Brisbane, Australia*

Background/ Introduction

Repeat infections of *Chlamydia* are very common and may represent a new infection, re-infection from an untreated partner or treatment failure.

Objectives

The aim of this cohort study is to estimate the proportion of women infected with *Chlamydia* who experience failure after treatment with 1 gram azithromycin.

Method

Women diagnosed with *Chlamydia* were followed for 8 weeks post treatment with 1 gram azithromycin and provided weekly genital specimens for further assay. The primary outcome was the proportion of women classified as having treatment failure at least 4 weeks after recruitment. Comprehensive sexual behavior data collection and the detection of Y chromosome DNA in vaginal swabs and genome sequencing were used to differentiate between *Chlamydia* re-infection and treatment failure. *Chlamydia* culture and MIC was also undertaken.

Results

There were 305 women recruited and 36 were diagnosed with repeat *Chlamydia* infection during follow up (11.8%; 95%CI: 8.4%, 16.0%). The median time till repeat infection was 7 weeks, with 25% of repeat infections diagnosed within 5 weeks. The risk of repeat infection increased with increasing organism load of initial infection (OR=1.6; 95%CI: 1.2, 2.8 for each additional log increase in load). Of those with repeat infection, 16 (44.4%; 95%CI: 27.9%, 61.9%) were classified as treatment failure; the overall risk of treatment failure was 5.2% (95%CI: 3.0%, 8.4%). There was no detectable shift in MIC between initial and repeat infections.

Conclusions

Using a combination of advanced laboratory techniques and sexual behavior data, we estimate that about 1 in 20 women with *Chlamydia* treated with azithromycin will fail treatment. Further laboratory investigation will determine whether there are any genomic characteristics of the infections associated with treatment failure in our cohort.

A20 Characteristics of pelvic inflammatory disease where no sexually transmitted infection is identified

Jane L Goller[1], Christopher K Fairley[2], Alysha M De Livera[1], Catriona S Bradshaw[2], Marcus Y Chen[2], Rebecca J Guy[3], Jane S Hocking[1]
[1]Melbourne School of Population and Global Health, University of Melbourne, Melbourne, Victoria, Australia, [2]Central Clinical School, Monash University and Melbourne Sexual Health Centre, Melbourne, Victoria, Australia, [3]Kirby Institute, University of New South Wales, Sydney, New South Wales, Australia

Background/ Introduction

Pelvic inflammatory disease (PID) occurs when pathogens, often sexually transmitted, ascend to the upper genital tract, yet a causative pathogen is not detected in a substantial proportion of diagnosed PID.

Objectives

In this cross-sectional study we aimed to assess the characteristics associated with PID in women in whom Chlamydia, gonorrhoea, Mycoplasma genitalium (MG), and bacterial vaginosis (BV) were not detected.

Method

Routinely collected demographic, behavioural and clinical data from new female sexual health clinic patients during 2006-2013 were extracted from the computerised medical record. Women were eligible if aged 16-49, had clinically diagnosed PID and tested for genital Chlamydia, gonorrhoea, MG and BV. PID cases were classified as pathogen-negative (testing negative for all four infections) or pathogen-positive(testing positive for at least one of Chlamydia, gonorrhoea, MG, BV). Vaginal inflammation was assessed by presence of increased polymorphonuclear leukocytes(PMNL) on high vaginal swab and defined as >/=5 PMNL per 1000 high powered field. Logistic regression was conducted to identify characteristics associated with pathogen-negative-PID.

Results

Among 330 women with clinically diagnosed PID, 204 (61.8%; 95%CI 56.3-67.1) had pathogen-negative-PID. Among the 126 pathogen-positive PID cases that tested positive for one or more infection, 49.2% (95%CI 40.4-58.1) had Chlamydia, 6.3% (95%CI 2.0-10.7) had gonorrhoea, 11.9%(95%CI 6.2-17.6) had MG, and 56.3% (95%CI 47.6-65.1) had BV. Compared with pathogen-positive-PID, pathogen-negative-PID cases were more likely to be aged >/=30 years (OR 1.7, 95% CI 1.0-3.0), had less evidence of vaginal inflammation (OR 0.5; 95%CI 0.3-0.9) and reported less unprotected sex (OR 0.6; 95%CI 0.4-1.0).

Conclusions

These findings raise questions whether these cases of pathogen-negative-PID represent false positive PID diagnoses, PID of another microbiological aetiology or PID where the cervical infection has cleared. However, until diagnostic biomarkers are available, PID treatment should be based on clinical features and sexual risk.

A21 Risk of pelvic inflammatory disease associated with *Chlamydia* and gonorrhoea infection among Australian sexual health clinic attendees

Jane L Goller[1], Christopher K Fairley[2], Alysha M De Livera[1], Catriona S Bradshaw[2], Marcus Y Chen[2], Rebecca J Guy[3], Julie Simpson[1], Jane S Hocking[1]
[1]*Melbourne School of Population and Global Health, University of Melbourne, Melbourne, Victoria, Australia,* [2]*Central Clinical School, Monash University and Melbourne Sexual Health Centre, Melbourne, Victoria, Australia,* [3]*Kirby Institute, University of New South Wales, Sydnet, New South Wales, Australia*

Background/ Introduction

Pelvic inflammatory disease(PID) is an important cause of female infertility and can occur when micro-organisms such as *Chlamydia* or gonorrhoea ascend to the upper genital tract. PID has been an outcome measure in several *Chlamydia* screening trials, however, few data have quantified the PID burden potentially avoidable by preventing *Chlamydia*.

Objectives

We estimated the population attributable fraction (PAF) of PID associated with a current *Chlamydia* or gonorrhoea infection among females 16-49 years attending an Australian sexual health clinic.

Method

Data were extracted from the clinic's electronic patient database for all females aged 16-49 years at first sexual health clinic visit between 2006-2013. *Chlamydia* and gonorrhoea tests were based on clinical and risk assessment. PID diagnosis was based on clinical examination findings. Using multivariable logistic regression, PAF estimates were adjusted for age and behavioural factors. Two separate analyses were undertaken; one among 'Chlamydia-tested' women and one among a subset of *Chlamydia*-tested women who were also tested for gonorrhoea ('*Chlamydia*+gonorrhoea tested'). A sensitivity analysis using multiple imputation was conducted to assess the impact of missing data on results.

Results

Among 15690 *Chlamydia*-tested women, 1279 (8.2%, 95%CI 7.7-8.6) were *Chlamydia* positive, 436 (2.8%, 95%CI 2.5-3.0) had PID diagnosed and the adjusted PAF for *Chlamydia* was 14.1% (95%CI 9.9-18.0). Among the *Chlamydia*+gonorrhoea tested subset (n=8839), 681 (7.7%, 95%CI 7.2-8.3) tested positive for *Chlamydia* only, 30 (0.3%, 95%CI 0.2-0.5) for gonorrhoea only, 22 (0.2%, 95%CI 0.2-0.4) for *Chlamydia* and gonorrhoea and 419 (4.7%, 95%CI 4.3-5.2) had PID diagnosed. The adjusted PAF was highest for *Chlamydia* only (12.4%, 95%CI 8.4-16.2) compared with gonorrhoea only (0.9%, 95%CI-0.1-1.8) or concurrent infections (1.0%, 95%CI 0.0-1.9).

Conclusions

In this high *Chlamydia* prevalence sexual health clinic population, eliminating a current *Chlamydia* infection might at most reduce PID by about 14%.

A22 Differential frequency of NKG2C/KLRC2 deletion in distinct African populations and susceptibility to Trachoma: a new method for imputation of NKG2C/KLRC2 genotypes from single nucleotide polymorphism (SNP) genotyping data

Adriana Goncalves[1], Pateh Makalo[2], Hassan Joof[2], Sarah Burr[1,2], Athumani Ramadhani[3], Patrick Massae[3], Aiweda Malisa[3], Tara Mtuy[1,3], Tamsyn Derrick[1,3], Anna R Last[1], Meno Nabicassa[4], Eunice Cassama[4], Joanna Houghton[1], Christine D Palmer[1], Matthew J Burton[1,3], David C W Mabey[1], Robin L Bailey[1], Martin Goodier[1], Martin J Holland[1,2], Chrissy h Roberts[1]

[1]London School of Hygiene and Tropical Medicine, London, UK, [2]Medical Research Council Unit, Fajara, Gambia, [3]Kilimanjaro Christian Medical Centre, Moshi, Tanzania, [4]Programa Nacional de Saude de Visao, Ministerio de Saude Publica, Bissau, Guinea-Bissau

Background/ Introduction

Repeated ocular infections with the intracellular pathogen Chlamydia trachomatis (Ct) causes Trachoma, a preventable blinding disease. Several studies suggest a role for Natural Killer (NK) cells in the immunopathology of Trachoma. KLRC2 encodes for NKG2C, a NK cell receptor that has been associated with several infectious and autoimmune diseases.

Objectives

The association between KLRC2 and intracellular bacterial infections has not been described so far. We investigated the association between KLRC2 deletion and Trachoma in different African populations where trachoma is or has been endemic, and described a new method for KLRC2 genotype imputation using single nucleotide polymorphism (SNP) genotyping data.

Method

A total of 1522 individuals from The Gambia, Guinea-Bissau and Tanzania were genotyped for KLRC2 deletion by sequence specific primer-PCR (SSP-PCR). Clinical grades of trachoma were obtained using the WHO simplified grading system. Blood was collected from a sample of 76 Gambians and peripheral blood mononuclear cells (PBMCs) were isolated by density gradient centrifugation for flow cytometry analysis of NKG2C expression on NK cells. KLRC2 deletion genotypes were imputed from commercial single nucleotide polymorphism (SNP) genotyping arrays in 1090 scarring (TS) cases and 1531 controls from the Gambia. Statistical analyses were performed using STATA and R statistical computing language.

Results

The frequency of the KLRC2 deletion is comparable among East-Africans, Europeans and East-Asians (~20%) but the proportion of the population carrying the KLRC2 deletion allele is significantly higher in West-Africans (33.2%; $p=1.110 \times 10^{-6}$). West-African populations have approximately two times the odds of having the KLRC2 deletion allele when compared to East-African Tanzanians (OR=1.88; 95% CI 1.46-2.43). There was no apparent relationship between KLRC2 genotype and trachomatous disease in West-African Gambians (p=0.909), East-African Tanzanians (p=0.417) or children with active disease (p=0.617). A newly described method uses information contained in three SNPs to predict KLRC2 genotypes with an accuracy of 94.5%.

Conclusions

KLRC2 deletion is present at high frequencies in different human populations. There was no evidence for an association between KLRC2 deletion and trachomatous disease. The newly described imputation method can be used to expand our understanding of the impact of KLRC2 and other deletions in human populations and disease.

A23 Investigating the relationships between conjunctival microbiome diversity, immune responses and trachomatous disease in Gambians

Christine D. Palmer[1], Pateh Makalo[2], Hassan Joof[2], Joanna Houghton[1], Tamsyn Derrick[1,4], Adriana Goncalves[1], David Nelson[3], Evelyn Toh[3], David C.W. Mabey[1], Robin L. Bailey[1], Matthew J. Burton[1,4], Sarah E. Burr[1], Chrissy h Roberts[1], Martin J. Holland[1,2]

[1]London School of Hygiene and Tropical Medicine, London, UK, [2]Medical Research Council Unit, Fajara, Gambia, [3]Indiana University, Indianapolis, USA, [4]Kilimanjaro Christian Medical Centre, Moshi, Tanzania

Background/ Introduction

Ocular *Chlamydia trachomatis* (*Ct*) infection causes trachoma, the leading infectious cause of blindness worldwide. The pathophysiology of trachoma is complex and multifactorial, and the factors involved in the inflammatory responses to repeated *Ct* infection that lead to conjunctival scarring, trichiasis and subsequent corneal opacity and blindness remain poorly understood.

Objectives

We have previously shown differences in conjunctival microbiome diversity between individuals with trachomatous scarring and controls. The aim of this study was to investigate the contribution of the conjunctival microbiome to the maintenance of host conjunctival associated lymphoid tissue responses at different stages of *Ct* pathology.

Method

Ocular swabs (n= 365) were collected into RNALater® and nucleic material was extracted using total RNA/DNA purification kits (Norgen). RNA was converted to cDNA using the SuperScript® VILO cDNA Synthesis Kit (Invitrogen) or the miScript II RT Kit (Qiagen). Conjunctival microbiome composition was analysed by 16S V1-V3 amplicon next generation sequencing (Illumina). Gene expression analysis was performed using Taqman® Low Density Array Micro Fluidic Cards (Applied Biosystems). Assessment of miRNA expression levels was carried out by qPCR using miScript Primer Assays and the miScript SYBR Green PCR kit (Qiagen). Statistical analyses were performed using R.

Results

Preliminary analyses revealed differential expression of multiple immune transcripts between subjects with scarring (TS), active disease (TF and TI) and controls. Levels of *MMP7* were elevated in TS ($p<0.01$) and active disease ($p<0.0001$) while transcripts of *SPARCL1* were lower in both disease groups compared to controls ($p<0.05$ and $p<0.001$). In contrast, NFkappaB transcripts were elevated in TS ($p<0.001$) but not active disease and *CD274* (*PD-L1*) transcripts were elevated in active disease ($p<0.001$) but not in TS. Levels of miR-147b and miR-155 were elevated in TS and active disease, respectively. Ocular microbiome diversity differed between subjects with scarring and controls.

Conclusions

Our preliminary analyses show differential expression levels of several immune transcripts and miRNAs between subjects with scarring or active disease and controls. We confirm previous findings of differential ocular microbiome diversity in individuals with conjunctival scarring, and analyses investigating the relationship between *Ct*, ocular microbiome and immune transcripts are ongoing.

A24 Identification and quantification of trachoma associated *Chlamydia trachomatis* antigens

Aleksandra Inic-Kanada[1], Katarina Smiljanic[2], Elisabeth Stein[1], Jelena Mihailovic[2], Petar Ristivojevic[3], Hadeel Chalabi[1], Maja Krstic[2], Nadine Schuerer[1], Marija Perusko[3], Sara Trifunovic[2], Dragana Stanic-Vucinic[2], Yeshigeta Belaw[4], Balgesa Elkheir[5], Tanja Cirkovic Velickovic[2], Talin Barisani-Asenbauer[1]

[1]OCUVAC – Center of Ocular Inflammation and Infection, Laura Bassi Centers of Expertise; Center for Pathophysiology, Infectology and Immunology; Medical University of Vienna, Vienna, Austria, [2]Center of Excellence for Molecular Food Sciences, University of Belgrade - Faculty of Chemistry, Belgrade, Serbia, [3]Innovation Center Ltd, University of Belgrade - Faculty of Chemistry, Belgrade, Serbia, [4]Jimma University, Jimma, Ethiopia, [5]Federal Ministry of Health, Karthum, Sudan

Background/ Introduction

The intracellular bacterium *Chlamydia trachomatis* (Ct) is an important human pathogen causing socioeconomic significant morbidities like preventable infectious blindness (trachoma) and female infertility.

Objectives

The aim of the present study was to i) identify Ct antigens associated with trachoma patients by immunoproteomics from proteins solubilized from elementary bodies (EBs) of ocular Ct serovar B (CtB) and ii) analyze the abundance of trachoma-associated Ct antigens using label-free quantitative (LFQ) proteomics.

Method

Electrophoretically separated Ct EB proteins were probed with human sera obtained from trachoma endemic countries, and the data were digitalized for statistical analysis after visualization of the reactive bands and identified by nano LC-high resolution mass spectrometry. Principal component analysis enabled visualization of the most relevant trachoma specific CtB antigens. Relative quantification of trachoma-associated antigens was achieved by LFQ through Q node of PEAKS Studio 7.5.

Results

The immunoproteomics study revealed 35 immunodominant chlamydial antigens, of which 14 were trachoma specific. The most prominent antigens were the major outer membrane protein (MOMP), different polymorphic membrane proteins (PmpE, PmpF, PmpG, and PmpH), the 60 kDa chaperonin (GroEL_1), the elongation factors (EF) G and Tu, and the novel trachoma major antigenic candidates EF-Ts, glycogen phosphorylase, putative zinc metalloprotease, RecA protein and trigger factor protein. LFQ revealed that several of those antigens are also among most abundant proteins of CtB (GroEL_1, MOMP, EF-Tu).

Conclusions

Our data add to the understanding of structure and function of proteins of the infectious form of CtB thereby extending the current knowledge on immunogenic antigens. The identified trachoma-associated chlamydial antigens could facilitate more specific ocular Ct diagnostics and vaccine development.

A25 Long-term trends in the incidence of *Chlamydia trachomatis* infection in Siberia (1998-2015)

Alexey Khryanin[1], Oleg Reshetnikov[2], Anastasiia Titenko[1]
[1]*Novosibirsk State Medical University, Novosibirsk, Russia,* [2]*Institute of Internal and Preventive Medicine, Novosibirsk, Russia*

Background/ Introduction

Siberian regions are among those with the highest risk of STI in the Russian Federation. They are characterized by continental climate with high summer temperatures (+30-35°C), as well as low winter temperatures (-30-35°C) that may result in immunosuppression of Siberian citizens.

Objectives

STI increasing rates including CT infection are a serious public problem for Siberia. The aim of the present study was to assess urogenital chlamydiosis incidence among the population of Novosibirsk (non-official capital of Western Siberia).

Method

The official statistics data on CT infection incidence over 1998-2015 were analyzed.

Results

The decrease in the incidence of CT infection over 1998 (320.0 cases per 100,000 citizens) to 2015 (74.0 cases per 100,000 people) was found, with the peak in 2009. It can be assumed that the reason of that is beginning of ELISA use. Furthermore, summer of 2009 was characterizes by large temperature swings, and high level of pollutants was registered this year. All these factors result in immunosuppression of Novosibirsk population and therefore the increase of morbidity. The main factors for CT infection incidence were 20-29 age group, female sex (69%), and winter season (72%).

Conclusions

The CT infection incidence in Siberia is higher than in Russia at average but less that in European countries. The incidence decreased by 77% since 1998 to 2015. Women predominate in the gender structure, age group 20-29 predominate in age structure. The highest incidence rates occurred in cold season.

A26 Ocular chlamydial genomic variants and disease severity in trachoma: A cross-sectional population-based genome wide association study

Anna R. Last[1], Chrissy h. Roberts[1], Francesc Coll[1], Jody Phelan[1], Sarah E. Burr[1,2], Eunice Cassama[3], Meno Nabicassa[3], Lesley T. Cutcliffe[4], Ian N. Clarke[4], David C.W. Mabey[1], Robin L. Bailey[1], Nicholas R. Thomson[1,5], Taane G. Clark[1], Martin J. Holland[1]

[1]London School of Hygiene and Tropical Medicine, London, UK, [2]Medical Research Council The Gambia Unit, Fajara, Gambia, [3]Ministério de Saúde Publica, Bissau, Guinea-Bissau, [4]University of Southampton, Southampton, UK, [5]Wellcome Trust Sanger Institute, Cambridge, UK

Background/ Introduction

Chlamydia trachomatis (Ct) is the commonest cause of bacterial sexually transmitted infection and the commonest infectious cause of blindness (trachoma) worldwide. Recurrent episodes of infection may cause chronic immunofibrogenic pathology leading to conjunctival scarring and blinding sequelae. Underlying host and pathogen factors responsible for such diverse clinical outcomes are unclear.

Objectives

To investigate Ct genotypic associations with disease severity using an objective in vivo conjunctival phenotype in active trachoma and Ct whole genome sequence (WGS) data in populations from a treatment-naïve geographically remote island setting of the Bijagós Archipelago of Guinea Bissau.

Method

A cross-sectional population-based trachoma survey was undertaken in 38 villages on four islands. Droplet digital PCR was used to detect and estimate Ct load from conjunctival swabs. Ct WGS data were obtained with next-generation Illumina sequencing. Single nucleotide polymorphisms (SNPs) were called against the reference genome Ct A/HAR-13. A permutation-based Ct genome-wide association study (GWAS) was performed to investigate SNP associations with conjunctival phenotype defined using a disease severity score which combined a conjunctival inflammation score and ocular Ct load.

Results

1507 conjunctival samples and corresponding clinical phenotype data were collected. Ct was detected in 220, and quantified in 184. WGS data were obtained from 126. 6244 SNP sites were identified across the Ct genome relative to Ct A/HAR-13. After quality filtering 129 genome-wide SNPs in 71 Ct sequences were included in the final analysis. Six SNPs were associated with disease severity at genome-wide significance within the genes glgA (OR=9.71, p*=0.022), trmD (OR=8.67, p*=0.037), alaS (OR=0.10, p*=0.032) and pmpE (OR=0.08, p*=0.009), the coding locus CTA0273 (OR=8.36, p*=0.042) and the intergenic region CTA0744- CTA0745 (OR=0.13, p*=0.043).

Conclusions

This is the first study to identify associations between alaS and CTA0273 and disease severity. These six markers provide direction for further in silico, in vitro and replication cohort studies to identify targets under selective pressure, causative variants and validate these findings to understand host-pathogen interactions in Ct pathogenesis.

A27 Immunization with a novel *Chlamydia* vaccine consisting of type III secretion components elicits cell-mediated and humoral immune responses and confers protection against genital tract infection and associated pathology

Steven Liang[1], David C. Bulir[1], Amanda Lee[1], Elizabeth Simms[1], Sylvia Chong[2], James B. Mahony[1,2]
[1]McMaster University, Hamilton, Canada, [2]St. Joseph's Hospital, Hamilton, Canada

Background/ Introduction

Despite decades of research, a *Chlamydia* vaccine has yet to be approved for human use. Cell-mediated and humoral immunity are both important for protection against *Chlamydia* infections. We have recently developed a novel chimeric antigen (BD584) consisting of three proteins from the chlamydial type III secretion (T3S) system.

Objectives

The objectives of this study were to characterize the immune response induced by immunization with BD584, and evaluate its efficacy for protecting mice against a genital tract infection with *Chlamydia*.

Method

Female C57BL/6 mice (8-12 weeks old) were immunized with 20 µg of BD584 and 10 µg of CpG adjuvant (BD584/CpG). Serum specific antibody titres to BD584 were determined using ELISA. Sera from immunized mice were assessed for their ability to inhibit *Chlamydia* infection *in vitro*. Antigen specific cell-mediated immune responses were assessed following *in vitro* stimulation of splenocytes harvested from immunized mice by ELISA and flow cytometry. Following immunization, mice were intravaginally challanged with 5×10^4 IFUs of *C. muridarum*. Bacterial load was quantified by qPCR, and pathology was assessed 50 days post infection.

Results

Mice immunized with BD584/CpG generated serum antibodies that inhibited *Chlamydia* infection *in vitro*. Splenocytes from immunized mice produced IFN-γ upon *in vitro* stimulation with BD584. Compared to control mice, immunized mice had significantly lower bacterial load and incidence of hydrosalpinx following intravaginal challenge with *Chlamydia*.

Conclusions

Antigens derived from the T3S system have been used as successful vaccine candidates against other pathogenic bacteria. BD584 consists of chlamydial T3S components which are highly conserved among different serovars of *C. trachomatis* and may represent a good candidate for a *Chlamydia* vaccine.

A28 Genomic evidence that the *Chlamydia abortus* vaccine strain 1B can cause disease

Morag Livingstone[1], Helena MB Seth-Smith[2], Michelle Sait[1,3], Simon Harris[2], Karine Laroucau[4], Konrad Sachse[5], Nicholas R Thomson[2], David Longbottom[1]
[1]*Moredun Research Institute, Edinburgh, UK,* [2]*Sanger Institute, Hinxton, UK,* [3]*University of Melbourne, Melbourne, Australia,* [4]*French Agency for Food, Environmental & Occupational Health Safety (ANSES), Maisons-Alfort, France,* [5]*Friedrich-Loeffler-Institut, Jena, Germany*

Background/ Introduction

The live, temperature-attenuated vaccine targeting *Chlamydia abortus*, the aetiological agent of Ovine Enzootic Abortion (OEA), has been implicated in cases of vaccine breakdown. This follows on from the identification of the 1B vaccine strain in the placentas of vaccinated ewes that had aborted, by PCR-RFLP typing.

Objectives

To perform full genome sequence and comparative analysis of the AB7 parental strain and derived nitrosoguanidine (NTG)-induced mutants, 1B (temperature sensitive mutant) and 1H (reversion mutant), and five strains isolated from cases of OEA from either vaccinated animals or animals that have had extensive contact with a vaccinated flock.

Method

C. abortus strains AB7, 1B-Cevac, 1B-Enzovax, 1H, 11-669_5380/2, 10DC0084, AB15, 6012 and 6181 genomes were sequenced using the Illumina HiSeq platform with 75-bp paired end reads generating a mean genome coverage of 135, 300, 14, 208, 40, 273, 169, 10 and 10x, respectively after mapping against the reference strain S26/3 using SMALT. All SNPs were manually checked against mapped reads with even the lower coverage samples providing sufficient data for confident base calls. Annotation was transferred from *C. abortus* strain S26/3 and manually curated using Artemis.

Results

We confirmed that AB7 belongs to a different phylogenetic lineage compared to the reference strain S26/3. The genomes of 1B-Enzovax and 1B-Cevac, both derived from the commercial vaccines, showed identical sequence. In contrast to earlier published work, the vaccine strain 1B was found to contain ten SNP differences compared to parent strain AB7. Unexpectedly, the 1H reversion mutant strain was found to be identical in sequence to 1B. The field strains isolated from OEA cases (vaccinated or in contact vaccinated animals) were also found to very tightly cluster phylogenetically with the vaccine strain.

Conclusions

If 1B and 1H are identical in sequence, is the temperature-sensitive phenotype of the vaccine real? Indeed, vaccine strain can be found in placentas of aborted vaccinated ewes suggesting growth and multiplication. Thus, vaccine-induced protection may arise as a consequence of the high organism dose administered rather than any attenuation.

A29 Anti-bacterial activity of 17 strains of lactobacilli against elementary bodies of *Chlamydia trachomatis*

Antonella Marangoni[1], Paola Nardini[1], Rogers Alberto Ñahui Palomino[2], Carola Parolin[2], Luca Laghi[3], Claudio Foschi[1], Roberto Cevenini[1], Beatrice Vitali[2]
[1]University of Bologna, DIMES, Microbiology, Bologna, Italy, [2]University of Bologna, FaBiT, Bologna, Italy, [3]University of Bologna, Centre of Foodomics, Department of Agro-Food Science and Technology, Cesena, Italy

Background/ Introduction

Chlamydia trachomatis (CT) is the most frequent bacterial sexually transmitted infection (STI) worldwide. The human vaginal microbioma plays a key-role in preventing a large number of urogenital diseases, including STIs. These protective functions are mainly attributed to *Lactobacillus* species dominating the vaginal niche of healthy women.

Objectives

Up to now only few studies have investigated the possible interaction between lactobacilli and CT. The aim of our study was to investigate anti-bacterial activity of 17 vaginal lactobacilli isolates against elementary bodies (EBs) of CT in relation to their metabolic profiles.

Method

Seventeen *Lactobacillus* strains, isolated from vaginal swabs of healthy pre-menopausal women were used. Lactobacilli cultures were centrifuged to separate cell pellets (CP) from cell-free supernatants (CFS).

All CP and CFS corresponding to 2.5×10^8, 2.5×10^7 and 2.5×10^5 CFU were mixed with 5×10^3 IFU of EBs of CT, serotype D.

Tubes were incubated for 7, 15 and 60 minutes and then centrifuged. Supernatants were used to infect confluent Hela cells. CT infectivity was evaluated after 48h of incubation.

^{1}H-NMR analysis of metabolic profiles of CFS was conducted on AVANCE spectrometer.

Statistical analyses were performed using GraphPad Prism software, applying Wilcoxon test.

Results

CT infectivity was significantly reduced only by CFS ($p=0.038$), in contrast to CP ($p=0.425$). CSF at the highest concentration showed the strongest anti-chlamydial activity. Under these conditions CFS were found to have $pH<4.5$, differently from the less concentrated ones.

The best anti-*Chlamydia* profile was shown by *L. crispatus* species.

Production of lactate and acidification of the vaginal environment seemed to be crucial for the activity, in addition to the consumption of the carbonate source represented by glucose.

Conclusions

Our results demonstrate the ability of different *Lactobacillus* strains of vaginal origin to inactivate *C. trachomatis* EBs through the production of extracellular metabolites.

The final goal is the selection of active lactobacilli in order to develop new pharmaceutical formulations based on probiotics for the prevention and treatment of CT infection.

A30 Tetracycline Resistance in *Chlamydia suis*: Transmission through co-infection

Hanna Marti[1], Hoyon Kim[1], Sandeep J. Joseph[2], Stacey Dojiri[1], Timothy D. Read[2], Deborah Dean[1,3]
[1]UCSF Benioff Children's Hospital Oakland Research Institute, Oakland, California, USA, [2]Emory University School of Medicine, Atlanta, Georgia, USA, [3]UCSF and UC Berkeley Departments of Bioengineering, Berkeley, California, USA

Background/ Introduction

The only example of an obligate intracellular bacterium naturally acquiring antibiotic resistance is *Chlamydia suis*. While acquisition of the *tet*(C)-containing transposon confers tetracycline resistance, and *in vitro* transposon transfer from *C. suis* to *C. trachomatis* but not *C. caviae* has been described, the implications for *in vivo* transmission are unknown.

Objectives

1) To identify genomic, transposon and antibiotic features required for efficient and stable HGT *in vitro* between tetracycline sensitive and resistant *C. suis* strains; and 2) To determine prokaryotic/eukaryotic sources of genes/genomic regions within the inserted transposon and flanking genomic regions that may provide stable insertion into *C. trachomatis*.

Method

Tetracycline-sensitive *C. suis* strain S45 and tetracycline-resistant strain Rogers132 that lacks *IS200* and *IS605* transposases but contains *tet*(C), repressor gene *tet*R(C) and various mobilization genes were i) co-infected or ii) added sequentially to McCoy cells. Plaque assays were performed to clonally purify recombinants, which were tested for S45 and Rogers132 specific markers. Clones that contained *tet*(C), were *ompA*- and *pmp*-positive for S45, and possessed minimal inhibitory concentrations (MIC) greater than S45 were considered potential recombinants and were whole-genome sequenced. BLASTN was employed for database mining to determine the microbial origins of the genes comprising the transposon.

Results

Seven potential recombinants were isolated. MICs for tetracycline were ~8µg/ml (similar to Rogers132). Tetracycline resistance of the recombinants was unstable after 3-4 passages unless grown in tetracycline at 2x the MIC of S45. Genomics revealed identical recombinants with insertion of the Rogers132 transposon between *nrq*F and a hypothetical gene with additional Rogers132 DNA flanking *fts*K in S45. The transposon region of *tet*(C), *tet*R(C), *IS200* and *IS605* was 100% homologous to that of *Snodgrassella spp.*, a bacterium in honeybee guts (an unlikely transposon source for *C. suis*), reflecting pressure from antibiotic use starting in the 1950s in beekeeping and animal husbandry.

Conclusions

Transposition of the transposon into S45 had low frequency, did not require *IS200/IS605* transposases, and was stable when grown in tetracycline. The unique insertion sites may facilitate transfer into other *Chlamydia*. *tet*(C) and *tet*R(C) homology with *Snodgrassella* indicate parallel antibiotic selective pressure, a Public Health threat from infected animal species.

A31 Proteome alterations in human monocytes during acute *Chlamydia trachomatis* infection

Mads Lausen Nielsen, Thomas Bouet Guldbæk Poulsen, Allan Stensballe, Svend Birkelund
Aalborg University, Aalborg, Denmark

Background/ Introduction

Different *Chlamydia trachomatis* serovars infect monocytes *in vitro*. Upon uptake, *C. trachomatis* activates the cell and reside intracellularly in a persistent and non-replicative state. Evaluating the monocyte response to *C. trachomatis* uptake could reveal novel insights into *Chlamydia* elimination pathways including serovar-specific differences in clearance mechanisms.

Objectives

We investigated the activation and proteomic changes in human monocytes during acute infection by *C. trachomatis* serovars D and L2 to improve the current understanding of the processes taking place in monocytes following *C. trachomatis* uptake.

Method

Blood was obtained from one healthy donor and peripheral blood mononuclear cells (PBMCs) were isolated by density gradient centrifugation. Monocytes were purified from PBMCs by immunomagnetic positive selection or by adherence. Monocytes were incubated with *C. trachomatis* serovars D or L2, LPS, and mock control over a time course of 6, 12, 18, and 24 hours. Monocyte proteomes were analyzed by ultra performance liquid chromatography tandem mass spectrometry (UPLC-MS/MS). Confocal microscopy was used to assess monocyte activation; infected monocytes were stained against chlamydial MOMP and COMC, and the propiece of interleukin-1alpha (IL-1α).

Results

First, we made a proteomic analysis of LPS activated monocytes to verify an analytical platform to study *Chlamydia*-monocyte interaction. Using UPLC-MS/MS we identified and quantified over 2700 proteins from different subcellular compartments and functional systems.

Next, we examined the infection and activation of *C. trachomatis* in monocytes. EBs of both serovars were visualized in monocytes to all investigated time points and induced IL-1α expression. Proteinase K-treated *Chlamydia* also induced IL-1α expression, but to a lesser extent, suggesting that the activation is only partially mediated by chlamydial LPS.
Results from the proteomic analysis of *Chlamydia*-infected monocytes will be presented.

Conclusions

These results confirm that *C. trachomatis* serovars D and L2 infect human monocytes and lead to production of IL-1α. Proteomic analysis of *Chlamydia*-infected monocytes will provide insight into the protein-based defense mechanisms elicited in human monocytes following *C. trachomatis* uptake.

A32 A unique insight into the MiRNA profile during genital *Chlamydia* infection

Yusuf O. Omosun[1,2], Tankya Simoneaux[1], Yuehao Wu[1], Khamia Ryans[1], Danielle McKeithen[1], Debra Ellerson[2], Roshan Pais[1], Francis O. Eko[1], Carolyn M. Black[2], Uriel Blas-Machado[3], Joseph U. Igietseme[1,2], Qing He[1,2]
[1]Department of Microbiology, Biochemistry & Immunology, Morehouse School of Medicine, Atlanta, Georgia, USA, [2]Centers for Disease Control and Prevention, Atlanta, Georgia, USA, [3]Department of Pathology, College of Veterinary Medicine, University of Georgia, Athens, Georgia, USA

Background/ Introduction

Chlamydia induced pathological sequelae in the female genital tract are the consequence of deleterious gene expression which give rise to pelvic inflammatory diseases, salpingitis and tubal factor infertility in women. Understanding the altered gene expression during chlamydial pathogenesis therefore is of importance.

Objectives

To identify novel and differentially expressed miRNAs in the genital tract of *Chlamydia* infected mice that are associated with chlamydial pathogenesis.

Method

Mice were divided into two groups: First, primary infection (one infection) and second, secondary Infection (two infections). Mice were sacrificed and genital tract tissues were collected at four time points; one, two, four, and eight weeks after infection. miRNA sequencing, pathology, cytokine analysis and fertility assay were performed.

Results

Secondary infected mice had higher bacteria loads and their infection lasted longer than primary infected mice. Pathological presentation showed that secondary infected mice had more ectasia and inflammation in the oviduct and uterus. miRNAs were differentially expressed in both the primary and secondary infection, however, the miRNA profile was different for both groups. Pathway analysis showed that the differentially regulated miRNAs might be regulating endothelial migration and focal adhesion of cells, extracellular matrix receptors, and adherens junction formation amongst other functions. In addition, we also discovered novel miRNAs that were only found in *Chlamydia*-infected mice.

Conclusions

The progression of chlamydial pathogenesis depends on host factors, which include miRNAs. We intend to determine to what extent these miRNAs could be regulating the outcomes that were observed in *Chlamydia* infection.

A33 Effectiveness of *Chlamydia trachomatis* screening-a randomised trial

Matti Lehtinen[1], Tiina Eriksson[1], Saara Kares[2], Kari Natunen[1], Helja-Marja Surcel[3], Mirja Puolakkainen[4], Jorma Paavonen[4]
[1]University of Tampere, Tampere, Finland, [2]FIMLAB, Tampere, Finland, [3]National Institute of Health and Welfare, Oulu, Finland, [4]University of Helsinki, Helsinki, Finland

Background/ Introduction

C.trachomatis is the most common sexually transmitted bacterial infection and a feasible target for systematic screening and treatment.

Objectives

We established a randomised trial on the effectiveness of *C. trachomatis* screening among young women.

Method

A cohort of 40 000 and 22 500 women born 1992-95 were invited and vaccinated with the bivalent human papillomavirus type (HPV) 16/18 vaccine at 13-15 years of age within a community randomized trial (CRT, EUDraCT 2007-001731-55), in 33 communities during 2007-2010. At the age of 18.5 years 11 505 participants attending the last CRT follow-up visit were randomized to C.trachomatis screening trial. At the age of 22 years women from 11 control communities are also enrolled.

Results

At the first screening round, the coverage among the 11 505 18.5 year-old women was approximately 30% with little variation between communities. C.trachomatis prevalence rate ranged from 0.7% to 8.3%, by community. The overall *C. trachomatis* prevalence rate was 4.0%. At age 22 years, 3 610 women from the 1992-93 birth cohorts have already been tested. The overall *C. trachomatis* prevalence rate was 2.1% (range from 0% to 6.3%, by community).

Conclusions

We observed an approximately 50% *C. trachomatis* prevalence rate reduction in women after one screening round. Ultimately, true impact of screening will be assessed by comparing the prevalence rate to the rate among age-matched, unscreened women in control communities.

A34 *Chlamydia trachomatis* genome-wide signatures of antibody and genetic selection in trachoma

Harry Pickering[1], Andy Teng[2], Nkoyo Faal[3], Hassan Joof[3], Pateh Malako[3], Mass Laye[3], Eunice Cassama[4], Meno Nabicassa[4], Anna Last[1], Sarah Burr[5], Sarah Rowland-Jones[6], Nick R. Thomson[7], Chrissy h Roberts[1], David C.W. Mabey[1], Robin L. Bailey[1], Richard Hayward[8], Luis M. de la Maza[9], Martin J. Holland[1]

[1]Clinical Research Department, Faculty of Infectious and Tropical Diseases, London School of Hygiene and Tropical Medicine, London, UK, [2]ImmPORT Therapeutics, Inc./Antigen Discovery Inc., 1 Technology Dr., Suite E309, Irvine, CA, USA, [3]Medical Research Council Laboratories, Fajara, Gambia, [4]Programa Nacional de Saúde de Visão, Ministério de Saúde Publica, Bissau, Guinea-Bissau, [5]Disease Control and Elimination Theme, Medical Research Council Unit, Fajara, Gambia, [6]Nuffield Department of Medicine, Target Discovery Institute, University of Oxford, Oxford, UK, [7]Department of Infectious and Tropical Diseases, London School of Hygiene and Tropical Medicine, London, UK, [8]Institute of Structural and Molecular Biology, Birkbeck & University College London, London, UK, [9]Department of Pathology and Laboratory Medicine, Medical Sciences I, Room D440, University of California, Irvine, CA, USA

Background/ Introduction

Ocular *Ct* infection provokes an immune response which promotes initial clearance of infection but in trachoma endemic communities often does not protect from future infections and may later contribute to immunopathology. Neutralising antibody responses can in the short term protect from reinfection and serve as correlates of immunity.

Objectives

We screened serum from a longitudinal trachoma cohort from The Gambia on a *Ct* proteome array. Whole-genome sequences from 126 ocular *Ct* isolates collected from a single population in Guinea-Bissau were used to test for signatures of selection as further evidence of immune selection pressure.

Method

Children aged 4-15 years from 9 Gambian villages were followed fortnightly for six months, at each visit conjunctival swabs were tested for *Ct* using an in-house 16S qPCR assay. Blood was taken at the start of the study from 90 children and serum was screened on a *Ct* (D/UW-3cx) proteome array (ImmPORT). Antigens with a differential antibody response between individuals with either no or short duration infections (protected) compared to individuals with long duration infections (non-protected) were identified. These were mapped to their Tajima's D value and dN/dS ratio, calculated from a population of ocular Ct strains in current co-circulation.

Results

Twenty-nine antigens were associated with higher antibody responses (P10000 < 0.05) in individuals with long duration infections, six antigens were associated with significantly higher responses in individuals with no or short duration infections. Ten of these twenty-nine antigens had negative Tajima's D values (P10000 < 0.05) of which five had evidence of positive selection (CT017, CT119, CT223, CT592 and CT664) and five had evidence of purifying selection (CT106, CT181, CT545, CT579 and CT841). Two of six antigens had negative Tajima's D values with evidence of purifying selection (CT029 and CT239).

Conclusions

Six differential antibody responses associated with protection however most associated with lack of protection and had evidence of purifying selection. These non-protective antigens may be acting as decoys, diverting the antibody response away from potentially protective epitopes. This immune evasion mechanism may help sustain *Ct* infection and facilitate reinfection.

A35 Endemic Australian *Chlamydia psittaci* strains from humans and parrots cluster within the highly virulent 6BC clade of this important zoonotic pathogen

James Branley[1], Nathan Bachmann[2], Martina Jelocnik[2], Garry Myers[3], Adam Polkinghorne[2]
[1]Nepean Hospital, Penrith, NSW, Australia, [2]University of the Sunshine Coast, Sippy Downs, QLD, Australia, [3]University of Technology Sydney, Sydney, NSW, Australia

Background/ Introduction

Chlamydia psittaci is an avian pathogen and zoonotic agent of atypical pneumonia. The most pathogenic *C. psittaci* cluster into the 6BC clade, hypothesized to have recently emerged globally. Exposure to infected parrots is a significant risk factor. Evidence is increasing that indirect exposure may also be an epidemiological factor.

Objectives

Psittacosis is endemic to the Blue Mountains, Australia with ongoing cases of psittacosis leading to serious illness over a 9 year period. The majority of human cases did not have explicit psittacine contact. The study's objectives were to characterise the identity and relationships of these Australian human and bird isolates.

Method

Sequencing was performed on six Australian human and a single avian *C. psittaci* strain isolated over a 9 year period. Only one patient had explicit contact with psittacines. Phylogenetic analysis was performed on the resulting near-full length genome sequences and against other available *C. psittaci* sequences using PhyML. Bayesian analysis of substitution rates and divergence time was performed on these samples along with 16 publically available *C. psittaci* genome sequences using BEAST. Evidence of recombination within the newly sequenced *C. psittaci* isolates was detected using Gubbins.

Results

All sequenced Australian human *C. psittaci* isolates, along with the native Australian parrot isolate, were remarkably similar, sharing < 100 SNPs. Phylogenetic analysis revealed that these newly sequenced strains clustered tightly within the highly pathogenic 6BC clade of *C. psittaci* with <200 SNPs separating all members. All *C. psittaci* strains in the 6BC clade, including the Australia isolates, have an identical recombination profile. Recalculation of the substitution rate for *C. psittaci* produced a significantly slower rate of 6.301×10^{-7} substitutes per year per site than that previously calculated, predicting the emergence of the 6BC clade approximately 2,000 years ago.

Conclusions

These findings reveal a potential Australian natural reservoir of *C. psittaci* strains from the 6BC clade, highlighting their potential role in the dissemination of these strains globally. This work also further reinforces the public health risks of inadvertent contact with *C. psittaci*-infected wild birds.

A36 Human immune responses in active trachoma and ocular *Chlamydia trachomatis* infection in Tanzanian children; a cross-sectional study

Athumani M. Ramadhani[1,2], Patrick Massae[2], Tamsyn Derrick[1,2], Tara Mtuy[1,2], David Jeffries[3], Chrissy h. Roberts[1], Helen A. Weiss[1], Robin L. Bailey[1], David C. W. Mabey[1], Martin J. Holland[1], Matthew J. Burton[1]

[1]*London School of Hygiene and Tropical Medicine, London, UK,* [2]*Kilimanjaro Christian Medical Centre, Moshi, Tanzania,* [3]*Medical Research Council Laboratories, Faraja, Gambia*

Background/ Introduction

Trachoma, caused by *Chlamydia trachomatis*, is the worlds leading infectious cause of blindness. Much of the pathology of trachomatous disease is thought to be caused by the host immune response to infection, However the immune response during active trachoma is not clearly understood.

Objectives

To characterise the host ocular response in active trachoma in a cohort of children from a trachoma endemic population

Method

We conducted a cross-sectional study in untreated children from a trachoma-endemic region of Northern Tanzania. Five hundred and six children aged 6 to 10 years were recruited. An ocular examination was performed followed by conjunctival swab sample collection. *C. trachomatis* was detected by droplet digital PCR. Expression of 91 human genes involved in the immune response was measured by quantitative real-time PCR (qPCR).

Results

The prevalence of follicles (TF), papillary hypertrophy (TI) and scarring (TS) were 33.6%, 31.6% and 28.5% respectively in this cohort. *C. trachomatis* plasmid was detected in 15.4% and chromosomal DNA was detected in 14.0% of individuals. Over 70% of *C. trachomatis* infection was detected in individuals with TF and TI, and most infected individuals without TF showed signs of mild follicular conjunctivitis. In addition to the upregulation of many pro-inflammatory cytokines, chemokines and matrix metalloproteinases, there was a strong upregulation of genes involved in the development and function of Th17 cells in response to *C. trachomatis* infection.

Conclusions

Gene expression characteristic of Th17 cells was observed suggesting these cells may be involved in the immune response to ocular *C. trachomatis* infection. Longitudinal study of children in this cohort further establish the role of these differentially-expressed targets and their contribution to protection from or development of progressive scarring trachoma.

A37 The impact of IFN-γ mediated Tryptophan limitation on the *Chlamydia trachomatis* proteome

Ole Østergaard, Frank Follmann, Anja W. Olsen, Niels H.H. Heegaard, Peter Andersen, Ida Rosenkrands
Statens Serum Institut, Copenhagen, Denmark

Background/ Introduction

Cellular host immunity against *C. trachomatis* is primarily mediated by the cytokine IFN-γ that acts through the induction of the enzyme indoleamine 2,3-dioxygenase, which degrades tryptophan (Trp). Trp depletion disrupts the normal chlamydial developmental cycle and halts the bacterium in a non-replicating persistent form (aberrant reticulate bodies,ARB).

Objectives

The current study describes a quantitative comparative proteome analysis of *C. trachomatis* D/UW-3/CX growth forms under normal and Trp limiting growth conditions.

Method

An *in vitro* model of persistent infection was established by infecting Hela 229 cells with *C. trachomatis*, and growth in RPMI medium was followed after IFN-γ treatment or under normal growth conditions for comparison. The bacteria were harvested after 20 hours (the RB form) and 40 hours (the EB and ARB form) of culturing. Protein lysates were prepared from the isolated bacteria, separated by SDS-PAGE and excised gel slices were analysed by high resolution LC-MS/MS. The MaxQuant software was used for label-free protein quantification and identification.

Results

We identified 686 (76%) of the predicted proteins and 89% were shared between the RB, EB and ARB forms. The ARB proteome was highly similar to the RB proteome, however, the most striking characteristics of the persistent form was the strong increase in the abundance of the tryptophan synthase components TrpA and TrpB representing 9% of the total protein content in this growth form. Furthermore, our analyses suggested that Trp limiting conditions affected the ARB protein profile in favour of low-Trp containing proteins.

Conclusions

We have studied the chlamydial evasion response to the host's strategy of decreasing bacterial replication, and shown that the Trp depleted environment is reflected in the protein repertoire of the chlamydial persistence phase.

A38 *Chlamydia trachomatis* detection using immunomagnet fluorescent nanoparticles

Luidmila Rubanik[1], Andrey Astachonok[1], Nikolay Poleshchuk[1], Genady Zhavnerko[2]
[1]*Republic Research and Practical Center for Epidemiology and Microbiology, Minsk, Belarus,*
[2]*Institute of chemistry of new materials of National Academy of Sciences of Belarus, Minsk, Belarus*

Background/ Introduction

Despite the existence of a fairly wide arsenal of laboratory methods (MFA, EIA, PCR, cell culture) each of them has its advantages and disadvantages. In this connection actual is the improvement of existing and development of new rapid and accurate method of laboratory diagnosis of *Chlamydia trachomatis* using nanotechnological approaches

Objectives

Development of a new effective technique for the *Chlamydia trachomatis* detection using activated sensor surfaces and functionally active composite conjugates in immunomagnet nanoparticles containing a fluorescent label

Method

The urogenital scraping material of 495 patients was studied using the cultural method, PCR, MFA, and a microchip constructed and fluorescent immunomagnet nanoparticles. *Chlamydia trachomatis* strain CT-869 passaged in McCoy cell culture was used as a positive control. The intact McCoy cell culture was used as a negative control. Standard 8-cell glass titer plates with a chemically modified surface and immobilized anti-*Chlamydia* antibodies were used as a base for creating a microchip sensor surface. Functionally active composite fluorescent immunomagnet microspheres (MMS) were used for the indication pathogen in the biological probes. The results were registered at a fluorescent microscope.

Results

The chosen nanotechnological approach to the *Chlamydia trachomatis* detection in biological material was shown to be efficient in patients suffering from urogenital pathologies. Highly informative values of the *Chlamydia trachomatis* indication were obtained when activated sensor surfaces and functionally active composite conjugates of immunomagnet particles containing a fluorescent label were used, i.e. sensitivity was 98,8%, specificity – 99,6%, accurancy – 99,2%. The MMS conjugates were shown to bind selectively and to concentrate pathogens on their surface. Shown that the pathogen could be detected even when its concentration in the sample was low.

Conclusions

Immunomagnet separation using MMS covered with a biocompatible coating and conjugated with affine anti*Chlamydia* antibodies was shown to detect *Chlamydia trachomatis* small amounts in biological material. An analytical microchip was developed and MMS conjugates with fluorescent labels making possible the pathogen indication were obtained.

A39 Exosomes from *Chlamydia* Infected Cells Stimulate Immune Responses through Dendritic Cell Activation

Raedeen S. Russell[1], Joseph U. Igietseme[2], Carolyn M. Black[2], Francis O. Eko[1]
[1]*Morehouse School of Medicine, Atlanta, Georgia, USA,* [2]*Centers for Disease Control and Prevention, Atlanta, Georgia, USA*

Background/ Introduction

Exosomes are vesicles that can package donor cell intracellular molecules and release their cargo into recipient cells to manipulate gene expression, cellular activity and physiologic responses. They have been shown to play a role in cancer and cardiovascular diseases but their role in response to *Chlamydia* has not been delineated.

Objectives

The objectives of this study were to characterize exosomes released from *Chlamydia muridarum* (MoPn)-infected cells, and define their role in immune activation.

Method

C57/BL6 mouse oviduct epithelial cells were infected with MoPn at a multiplicity of infection of 5. After 3 hours of infection cells were washed to remove unbound *Chlamydia.* Fresh media was added and exosomes were isolated by differential ultra-centrifugation from the conditioned media at 1h and 48h of incubation. The concentration of exosomes was determined using the NanoSight and the protein concentration by the Nanodrop. Exosomes were co-cultured with naïve (uninfected) bone marrow derived cells (BMDC) and FACS analysis was used to study the profile of surface markers.

Results

Exosome release from epithelial cells increased between 1h and 48h. Infected cells showed the highest concentration of exosomes at 48h. Exosomes from infected cells contained chlamydial proteins, and about 50% fewer proteins than exosomes from uninfected cells. BMDCs co-cultured with exosomes from infected cells showed a difference in surface marker expression, including higher expression of costimulatory molecules required for T-cell activation. Additionally, BMDCs co-cultured with exosomes from MoPn infected C57/BL6 cells had increased MHCII and CD86 expression at 1h and 48h, and they had a higher expression of CD40 at 48h, compared to BMDCs co-cultured with exosomes from uninfected cells.

Conclusions

Exosomes may play a role in chlamydial disease and host response by enhancing immune responses through dendritic cell activation.

A40 Towards elimination of blinding trachoma in Ghana: a review of post treatment surveillance methodologies and endgame challenges

Laura Senyonjo[1,5], Oscar Debrah[2], David Agyemang[3], Didier Bakajika[3], Ernest Mensah[4], Nana Biritwum[2], Robin Bailey[5]
[1]Sightsavers, Haywards Heath, UK, [2]Ghana Health Services, Accra, Ghana, [3]Sightsavers, Accra, Ghana, [4]FHI, Accra, Ghana, [5]London School of Hygiene and Tropical Medicine, London, UK

Background/ Introduction

Trachoma was endemic in two regions of Northern Ghana. After a successful intervention, the country stopped distribution of azithromycin in 2008. Subsequently, an on-going trachoma surveillance system has been implemented and in 2015-2016, a final survey was conducted, aimed at providing evidence that elimination of blinding trachoma has been achieved.

Objectives

The purpose of the study was to undertake an in-depth review of the operationalisation of the trachoma surveillance system in Ghana. It further aimed to capture the endgame challenges and lessons learnt in regards to the verification of the elimination of blinding trachoma in Ghana.

Method

The presentation primarily focuses on the findings of the qualitative component of this study, which involved a document analysis and a number of in-depth interviews with key informants from all levels of the health system. Semi-structrured topic guides were used to guide the discussions with a range of informants, from the national level to community volunteers. This covered topics such as the usefulness and adequacy of the system used, system quality and performance, resources and operationlisation gaps and integration of activities with other systems.

The analysis will include a three-stage thematic coding approach, using both iterative and deductive approaches.

Results

The presentation will provide a description of the surveillance system employed in Ghana, including the on-going and survey activities. The findings from the qualitative study in Ghana will help highlight the challenges in operationalising a surveillance system for trachoma, including human resource capacity and motivation; trichiasis case finding and the use of community volunteers; diagnostic challenges (especially for infection); the usefulness and methodological limitations in approaches used and opportunities for integration of activities with the health system and other infections. The data has been collected but analysis is currently on-going and will be ready by the end of August 2016.

Conclusions

Ghana is further along the trachoma elimination pathway than most countries and has an opportunity to share experiences and lessons learnt from its elimination programme. This can inform activities in other countries, helping contribute to the achievement of global targets for the elimination of blinding trachoma by 2020.

A41 Genomic variation of genus *Chlamydia* detected at the pan-genome level

Olga Sigalova[1], Andrey Chaplin[2], Olga Bochkareva[1], Valentina Burskaya[5], Pavel Shelyakin[1], Vsevolod Filaretov[1], Evgeny Akkuratov[3], Mikhail S. Gelfand[1,4]
[1]*Institute for Information Transmission Problems (the Kharkevich Institute), RAS, Moscow, Russia,* [2]*Microbiology and Virology Department, Pirogov Russian National Research Medical University, Moscow, Russia,* [3]*Institute of Translational Biomedicine, St. Petersburg State University, St. Petersburg, Russia,* [4]*Faculty of Bioengineering and Bioinformatics, Lomonosov Moscow State University, Moscow, Russia,* [5]*Biological faculty, Lomonosov Moscow State University, Moscow, Russia*

Background/ Introduction

Chlamydia are ancient intracellular pathogens with reduced through strikingly stable genome. The evolutionary success of these bacteria is likely to result from the interplay between high variability and strong selection, the former, however, being masked by almost complete absence of neutrally evolving regions in the chlamydial genome.

Objectives

Our objective was to systematically characterize plasticity of *Chlamydia* genome at the pan-genome level. The focus was placed on the analysis of the non-universal genes, orthologous groups with pseudogenes, and gene families with multiple paralogs.

Method

All complete genomes of *Chlamydia* available by June 2015 were downloaded from the NCBI FTP site; duplicates and genomes with assembly anomalies were filtered out. Orthologous groups of genes were identified with OrthoMCL. Pseudogenes were predicted during the RAST annotation pipeline. Alignments were made with MUSCLE and MACSE. The phylogeny was reconstructed with RAxML (GTRGAMMA and PROTGAMMABLOSUM62 models, 1000 bootstraps). The comparison and clustering of trees for individual genes and the core-genome concatenate was done in Treedist (the PHYLIP package). Genome rearrangements were reconstructed with MGRA . Sites under positive selection were identified with codeml (the PAML package).

Results

The comparative genomic analysis enabled identification of several types of neutrally evolving sequences and regions under positive selection. Frequent domain loss as well as phase and antigen variation were detected in gene families with multiple paralogs. The metabolic reconstruction indicated parallel loss of several nonessential pathways. Moreover, a significant fraction of periphery genes was comprised of either shortened or frameshifted copies of universal genes. The evolutionary history of genes was traced by comparing individual gene trees, analysis of genome rearrangements, and assessing selection strength within coding and intergenic regions for orthologous groups with pseudogenes and with potential homoplasies.

Conclusions

Unlike many other intracellular bacteria, *Chlamydia* are successful pathogens that have maintained stability of their genome for millions of years, frequently switching hosts and conquering novel niches. The pan-genome analysis indicates that their evolutionary success probably results from high variability shaped by strong selection forces and efficient homologous recombination.

A42 Growth Kinetics of Plasmid-Cured and Plasmid-Bearing *Chlamydia muridarum*

Rachel Skilton[1], Yibing Wang[1], Catherine Winstanley[1], Colette O'Neill[1], Kyle Ramsey[2], Ian N. Clarke[1]
[1]University of Southampton, Southampton, UK, [2]Midwestern University, Chicago, USA

Background/ Introduction

Plasmid-free isolates of *C.trachomatis* have slower growth rates than cognate plasmid bearing strains and display a specific morphological phenotype *in vitro*. Animal infection with plasmid-free isolates have reduced pathology which has led to speculation that the plasmid is a virulence factor and virulence manifests from a range of complex properties.

Objectives

In contrast to *C.trachomatis,* plasmid-free isolates of *C.muridarum* have been reported to have similar growth kinetics to the cognate plasmid bearing wild-type. Thus, the aim of this study was to define the plasmid-free phenotype of *C.muridarum* more fully by accurately comparing the growth rate and bacterial 'fitness' between strains.

Method

C.muridarum (strain Nigg) transformed with the *C.trachomatis* plasmid backbone but carrying CDS2 from *C.muridarum* (pGFP::SW2NiggCDS2) was cured by treatment with novabiocin. Plasmid-cured *C.muridarum* (Nigg P-) were selected by their typical 'bulls-eye' phenotype and absence of green fluorescence. *C.muridarum* containing wild-type plasmid (Nigg P+) and cured plasmid (Nigg P-) were grown over a full developmental cycle and sampled at set intervals. Morphological observations were carried out by confocal and transmission electron microscopy, plus qPCR and infectivity assays were performed to determine growth characteristics.

Results

The infectivity data demonstrated that the plasmid-cured inclusions (Nigg P-) were smaller and contained less infectious EB's at comparable time points to the plasmid-bearing strain (Nigg P+). Confocal images taken at the set time intervals over the developmental cycle demonstrated that the plasmid-bearing strain (Nigg P+) developed larger inclusions at a faster rate than the plasmid-cured strain (Nigg P-). Quantitative PCR data confirmed that the plasmid-cured strain (Nigg P-) grew at a significantly slower rate over the time course compared to the plasmid-bearing strain (Nigg P+) and, in addition, took longer to reach maturity.

Conclusions

Plasmid-cured *C.muridarum* (Nigg P-) grows more slowly than plasmid-bearing *C.muridarum* (Nigg P+). These data are comparable with similar observations for plasmid-free and plasmid-bearing *C.trachomatis.*

A43 Age difference between heterosexual partners, its implications for the spread of *Chlamydia trachomatis* and the impact of screening on age-specific prevalence

Joost H. Smid[1], Victor Garcia[1], Christian L. Althaus[1], Catherine H. Mercer[2], Nicola Low[1]
[1]*Institute of Social and Preventive Medicine, Universität Bern, Bern, Switzerland,* [2]*Research Department of Infection and Population Health, University College London, London, UK*

Background/ Introduction

Data on *Chlamydia* prevalence and coverage of opportunistic screening for *Chlamydia trachomatis* over time show discrepancies with the expected impact of *Chlamydia* screening interventions predicted by mathematical models. These discrepancies demonstrate the need to re-examine modelling assumptions and predictions and epidemiological data about *Chlamydia* screening and sexual mixing patterns.

Objectives

This study aimed to re-investigate the impact of *Chlamydia* screening at the population level through a detailed investigation of sex- and age-specific population level indicators of sexual behaviour and of *C. trachomatis* infection characteristics in an age-structured mathematical model for heterosexual *Chlamydia* transmission.

Method

We developed an age-structured, compartmental model for heterosexual transmission of *C. trachomatis* that included sex- and age-specific partner age preference and mixing between sexual activity classes. The model was parameterised using sexual behavioural data from the third British National Survey of Sexual Attitudes and Lifestyles (Natsal-3). We fitted the model to observed *Chlamydia* prevalence data from Natsal-3 using a Bayesian inferential framework.

Results

Natsal-3 data show that the shape, scale and skewness of the distributions of the ages of new partners at the moment of first sexual intercourse with them depends on the age and gender of the participant. On average, males reported sex with younger partners (median: -6.4; IQR: [-3.7, -9.9] years); females reported having partners of similar ages (median: -0.2; IQR: [-2.5, 1.2] years). Different assumptions including about age-mixing can influence the age-specific *Chlamydia* prevalence estimated from the model. The Bayesian inferential framework allowed us to investigate these assumptions, hypotheses about naturally acquired immunity and their impact on screening interventions.

Conclusions

The influences of sex, age and sexual activity level on partner age preference are complex and affect sex- and age-specific prevalence of *C. trachomatis* infection in a heterosexual population. These interactions should be incorporated into mathematical models that aim to provide insights into the impact of *Chlamydia* screening interventions.

A44 Vaginal microbiota composition and association with *Chlamydia trachomatis* infection among young women attending a STI clinic in France

Jeanne Tamarelle[1,3], Bertille de Barbeyrac[4], Isabelle Le Hen[5], Anne Thiébaut[1,2], Cécile Bébéar[4], Jacques Ravel[6,1], Elisabeth Delarocque-Astagneau[1,3]

[1]Institut Pasteur, Paris, France, [2]INSERM, Paris, France, [3]Université Versailles Saint Quentin en Yvelines, Montigny-le-Bretonneux, France, [4]National Reference Centre (CNR) for chlamydial infections, Bordeaux, France, [5]Maison départementale de la santé CDAG/CIDDIST, Bordeaux, France, [6]Institute for Genome Sciences, University of Maryland School of Medicine, Baltimore, USA

Background/ Introduction

New molecular techniques have permitted to describe groups of bacterial communities in the vagina (community state types (CST)) that could play an important role in favoring or preventing *Chlamydia trachomatis* (Ct) infection, persistence and evolution towards Pelvic Inflammatory Disease (PID).

Objectives

Here, we sought to characterize the vaginal microbiota of a sample of women attending a STI clinic in France and determine whether any particular CST was associated with a greater susceptibility to Ct infection.

Method

A cross sectional study on vaginal microbiota composition among 18-25 years old women attending a STI clinic was carried out in June 2015. Participants provided vaginal sample for routine Ct screening and sociodemographic data were collected. Ct screening was carried out at the National Reference Center for chlamydial infections using the Aptima-combo 2 Transcription-Mediated-Amplification assay. Vaginal microbiota composition was studied using high-throughput 16S RNA genome sequencing (University of Maryland). Statistical analysis was performed using Stata 12.0.

Results

One hundred and forty-four women were included in the study. Analysis will allow to characterize the vaginal microbiota of young women for the first time in France. Association between vaginal CST and Ct infection will be studied, controlling for sociodemographic factors such as age, origin, sexual orientation and motives for consultation.

Conclusions

It will help us to generate hypothesis on the role of the vaginal microbiota on the natural history of Ct infection, which will be further investigated in the PID-Prev trial aiming at evaluating systematic screening for Ct infection at a mean to prevent PID.

A45 Prevalence of *C. psittaci* in avian samples collected in pet shops in Croatia

Danijela Horvatek Tomic, Zeljko Gottstein, Maja Lukac, Ana Marquiza Quilicot, Estella Prukner-Radovcic
Department of Poultry Diseases with Clinic, Faculty of Veterinary Medicine University of Zagreb, Zagreb, Croatia

Background/ Introduction

Birds, especially parrots, are one of the most popular pets in Croatia, but they can harbour *Chlamydia*, especially C. psittaci, potential zoonotic agents with a great significance for human and animal health. Birds are mainly sold through pet shops, presenting a possible source of infection for employees and buyers.

Objectives

In Croatia it is obligatory to test the birds in the pet shops for the presence of C. psittaci. The aim of this study was to detect the prevalence of C. psittaci in samples taken from the pet shops, to determine the potential risk for both human and birds' health.

Method

During the five-year period (2011-2015) altogether 485 samples from pet shops were submitted for the testing of the presence of C. psittaci. The samples obtained were pooled faecal samples, containing faeces of different bird species, currently present in the examined stores. The DNA was extracted by using commercially available kit. The extracted DNA were examined by specific *Chlamydia*ceae real-time PCR targeting the 23S rRNA gene, and C. psittaci-specific real-time PCR targeting the incA gene.

Results

Altogether 34 samples were found positive (7.01%) over the examined time period. The majority of positive samples belonged to different parrot species. It is evident that the number of positive samples varied over the years, from 4 in 2014 up to 11 in 2015, which represents 3.36% to 9.09% of positive samples, respectively. Genotyping of C. psittaci is still in progress, to reveal the presence of different genotypes in examined bird species. During these 5 years, in three workers and in one parrot owner psittacosis was confirmed.

Conclusions

The occurrence of C. psittaci in faecal samples collected in different pet shops all over Croatia suggests potential breeder but also environmental contamination and may raise public health concern. The increasing number of positive samples in 2015 confirm the necessity for obligatory testing of pet shops all over the country.

A46 *Simkania negevensis*, an emerging pathogen associated with lower respiratory tract infections? Lessons from *in vitro* experiments and clinical studies

Manon Vouga[1,2], David Baud[1,2], Gilbert Greub[1,3]
[1]Insitute of Microbiology, Lausanne, Switzerland, [2]Department Femme-Mère-Enfant, Lausanne, Switzerland, [3]Infectious Disease Service, Lausanne, Switzerland

Background/ Introduction

Simkania negevensis is an emerging *Chlamydia*-related bacterium discovered in 1993. Evidence of human exposition has been reported worldwide and current data suggest an association with pneumonia and bronchiolitis, while no significant associations were found with asthma, acute lung rejection and exacerbation of COPD.

Objectives

Controversies still subsist on the pathogenic role of S. negevensis in human diseases, especially due to lack of reliability of previous diagnostic methods. Our work aims at providing further information on the importance of S. negevensis infections in lower respiratory tract diseases.

Method

We developed a specific quantitative PCR. Specific primers and probe were chosen targeting the 16S rRNA gene and subsequently used to conduct a retrospective study of S. negevensis prevalence among Swiss patients; bronchoalveolar lavages from adult patients with various pulmonary symptoms (total 200) and children with symptoms compatible with bronchiolitis (total 200) were tested. We also evaluated, in vitro, the characteristics of S. negevensis infection in pneumocytes (A549 cell line) using (i) the same quantitative PCR (ii) immunofluorescence and (iii) a mortality assay, based on propidium iodide incorporation.

Results

The PCR exhibited high specificity (<99%) and sensitivity (< 10 copies/µl) as well as low intra-run and inter-run variabilities. Out of the 150 samples from adult patients tested, all were negative. Results were confirmed by a pan-*Chlamydiales* PCR. Subsequent testings are ongoing.
In vitro experiments revealed efficient replication of S. negevensis in pneumocytes within 6 days. Infectivity was higher in pneumocytes compared to control Vero cells. No specific cytopathic effects were observed, as shown by similar mortality rates in infected and uninfected cells. A strong association with the endoplasmic reticulum and mitochondria was observed, without Golgi apparatus fragmentation.

Conclusions

We confirmed that pneumocytes support S. negevensis replication and suggest that S. negevensis infection might persist for a prolonged time in pneumocytes. A role in chronic infections could be suspected. Clinical data suggest a low prevalence and do not support the pathogenic role of S. negevensis in adult Swiss patients.

A47 The impact of sexual behaviour and underlying psychological determinants on *Chlamydia* transmission: a mathematical modelling study

Daphne A. van Wees[1], Chantal den Daas[1], Mirjam E. Kretzschmar[1,2], Janneke C.M. Heijne[1]
[1]*National Institute for Public Health and the Environment (RIVM), Bilthoven, Utrecht, The Netherlands,*
[2]*Julius Centre for Health Sciences and Primary Care, University Medical Centre Utrecht, Utrecht, Utrecht, The Netherlands*

Background/ Introduction

Transmission of *Chlamydia trachomatis* (*Chlamydia*) is influenced by individuals' psychological determinants, such as risk perception and impulsiveness. However, these psychological determinants are rarely incorporated in mathematical models predicting the impact of intervention measures to control transmission of *Chlamydia*. Adding these factors to models might be essential for understanding *Chlamydia* control.

Objectives

To explore the influence of incorporating psychological determinants in mathematical models on the estimated impact of interventions in reducing *Chlamydia* prevalence and re-infection rates.

Method

We developed a pair compartmental model with a susceptible-infected-recovered-susceptible (SIRS) structure representing a heterosexual population of men and women aged 16 - 24 years. The parameters of the models were informed by data from a pilot study among heterosexual students conducted in 2016 assessing sexual behaviour (e.g. number of partners, condom use), psychological determinants (e.g. risk perception, impulsiveness) and self-reported *Chlamydia* infection using an online questionnaire. The questions were based on several existing and validated questionnaires. Answers to psychological determinant questions involved a 5-point scale, ranging from low to high risk perception/impulsiveness.

Results

The model fitted the data well and was able to accurately predict re-infection rates found in the literature. We compared a configuration of the model which incorporated sexual risk groups based on reported partners in the last year with a configuration in which sexual risk groups were further subdivided according to psychological determinants. The quantification of psychological determinants in subgroups was based on the distribution of answers over the 5-point scale. The impact of different interventions aimed at encouraging preventive health behaviour on reducing *Chlamydia* prevalence and re-infection rates was estimated in both configurations and compared.

Conclusions

Mathematical models incorporating psychological determinants could improve the estimation of the impact of interventions tailored to specific subgroups on *Chlamydia* transmission. These models might thereby be able to identify successful interventions aimed at changing psychological determinants for the future.

A48 Assessment of risk factors for *Chlamydia trachomatis* exposure in the female population and in cervical cancer patients in Mongolia by a new multiplex serology assay

Martina Willhauck-Fleckenstein[1], Bollorma Dondog[1], Helja-Marja Surcel[2], Katrin Hufnagel[1], Markus Schmitt[1], Dana Holzinger[1], Juliane Schröter[1], Tim Waterboer[1], Michael Pawlita[1]
[1]*German Cancer Research Center, Division Molecular Diagnostics of Oncogenic Infections, Heidelberg, Germany,* [2]*National Institute for Health and Welfare, Oulu, Finland*

Background/ Introduction

HPV (*Human Papilloma Virus*) infection is the leading cause for the development of cervical cancer. Cofactors like smoking and multiparity are known while other sexually transmitted infections (STI) especially with *Chlamydia trachomatis* (Ct) are discussed controversially.

Objectives

Development and validation of a new Ct multiplex serology assay (CtMS), analysis of risk factors for Ct infection and of a potential association of Ct infection with incident cervical cancer in the female Mongolian population.

Method

Recombinantly expressed, affinity-purified GST fusion proteins of Ct MOMP, PorB and TARP (two fragments) bound to fluorescent Luminex beads were used as antigens. The Ct plasmid-derived protein Pgp3 was added later. CtMS was validated against commercial ELISA, MIF and presence of Ct-DNA in cervical exfoliated cells. Antibody reactivity with at least two Ct proteins or strong anti-Momp responses alone (>1000 MFI) defined Ct seropositivity. Ct serostatus was determined 985 Mongolian women from a population-based HPV prevalence study (Dondog et al., 2008) and 96 from a Mongolian invasive cervical carcinoma (CxCa) series (Halec et al., 2013).

Results

CtMS positivity was present in 86% of CT-DNA+ woman. Agreement with commercial ELISA was moderate (kappa 0.46), apparently due to increased sensitivity of CtMS. Seropositivity to Pgp3 was most frequent and in young women appears to occur prior to seropositivity to the other Ct proteins. Risk factors significantly associated with CtMS seropositivity were life time number of sex partners >2 (OR 2.6; 95% CI 1.9–3.8), age at first intercourse <19 years (1.9;1.2–2.9), full term pregnancies >2 (2.9;1.5–5.8), lower education level (2.2;1.6–3.0) and mucosal HR-HPV-infection (1.4;1.0–1.9). Comparing CxCa cases versus disease-free controls was significantly associated with CxCa (2.7;1.1–6.8).

Conclusions

Newly developed CtMS is a useful tool for assessing prevalence and risk factors of Ct infection in large epidemiological studies. A pilot case-control study in Mongolia demonstrated a significant association of Ct exposure and incident CxCa. Pgp3 appears as the antigen most suited to identify incident infection.

A49 Improving the understanding of *Chlamydia* epidemiology in Europe - scoping for the rationale and feasibility of a European Union prevalence survey

Sarah C Woodhall[1], Aura Andreasen[1], Otilia Mardh[2], Gianfranco Spiteri[2], Gwenda Hughes[1]
[1]*Public Health England, London, UK,* [2]*European Centre for Disease Prevention and Control (ECDC), Stockholm, Sweden*

Background/ Introduction

European-wide surveillance for genital chlamydial infection currently relies on reports of diagnosed cases. There is considerable variation in reported cases by country, due to substantial heterogeneity in availability of diagnostics, surveillance strategies, and testing policies. The epidemiological utility of these data is therefore limited.

Objectives

To determine the rationale and feasibility of a European Union/European Economic Area (EU/EEA)-wide survey of *Chlamydia* prevalence and describe key methodological issues for consideration in survey development.

Method

We reviewed existing literature and updated a previously-published systematic review of *Chlamydia* prevalence surveys. Interviews were held with key informants to identify strengths and weaknesses of previously-conducted studies and to identify European-wide infrastructure for conducting a survey. Illustrative case studies were compiled, along with a matrix to compare the characteristics of different methods against objectives of a *Chlamydia* prevalence survey.

Results

Up to 2015, seven estimates of *Chlamydia* prevalence as part of nationally-representative, general population surveys had been conducted in EU/EEA countries. Key considerations for an EU/EEA-wide survey include defining primary objectives (e.g. country comparisons, identifying risk groups, monitoring time-trends), sampling strategy (e.g. general population, clinical/educational settings) and choice of outcome measure (e.g. current infection measured using nucleic acid amplification tests of urogenital samples, cumulative infection incidence measured using *C. trachomatis* antibody tests of sera). The survey could include testing of biological samples collected within existing nationally-representative health surveys, and researcher-led surveys in clinical/educational/general population samples.

Conclusions

A change in focus is needed to understand and monitor the epidemiology of *Chlamydia* effectively at the European level. Although estimating the prevalence of *Chlamydia* is challenging, examples of well-conducted surveys exist and there may be opportunities to build on existing survey models and infrastructure in future years.

A50 Protective effects of an inactivated vaccine against *Chlamydia abortus* in pregnant yaks

Zhaocai Li[1], Jizhang Zhou[1], Xiaoan Cao[1], Zhongzi Lou[1], Jinshan Cai[2], Ruilin Ma[2]
[1]*Lanzhou Veterinary Research Institute, Lanzhou, Gansu, China,* [2]*Center for Animal Disease Control and Prevention in Qinghai Province, Xi'ning, Qinghai, China*

Background/ Introduction

The yaks (*Bos grunniens*) provide the basic material for the Tibetan people daily life in the Qinghai-Tibetan Plateau, China. However, abortion caused by *Chlamydia* abortus in yaks is a serious problem, which also caused a huge economy loss in local area

Objectives

Herein we generated an inactivated vaccine using a *Chlamydia abortus* strain isolated from aborted yak and evaluated its protective effects in pregnant yaks.

Method

The *Chlamydia abortus* strain was proliferated in embryonated eggs. To prepare the vaccine, the obtained membrane of the yolk sacs was inactivated and combined with Montanide ISA 206 VG as adjuvant in a 1:1 ratio. A total of 60 pregnant yaks (pregnancy within 1.5 months) were either vaccinated (n=45) or used as control (which were challenged by a *Chlamydia* abortus strain at dose of 5×10^7 CFU/animal). The vaccinated animals were challenged at dose of 5×10^7 (n=15), 5×10^8 (n=15), 5×10^9 (n=15) CFU/animal. Then the immunogenicity of the inactivated vaccine was evaluated.

Results

The result showed that a single immunization with the inactivated vaccine significantly increased the GMT of IgG antibodies against *Chlamydia abortus* as early as 7 d post vaccination and the IgG2a antibody isotype predominated. In addition, increased in vitro neutralization titers were observed. The vaccine in yaks also induced a strong antigen-specific T-cell immune response, as indicated by a high number of CD4+ and CD8+cells, as well as the concentration of IFN-γ. Moreover, no abortion was observed in yaks in the vaccinated group after challenge while 14 yaks aborted (14/15) in the control group.

Conclusions

The inactivated vaccine showed a good protection against *Chlamydia abortus* strain challenge and could be used to control the chlamydosis in yaks.

A51 Contrasts in *Chlamydia*: genomic analysis of European *Chlamydia abortus*

Helena MB Seth-Smith[1], Michelle Sait[2,3], Morag Livingstone[2], Simon Harris[1], Nicholas Thomson[1], David Longbottom[2]
[1]Sanger Institute, Cambridge, UK, [2]Moredun Research Institute, Edinburgh, UK, [3]Department of Microbiology and Immunology, Peter Doherty Institute for Infection and Immunity, The University of Melbourne, Australia

Background/ Introduction

Chlamydia abortus is an economically important livestock pathogen, causing ovine enzootic abortion (OEA), and can also cause zoonotic infections in humans affecting pregnancy outcome. Large scale genomic studies on other chlamydial species are giving insights into the biology of these organisms but have not yet been performed on *C. abortus*.

Objectives

To investigate a broad collection of European strains of *C. abortus*, using next generation sequencing methods, looking at diversity, geographic distribution and genome dynamics.

Method

A collection of 68 strains was assembled, originating primarily from the UK, Germany and France, but also from Greece, Tunisia, Namibia and the USA. All strains were subject to Illumina sequencing and subsequent tailored analysis including mapping against the reference strain S26/3, phylogenetics and recombination analysis.

Results

The population of *C. abortus* currently circulating in European livestock shows significantly less variation compared to *C. trachomatis* and *C. psittaci*. The phylogeny shows a single large clade, with strong geographical signatures, and two more distantly related Greek strains, LLG and POS. This suggests that isolates causing the majority of disease are descended from a more diverse, unsampled source population, or more likely that there have been significant population bottlenecks during the current species expansion. Some importing of strains between the UK to Germany is suggested by the phylogeny. No recombination was identified within *C. abortus*.

Conclusions

The diversity within *C. abortus* appears to be much lower compared to other species in this genus, suggesting a recent clonal expansion into European herds. This may be associated with the strong geographical signatures found within the phylogeny and the clonal nature of the sampled population.

A52 Diversity and antibiotic resistance determinants of Swiss *C. suis* strains determined by genome sequencing

Helena MB Seth-Smith[1], Nathan Bachmann[2], Sabrina Wanninger[1], Adam Polkinghorne[2], Nicole Borel[1]
[1]*Institute of Veterinary Pathology, University of Zurich, Zurich, Switzerland,* [2]*University of the Sunshine Coast, Sunshine Coast, Australia*

Background/ Introduction

Chlamydia suis has been found to be endemic in Swiss pig herds. The diversity and background of these strains is unknown, but several are phenotypically tetracycline resistant (Tet[R]). Tet[R] determinants have previously been found in *C. suis* strains, but data on the genomic context and possible variation is lacking.

Objectives

We have tracked several farms and individual animals during antibiotic treatment to investigate the diversity of strains and the changes in infection pre- and post-treatment.
Our aim is to determine the genomic basis of tetracycline resistance in Swiss strains of *C. suis*.

Method

Next generation Illumina sequencing was applied to a selection of Tet[S] and Tet[R] strains of *C. suis* isolated in Switzerland. Data was analysed phylogenetically to assess the diversity of strains from Swiss farms, and to investigate sequential strains from animals pre- and post-antibiotic treatment. *De novo* assembly and annotation was used to identify the presence, location and arrangement of any antibiotic resistance determinants.

Results

Phylogenetic analysis showed significant strain diversity from farms in what is a geographically limited area. Several sequenced Tet[R] *C. suis* isolates show genomic evidence of resistance genes in the same genetic locus as has been previously described. The genomic analysis further revealed that the composition of this region in all Tet[R] isolates is highly variable in terms of (i) the number of predicted mobilisation and/or hypothetical proteins; and (ii) suspected insertions into the *tetR* gene.

Conclusions

Genomics gives detailed information on *C. suis* diversity and geographical clustering, and is the best tool to track events during antibiotic treatment. *C. suis* strains carrying antibiotic resistant determinants are commonly found in Swiss pigs. Preliminary data suggests that determinants were acquired ancestrally by one clade and have since rearranged.

POSTER SESSION B

B1 Rapid *Chlamydia trachomatis* genotyping assay designed using genome wide orthologous SNP information

Patiyan Andersson, Judith Wilson, Deborah Holt, Philip M. Giffard
Menzies School of Health Research, Darwin, Australia

Background/ Introduction

Due to the relatively low sequence variability in the *C. trachomatis* genome, most genotyping assays to-date target the few highly variable loci present, such as the *ompA* gene. However, these regions may not correlate with the whole genome phylogeny and thus may obscure epidemiological patterns.

Objectives

The aim was to develop an efficient and low cost genotyping assay for *C. trachomatis*, based on genome-wide orthologous single nucleotide polymorphisms (SNPs), and that divides the species into the major evolutionary lineages, and also discriminates the *ompA* variants.

Method

Orthologous SNPs were defined by alignment of 65 *C. trachomatis* genome sequences representative of known the global diversity. SNP sets optimised for combinatorial resolving power were derived using the software Minimum SNPs. The metric for resolving power was the Simpsons Index of Diversity, as determined *in silico* using the 65 genome sequences. PCR amplifiable fragments containing the SNPs were developed. High resolution melting analysis (HRMA) procedures to discriminate variants of amplified fragments were devised. The resolving power of HRMA was predicted *in silico*, and then determined in practice. The concordance between the genotypes, phylogeny, and *ompA* allelic state was assessed.

Results

In silico analyses yielded a prediction that HRMA of just two amplified fragments, nucleated by two SNPs, in *Jali1891* and *ompA*, would resolve *C. trachomatis* into 15 groups. Further, the groups were predicted to be highly concordant with the major lineages in orthologous SNPs-based phylogeny, and also with *ompA* serovars. HRMA assays were developed, and tested using 35 cultured isolates of known genome sequence, representing much of *C. trachomatis* diversity. The results were in accordance with in silico predictions. Preliminary experiments indicate that the method may be used for direct analysis of clinical specimens.

Conclusions

A method for resolving *C. trachomatis* into 15 groups highly concordant with the major phylogenetic lineages and *ompA* serotypes has been developed. The method requires two PCR reactions followed by HRMA, using a real time PCR platform. The HRMA format allows rapid and high-throughput analysis suitable for large epidemiological studies.

B2 New insights in the outbreak pattern of Lymphogranuloma venereum strains in France

Olivia Peuchant[1,2], Arabella Touati[1,2], Clément Sperandio[1,2], Nadège Hénin[1,2], Cécile Laurier-Nadalié[1,2], Cécile Bébéar[1,2], Bertille de Barbeyrac[1,3]

[1]1Univ. Bordeaux, USC EA3671 Mycoplasmal and chlamydial Infections in Humans, and Reference Center for Chlamydiae, Bordeaux, France, [2]INRA, USC EA3671 Mycoplasmal and chlamydial Infections in Humans, and National Reference Center for Chlamydiae, Bordeaux, France, [3]Bordeaux University Hospital, Department of Bacteriology, Bordeaux, France

Background/ Introduction

The French Reference Centre for *Chlamydiae* monitors the LGV outbreak by using two real-time PCRs targeting the pmpH gene to identify L and L2b strains, respectively, in *Chlamydia trachomatis* positive ano-rectal specimens. Almost all cases are caused by L2b variant, suggesting a single source of origin for the LGV outbreak.

Objectives

Because of the recent description of new L2 variants, as well as the co-circulation of variants, we decided to investigate if genetic variations exist within the LGV strains circulating in France since 2010, by sequencing of the ompA gene of clinical specimens typed as L2b.

Method

Between January 2010 and April 2015, 129 French LGV-positive ano-rectal specimens typed as L2b were retrospectively selected, based on high bacterial load corresponding to a cycle threshold £ 25. Amplification of the ompA gene was performed directly on specimens. A 1,100 bp-fragment was amplified by a nested PCR and sequenced in both directions. In case of discrepancies between the sequencing of the ompA gene and the results of pmpH PCR, the pmpH gene was sequenced. Clinical data and sexual behavior were also collected.

Results

A LGV genovar was confirmed for 117 specimens. The majority (71/117) had an ompA sequence identical to the L2b/UCH-1/proctitis reference strain. In addition, we could identify 4 new genetic L2b ompA variants in 16 specimens. Thirty specimens had an ompA sequence identical to the L2/434/BU reference strain. Analysis of the pmpH gene of these 30 specimens, showed the presence of the 9-bp insertion specific for L2b, explaining the positive amplification by real-time PCR. The characteristics of patients did not differ with regard to clinical data, sexual behavior, according to the LGV genotypes involved.

Conclusions

The outbreak is not anymore dominated by L2b strains but also involved L2 strains and other L2b variants. Moreover, these results raise the question of specificity of the PCR based on L2b pmpH gene since about 25% of strains were misidentified as L2b.

B3 Did L strains responsible for LGV proctitis spread among people with genital *Chlamydia trachomatis* infection In France in 2013?

Arabella Touati[1,2], Chantal Vernay-Vaisse[3], Michel Janier[4], Isabelle Le Hen[5], Cécile Charlois[6], Philippe Dhotte[6], Dominique Decré[7], Cécile Bébéar[1,2], Bertille de Barbeyrac[1,2]
[1]1Univ. Bordeaux, USC EA3671 Mycoplasmal and chlamydial Infections in Humans, and National Reference Center for Chlamydiae, Bordeaux, France, [2]INRA, USC EA3671 Mycoplasmal and chlamydial Infections in Humans, and National Reference Center for Chlamydiae, Bordeaux, France, [3]STI Center CDAG-CIDDIST CG13, Marseille, France, [4]University Hospital Saint Louis AP-HP, Paris, France, [5]STI Center CDAG-CIDDIST CG33, Bordeaux, France, [6]STI Center CDAG CIDDIST CG 75, Paris, France, [7]AP-HP, Groupe Hospitalier des Hôpitaux Universitaires de l'Est Parisien, Département de Bactériologie, Paris, France

Background/ Introduction

A national LGV surveillance network was implemented in France in 2010 in which all *C. trachomatis* (CT) rectal strains were genotyped. While recent data showed an increasing prevalence of rectal LGV in France in 2013, no routine surveillance for the presence of LGV in non rectal specimens exists.

Objectives

Because LGV urethritis exists, and because of the contrast between the high number of rectal LGV cases and the rarity of genital cases, we decided to conduct this study to determine if there was evidence of presence of L strains in non rectal specimens of CT-infected population in 2013.

Method

A total of 1802 non rectal CT-positive specimens (37 throat swabs, 36 male urethral and 670 urine specimens, and 842 vaginal, 96 cervical and 121 female urine specimens) were retrospectively analyzed using LGV-specific real-time PCR. The specimens were collected consecutively in 2013 at 6 Sexually Transmitted Infections (STI) screening centers in Paris, Marseille, and Bordeaux, France. Demographic data, STI history, sexual behavior in the last 6 months were recorded.

Results

The specimens were collected from 738 men and 1064 women: 97 were men who have sex with men (MSM), 22 were women who have sex with women, 1292 were heterosexuals and 391 had no documented sexual orientation. This was a high STI risk population: 69.5% reported having had 3 or more casual partners in the last 6 months and 27.9% declared having had unsafe sex, 11% had history of STI and 6% were co-infected with Neisseria gonorrhoeae. We did not find any single case of LGV infection in heterosexuals. Interestingly, three specimens positive for L2b strain were collected from MSM.

Conclusions

Our study showed no evidence for spread of LGV infections in women and heterosexual men in France in 2013. L2b strains seem to be restricted to the MSM population.

B4 Lymphogranuloma venereum proctitis cases are still increasing in France

Bertille de Barbeyrac[1,2], Arabella Touati[1,2], Cécile Laurier-Nadalié[1,2], Chloé Le Roy[1,2], Laure Imounga[1,2], Nadège Hénin[1,2], Olivia Peuchant[1,2], Ndeindo Ndeikoundam[3], Cécile Bébéar[1,2], Guy La Ruche[3]

[1]Univ., USC EA3671 Mycoplasmal and chlamydial Infections in Humans, and National Reference Center for Chlamydiae, Bordeaux, France, [2]INRA, USC EA3671 Mycoplasmal and chlamydial Infections in Humans, and National Reference Center for Chlamydiae, Bordeaux, France, [3]French Institute for Public Health Surveillance, Saint-Maurice, France

Background/ Introduction

In large European metropolitan areas, Lymphogranuloma venereum (LGV) outbreak has been ongoing for over 10 years and is responsible for proctitis mainly among men who have sex with men (MSM). A voluntary surveillance system for *C. trachomatis* (CT) proctitis has been established in France since 2004.

Objectives

Based on the data of the National Reference Center (NRC) for *Chlamydiae*, Bordeaux, France, this study aimed to describe the epidemiology of LGV and non-LGV proctitis in France and to examine the characteristics of affected populations.

Method

The French surveillance network includes clinicians, biologists and NRC. Biologists sent rectal CT-positive samples to the NRC where the strains were typed by using two real-time PCR targeting pmpH gene specific of L and L2b strains. Clinical, biological and sexual risk behavioural variables were compared in men with LGV proctitis and with non-LGV proctitis according the HIV status using appropriate statistical tests over the period 2010-2014.

Results

A total of 2,627 LGV cases were recorded from 2004 to 2015 of which 1,747 occurred from 2010 to 2015. The number of LGV diagnoses was multiplied by 2.4 between 2012 and 2015 and the number of recurrence reached 10% in 2015. LGV proctitis continues to affect a core group: HIV-infected MSM who engage in high-risk sexual practices. They were older and more often infected with syphilis than men with non-LGV proctitis, were usually symptomatic and mainly lived in Paris. Those who acquired LGV reinfection had concurrent hepatitis C and syphilis more often than those with a single episode.

Conclusions

A steady annual increase in the number of LGV cases and in the number of LGV recurrences was observed since 2012, demonstrating that the LGV epidemic is not under control and requires providing better information about the disease to affected patients and physicians of all specialties who take care them.

B5 Tetracycline resistant *Chlamydia suis* in Swiss fattening pigs

Sabrina Wanninger[1], Karolin Hoffmann[1], Manuela Donati[2], Antonietta Di Francesco[3], Michael Hässig[4], Nicole Borel[1]
[1]Institute of Veterinary Pathology, Zurich, Switzerland, [2]Section of Microbiology DIMES, Bologna, Italy, [3]Department of Veterinary Medical Sciences, Bologna, Italy, [4]Department of Farm Animals, Zurich, Switzerland

Background/ Introduction

The emergence of tetracycline-resistant (Tet[R]) *Chlamydia suis* strains in the US and Europe implicates pigs as a potential reservoir for tetracycline resistance determinants. In a recent Swiss study, each of 29 investigated fattening pig farms was positive for *C. suis* in fecal swabs.

Objectives

This study aims to investigate the presence of Tet[R] *C. suis* strains in pigs with/without antibiotic treatment, at the beginning and end of the fattening period, respectively. Additionally, tetracycline susceptibility of isolates was evaluated *in vitro* for correlation with the presence of the tetracycline (Tet) resistance gene determined by PCR.

Method

Duplicate fecal swab samples from *C. suis* PCR-positive pigs from 29 farms were used for isolation in LLC-MK2 cells. Isolated strains were tested *in vitro* for Tet susceptibility. Minimum inhibitory and minimum bactericidal concentrations were determined. Genomic DNA was extracted from *Chlamydia*-positive cell cultures using the QIAamp DNA mini kit and the presence/load of *C. suis* was confirmed by real-time PCR and Arraymate Microarray. A PCR amplifying a 525 bp fragment of the *tet*(C) region was performed on *C. suis*-positive isolates. Results were compared to epidemiological data regarding oral prophylactic antibiotic treatment in sampled pigs.

Results

C. suis inhabited the intestinal tract of nearly all examined pigs and its presence was positively correlated with diarrhea. Antibiotic treatment did not affect fecal shedding of *C. suis*. Tet[R] *C. suis* strains were only present in pigs which had received antibiotic treatment, not in untreated herds. However, the presence of the Tet resistance gene determined by PCR did not correlate with the *in vitro* tetracycline resistance, as determined by susceptibility testing.

Conclusions

Our results indicate selective pressure on Tet[R] *C. suis* strains in fattening pigs related to prior antibiotic treatment. *In vitro,* the regulation of Tet resistance in *C. suis* appears more complex than previously anticipated and needs further investigation. *In vivo*, Tet[R] *C. suis* strains in feces might contaminate the environment.

B6 A performance evaluation of the ATLAS Genetics io™ system: a novel and rapid point-of-care in vitro diagnostic test for *Chlamydia trachomatis*

Emma Cousins[1], Emma M. Harding-Esch[2,1], Christine Chow[1], Laura Phillips[1], Catherine L. Hall[1], Sebastian S. Fuller[1], Kevin Dunbar[2], Marc Green[3], Daniel P. Shenton[3], Stephanie Bannister[3], John Clarkson[3], Catherine M. Lowndes[2], S Tariq Sadiq[1,2]
[1]St George's, University of London, London, UK, [2]Public Health England, Colindale, London, UK, [3]Atlas Genetics, Bath, UK

Background/ Introduction

Rapid Point-Of-Care Tests (POCTs) for *Chlamydia trachomatis* (CT) may reduce onward transmission and reproductive sexual health (RSH) sequelae by decreasing turnaround times between diagnosis and treatment. The io™ single module system (Atlas Genetics) runs clinical samples in a microfluidic cartridge, without needing further processing, delivering results in 30 minutes.

Objectives

We evaluated the performance of io™ in RSH clinics representing a variety of urban centres across the UK. These form part of a unique network of clinics working with the Applied Diagnostic Research and Evaluation Unit (ADREU) based at St George's, University of London.

Method

io™ performance was compared against BD Viper™ Nucleic Acid Amplification Test (NAAT). ADREU provided the infrastructure to deliver protocol development, fast-tracked ethics approvals and study implementation and management. 306 females aged ≥16, were recruited prospectively and provided an additional-to-routine self-collected vulvovaginal swab (VVS). Samples were shipped refrigerated within 10 days of collection to ADREU testing laboratories, and immediately tested for CT infection on io™ and residuals stored at -20°C. Discrepant results were reconciled using the Artus® CT/NG assay.

Results

The prevalence of CT was 8.2%. 266/306 (87%) tests were successful on a first run. Concordant results were obtained for 96.7% of specimens. Sensitivity and specificity were 95.5% (95%CI 77.2-99.9) and 96.8% (95%CI 93.9-98.6), respectively. Positive (PPV) and negative (NPV) predictive values of 72.4% (95%CI 52.8-87.3) and 99.6% (95%CI 97.8-100.0), respectively, were calculated. The time from sample to result was 30 minutes for all samples.

Conclusions

io™, a single-module molecular CT POCT, has sensitivity and specificity >95% in fresh VVS. Although PPV does not meet British Association for Sexual Health and HIV CT-testing qualifications, high NPV and rapid turnaround suggest that it would have utility in high risk RSH clinic populations, provided positives are confirmed.

B7 Is *Chlamydophila psittaci* an underdiagnosed infection?

Judit Deák
University of Szeged, Szeged, Hungary

Background/ Introduction

Chlamydophila psittaci (C. psittaci) infection is regarded as a serious or often deadly zoonotic infection in humans. The source of infection may be close contact with birds. Without adequate antibiotic tratment, the lethality of the infection is high.

Objectives

Until 2002 , 1-6 cases were detected annually in Hungary. This was followed by a jump in 2003 to 85, and in 2005 to 140, with 29 and 28 cases in 2006 and 2007. 300 patients were examined in 2013 (January - December) for C. psittaci-specific IgM and IgG.

Method

Sputum, biopsy and blood samples are suitable for diagnosis, with cultivation (on cell cultures or embryonated eggs), by serological and PCR methods. In our studies, microimmunofluorescence was used to determine Chlamydophila *pneumoniae*, *Chlamydia trachomatis* and C. psittaci-specific IgM and IgG. Seropositive subjects were defined as those with IgM titres $\geq$1:10 and IgG titres of $\geq$1:16, and seronegative subjects as those whose titres were <1:10 and <1:16, respectively. To rule out the presence of cross-reactive antibodies, testing was also performed for Chlamydophila *pneumoniae* and *Chlamydia trachomatis*.

Results

11 positive cases and 5 borderline positive cases were diagnosed in November and December 2013. The majority of the positive patients were employed at a same poultry meat-processing plant in South-East Hungary. One patient was employed as a lawyer in the city of Szeged. The remaining patients live in different towns or villages near the factory. They were treated with macrolide and doxycycline antibiotics in different hospitals. The clinical or radiological diagnosis was serious or mild pneumonia.

Conclusions

Such infections must be registered officially in Hungary. As this is an occupationally-exposed disease, registration with the health authorities is compulsory. The antibiotic tratment of occupationally-exposed subjects is urgent when infection is suspected. Transfer of clinical samples is compulsory to the National-Health-Centre in Budapest., where our serological diagnosis were confirmed.

B8 Genital *Chlamydia trachomatis* and *Neisseria gonorrhoeae* infections among women in sub-Saharan Africa: A systematic review & meta-analysis

Jan Henk Dubbink[1,3], Stephan P. Verweij[2], Helen E. Struthers[1,4], Sander Ouburg[2], James A. McIntyre[1,4], Servaas A. Morré[2,3], Remco P.H. Peters[1,5]
[1]Anova Health Institute, Johannesburg, South Africa, [2]VU University Medical Center, Amsterdam, The Netherlands, [3]Maastricht University, Maastricht, The Netherlands, [4]University of Cape Town, Cape Town, South Africa, [5]University of Pretoria, Pretoria, South Africa

Background/ Introduction

C. trachomatis and *N. gonorrhoeae* constitute a major public health problem among women, but the burden of infection in sub-Saharan Africa is poorly documented. We conducted a systematic review and meta-analysis of genital and extra-genital *C. trachomatis* and *N. gonorrhoeae* infection in women in sub-Saharan Africa.

Objectives

To inform health policies and STI control strategies for women living in low-resource settings by providing insight into the distribution of genital and extra-genital *C. trachomatis* and *N. gonorrhoeae* infections.

Method

We searched Medline, EMBASE and Web of Science over a 10 years period for studies on epidemiology of genital and extra-genital chlamydial infection and gonorrhoea in women in all countries of sub-Saharan Africa. A total of 102 study results were included, with data available for 24/49 of sub-Saharan countries. We assessed geographic and demographic difference in prevalence and incidence of infection. Weighted mean prevalence estimates were calculated per population group using a random-effect model.

Results

Weighted prevalence of both chlamydial infection and gonorrhoea was significantly lower among women in community-based studies (3.9%; 95% CI 2.9-5.1% and 2.2%; 95% CI 1.2-4.0%) than for women recruited at primary healthcare facilities (6.3%; 95% CI 4.8-8.1% and 4.3%; 95% CI 3.3-5.6%, $p<0.001$, respectively). Prevalence of *Chlamydia* among sex workers was 5.5% (95% CI; 4.2-7.3%) and gonorrhoea 7.6% (95% CI; 5.4-11%). Geographic differences were observed. Seven studies reported on incidence which varied between 0.75-28 and 2.8-17 per 100 person-years-at-risk for chlamydial infection and gonorrhoea, respectively. Only two studies reported on extra-genital infections.

Conclusions

This overview underlines a high prevalence of genital *C. trachomatis* and *N. gonorrhoeae* in women in different settings in sub-Saharan Africa. Better control strategies are warranted to reduce the burden of infection and prevent long-term complications of these infections.

B9 Evaluation of syndromic management guidelines for treatment of sexually transmitted infections in South African women

Lisette van der Eem[1,2], Jan Henk Dubbink[1,3], Helen S. Struthers[1,5], James A. McIntyre[1,5], Sander Ouburg[4], Servaas A. Morré[3,4], Marleen M. Kock[6,7], Remco P.H. Peters[1,6]
[1]Anova Health Institute, Johannesburg, South Africa, [2]African Women Foundation, Amsterdam, The Netherlands, [3]Maastricht University, Maastricht, The Netherlands, [4]VU University Medical Center, Amsterdam, The Netherlands, [5]University of Cape Town, Cape Town, South Africa, [6]University of Pretoria, Pretoria, South Africa, [7]Tshwane Academic Division, Pretoria, South Africa

Background/ Introduction

Sexually transmitted infections (STI) in women represent a global public health problem. Many low resource countries, including South Africa, use a syndromic management of vaginal discharge syndrome (VDS) for STI control.

Objectives

To evaluate performance of three different guidelines for the management of vaginal discharge syndrome (VDS) for women living in a rural setting in South Africa.

Method

We conducted a secondary analysis of data from a cross-sectional study in Mopani District, South Africa. The 2015 and 2008 guidelines of the South African Department of Health (DoH) and the most recent WHO guidelines were evaluated for adequate treatment of genital *Chlamydia trachomatis*, *Neisseria gonorrhoeae*, *Mycoplasma genitalium*, and *Trichomonas vaginalis* infection.

Results

Of the 489 women included in this analysis, 171(35%) presented with VDS according to the DoH and 146(30%) per WHO definition of VDS respectively. Fourty-two (56%) of the women with VDS would be treated adequately for these STI when using the 2015 DoH guideline, whereas 76% (p=0.01) and 64% (p=0.35) would receive adequate treatment with the 2008 DoH and WHO guidelines respectively. Of the symptomatic women who tested negative for all four STI, STI treatment would have been indicated for 36% as per 2015 DoH guideline compared to 69% (p<0.001) respectively 67% (p<0.001) per 2008 DoH and WHO guidelines.

Conclusions

Up to three quarters of symptomatic women infected with these STI would receive adequate treatment when using the syndromic management approach, with significant differences between the different guidelines. Many symptomatic women without STI receive broad-spectrum antibiotics. Innovative approaches are warranted to improve STI control in settings with syndromic approach.

B10 Cell mediated immunity response to *C. pneumoniae* infection in Moroccan patients with cardiovascular diseases

Loubna Elyazouli[1,3], Fouad Seghrouchni[4], Naima Elmdaghri[1], Hicham Hejaji[2], Mohamed Bouazza[5], Aziz Alami[2], Abdelouahed Amraoui[5], Nadia Dakka[3], Fouzia Radouani[1]

[1]Institut Pasteur, Laboratory of Chlamydiae and Mycoplasmas, Casablanca, Morocco, [2]Cardiovascular Surgery Service , Ibn Rochd CHU, Casablanca, Morocco, [3]Biochemistry and immunology Laboratory, Faculty of Sciences Rabat Agdal, Rabat, Morocco, [4]Cellular Immunology Labortory, Institut National d'Hygiène, Rabat, Morocco, [5]Ophtalmoogy Departement, Casablanca, Morocco

Background/ Introduction

Chlamydophila pneumoniae (*C. pneumoniae*) is a common respiratory pathogen that causes a chronic and persistent airway infection and strongly involved in cardiovascular diseases.

Objectives

The main objective of our study is to explore the cell mediated immune response to *C. pneumoniae* infection in patients with cardiovascular diseases evaluating the CD14, CD8 and CD4 expression.

Method

A total of 27 patients with cardiovascular diseases (12 *C. pneumoniae* positive and 15 negative) and 32 controls (7 *C. pneumoniae* positive and 25 negative) recruited respectively in cardiovascular surgery and Ophthalmology departments. Blood samples were collected in EDTA tubes and C. pneumoniae DNA was detected in peripheral blood mononuclear cells by Nested PCR. To measure the expression of CD4, CD8 and CD14, blood cells were stained by anti CD4+, anti CD8+ and anti CD14+ monoclonal antibodies. The analysis was performed by Flow Cytometry and FlowJo software. The data were statistically analyzed by MedCalc and $p<0.05$ was considerate significant.

Results

The results showed an up-expression of CD4, CD8 and CD14 in infected subjects with *C. pneumoniae* among patients and controls (CD4 Cpn(+)= 1068.89 vs CD4 Cpn(-)= 581.6; CD8 Cpn(+)= 1691.52 vs CD8 Cpn(-)= 625.05; CD14 Cpn(+)= 1502.47 vs CD14 Cpn(-)= 968.17) with a significant difference ($p<0.0001$). Furthermore, the comparison of CD4, CD8 and CD14 expression between infected patients and infected controls showed a significant increase expression in the first group (CD4 Cpn(+) patients= 1304.9 vs CD4 Cpn(+) controls= 728 ; CD8 Cpn(+) patients= 2171.5 vs CD8 Cpn(+) controls= 868; CD14 Cpn(+) patients= 1632.9 vs CD14 Cpn(+) controls= 1278; $p<0.05$).

Conclusions

These data provide incentive to further explore the role of *C. pneumoniae* in stimulating and changing mechanisms of cell-mediated immune response induced by its antigens. Which may alter immunity response, by an up-expression of CD4, CD8 and CD14 involved in the inflammation mechanism and therefore the development of fatal atherosclerosis.

B11 The role of *Chlamydia pneumoniae* (CP), *Chlamydia trachomatis* (CT) and CT genovars, in women with lower abdominal pain (LAP)

Eleanne van Ess[1], Sander Ouburg[1], Svetlana Dubrovina[2], Servaas A. Morré[1], Joke Spaargaren[1]
[1]VU University Medical Center, Amsterdam, The Netherlands, [2]Scientific Research Institute of Obstetrics and Pediatrics, State Medical University, Rostov-on-Don, Russia

Background/ Introduction

Upper genital tract infections (UGTI) lead to local tissue damage on the basis of infection and inflammation. CT is a major cause of late complication development in women. Also pulmonary CP (Manam 2013) has been suggested to play a role in enhancing severity of UGTI with CT.

Objectives

The aim of this study was to investigate the potential relation between *C. trachomatis* DNA positivity and the presence of serological responses to *C. pneumoniae* and/or *C. trachomatis* in women with and without LAP to predict upper genital tract progression and if so, whether a relationship was genovar dependent.

Method

711 Dutch Caucasian women attending the STD outpatient clinic in Amsterdam participated in this prospective study. The presence of CT DNA in the urogenital tract was assessed by PCR and sera were collected for analysis of systemic IgG antibodies (Medac Diagnostika, Germany) against CP and CT at the time of consultation. Genovars were determined by PCR based RFLP. *N. gonorrhoeae* infections were excluded according previously described the methods. Questionnaires were filled in regarding their self reported complaints including recent lower abdominal pain (not gastrointestinal or menses related).

Results

From 711 women tested 240 (33.8%) were found CT-DNA positive (1:2 collection-strategy; CT DNA positivity was not associated with LAP); of those 211 had IgG antibodies against CP and of those 40 (19%) reported LAP while of the 29 CP-IgG negative women 2 reported LAP (6.9%), *p*=0.12; OR 3.2. The results did not change when the CT-IgG status was included in the model. Neither when the genovar distribution was added. Among the 471 CT DNA negative women 398 were CP-IgG positive and of those 60 reported LAP (15.1%) whereas of the 73 CP-IgG negative women, 13 reported LAP (17.8%), *ns*.

Conclusions

A previous CP infection might influence the risk to develop LAP when an urogenital CT infection is contracted. Whether the modulation of the host immuneresponse by CP and/or in combination with host factors (*e.g.* SNP) contribute to the course and symptomatology of CT infections is under investigation.

B12 Evaluation of the accuracy of the Mikrogen multi target serology assay for the prediction of tubal pathology (TP) in subfertile women: comparison with the Medac MOMP IgG pELISA

Eleanne F. van Ess[1], Joke Spaargaren[1], Sander Ouburg[1], Jolein Pleijster[1], Jolande A. Land[2], Servaas A. Morré[1]
[1]VU University Medical Center, Amsterdam, The Netherlands, [2]University Medical Center Groningen, Groningen, The Netherlands

Background/ Introduction

CT infection is the major cause of tubal factor infertility. In the clinical fertility workup CT IgG status is used to assess the risk of TP. Only women at high risk will undergo invasive additional testing, *i.e.* laparoscopy. There is still a need for more accurate CT IgG tests.

Objectives

We evaluated whether the Mikrogen multi target assay has a better predictive value for TP than the currently widely used one target assay (MOMP) from Medac, in order to accurately lead patients to diagnostics (laparoscopy) and treatment (IVF) options.

Method

101 women who attended the fertility clinic of the UMC Groningen, The Netherlands, between 2007-2011 were included in this study. All patients underwent a laparoscopy to diagnose and classify TP. TP was defined as extensive adhesions and/or distal occlusion of at least one tube. Controls had no adhesions and no tubal occlusions. Serum was tested with the Medac pELISA (MOMPA) and subsequently with the multitarget Mikrogen ELISA (MOMP-CPAF-TARP). Results of both ELISAs (pos-neg-greyzone) were compared for their accuracy to identify TP. In addition, the Mikrogen line assay (MOMPA-TARP-CPAF-HSP60-OMP2: individual targets) will be analyzed on all samples in the upcoming months.

Results

Out of 101 patients 48 had TP and 53 were controls. Of the TP patients 64.5% had a positive CT serology with the Mikrogen ELISA, whereas 41.6% had a positive Medac pELISA. Although 35.4% of women in the TP group tested negative with Medac pELISA they tested either positive or grey zone with Mikrogen ELISA. Eight patients with TP had negative Mikrogen CT ELISA results versus 25 negative Medac pELISA. In the control group the Mikrogen ELISA had a false positive rate of 54.7%, versus 64.2% in Medac.

Conclusions

Preliminary results suggest that the Mikrogen ELISA has a higher accuracy to predict TP. To reduce the possible false positive rate of the Mikrogen assay the effect of changing cut-off values is examined; the contribution of the individual antibody targets for TP prediction is currently analyzed and will be presented.

B13 Lactoferrin-Lactobacilli interplay in *Chlamydia trachomatis* infection

Simone Filardo, Marisa Di Pietro, Alessia Bressan, Giovanna Schiavoni, Paola Mastromarino, Rosa Sessa
Department of Public Health and Infectious Diseases, Sapienza University, Rome, Italy

Background/ Introduction

In recent years, the incidence of *Chlamydia trachomatis* (CT) infection has increased worldwide and the genital infection is still considered an important public health problem. The interest of the scientific community has turned to several natural defense factors in order to better understand the etiopathogenesis of CT genital infection.

Objectives

The aim of our study was to evaluate, for the first time, the effect of lactoferrin (Lf) on CT infection cycle. We also evaluated the Lf ability in modulating the CT-mediated inflammatory state. In addition, *Lactobacillus* spp. have been considered in order to mirror the healthy genital microbiota.

Method

CT L2 strain 434/Bu (MOI: 0.05 IFU/cell) was used to infect HeLa-229 cells in the presence or absence of bLf (100µg/mL) and/or *L. brevis* (LB) strain CD2 (MOI: 1000 CFU/cell). Different phases of CT infection cycle were evaluated: i. Pre-treatment of CT elementary bodies; ii. Pre-incubation of HeLa-229 for 1 or 3 hours followed by CT infection; iii. Infection of HeLa-229 with CT; iv. Multiplication of CT. IL-6 and IL-8 levels were determined in supernatants by ELISA. Statistical analysis was performed by using a two-tailed t-test for independent samples. A value of P<0.05 was considered statistically significant.

Results

The main result of our study was observed in the CT infection phase, where Lf together with LB was able to hinder the adhesion and the entry of CT elementary bodies within the host cell, as shown by the significant decrease in chlamydial IFUs in infected cells in the presence of Lf and LB as compared to infected cells alone (P<0.001). IL-6 and IL-8 levels were significantly reduced in CT infected cells following Lf treatment.

Conclusions

The ability of Lf, together with LB, in inhibiting CT infection and reducing the associated inflammatory state may open the way to further studies in order to develop novel potential approaches for the prevention of CT genital infection.

B14 Mechanisms of *Chlamydia trachomatis* uptake into eukaryotic cells: an updated view

Charlotte Ford[1], Andrea Nans[2], Emmanuel Boucrot[1], Richard Hayward[1]
[1]*ISMB, London, UK,* [2]*The Francis Crick Institute, London, UK*

Background/ Introduction

Intracellular pathogens have evolved various strategies for entry into nonphagocytic cells to take advantage of the host environment. *Chlamydia trachomatis* is a major cause of human disease yet very little is known about the mechanisms they use for uptake into cells, other than actin reorganisation triggered by TARP and Rac.

Objectives

This study aims to clarify molecular mechanisms of bacterial uptake in light of recent ultrastructural studies, where snapshots of several morphologically distinct structures are observed at *Chlamydia* entry sites (Nans, Saibil, & Hayward, 2014).

Method

combination of biochemical, molecular biological and microscopic techniques to explore pathways of actin organisation including pharmacological inhibition, transfection, colocalisation and mutational analysis, confocal microscopy of fixed and live samples.

Results

Chlamydia associate with diverse actin structures during bacterial entry, including filopodia and phagocytic cups, and are taken up into PI3P-rich early endosomal-like structures.

Conclusions

Along with filopodial capture, a major route of entry for the bacteria is through an amiloride and PI3K-sensitive pathway which resembles macropinocytosis.

Nans, A., Saibil, H.R. & Hayward, R.D., 2014. Pathogen-host reorganization during *Chlamydia* invasion revealed by cryo-electron tomography. Cellular Microbiology, 16(10), pp.1457-1472.

B15 *Chlamydia trachomatis* and carcinoma, antigen and antibody detection, is there a connection?

Tatjana Grdanoska[1], Kiril Mihajlov[1], Gordana Jankoska[1], Elena Trajkovska Dokic[1], Dragan Tanturovski[2], Biljana Surbevska[1], Milena Petrovska[1], Zaklina Cekovska[1], Nikola Panovski[1]

[1]*Institute of Medical Microbiology and Parasitology,Medical Faculty, Skopje, Macedonia*, [2]*Clinic of Gynecology and Obstetrics, Clinical Center, Skopje, Macedonia*

Background/ Introduction

chlamydial infections has attracted rising attention. The following data show: in 1996 a total number of 835 samples were sent for detection of *C. trachomatis*. In 2015 a number of 9 612 samples were recived for same analysis. Anamnestic data give the first information, which points to *Chlamydia* infection.

Objectives

· To determine the positivity to *Chlamydia* antigen;
· To determine the positivity to *Chlamydia* in the aimed group of patients
· To determine the positivity of specific antibodies in the examined population
· To determine the positivity pathogenic bacteria and candida, presence of normal flora

Method

A total of 74 specimens from female were examined, 30 examines were control group and 44 with aimed diagnosis. Materials were examined for presence of chlamydial antigen and specific antibodies. The specimens were collected at the Clinic of Gynecology and Obstetrics, Clinical Center in Skopje. Direct detection of *Chlamydia* antigen was performed by the method of Direct Immunofluorescence (DIF). as a highly sensitive and specific test used. Detection of chlamydial abs was performed with ImmunoComb test for detection of IgA and IgG classes as well. The presence of other cultivable pathogenic bacteria and candida was examined by routine cultivable methods.

Results

The age of analysed patients was: 1991-95 (20pts), !986-90 (20pts), 1981-85 (15pts), 1976-80 (11pts), 1971-75 (4pts), 1965- 70 (4pts).

chlamydial antigen was detected in 23pts (31,1%).The positivity in the control grpoup was 8pts (10.8%), in aimed group 15pts (20,3%). IgA were detected only in 2pts (2,7%) from the aimed group (1:16 and >;1:32). IgG were detected in 3 pts,(4,1%) one from the control and 2pts from the aimed group (1:256, :64, :128). Other bacteria detected were: Gardnerela vaginalis in 9pts (12,2%), Ureaplasma urealyticum in 2pts (2,7%) , Candida albicans in 2pts (2,7%).

Normal flora was reduced or absent in7pts (9,4%)..

Conclusions

chlamydial antigen was detected in 23pts (31,1%). The individuals often did not show serum positivity. According to results from individuals that were positive for chlamydial antigen, ones with specific diagnosis were more frequently positive. This could be a result of microrganisams ability or weeknes of the host.

B16 *Chlamydia trachomatis* genotypes in a cross sectional study of urogenital specimens from remote Northern and Central Australia, and implications for child protection

Philip M Giffard[1,2], Nicole C Brenner[1], Sepehr N Tabrizi[3,4], Suzanne M Garland[3,4], Deborah C Holt[1], Patiyan Andersson[1], Rachael A Lilliebridge[1], Steven YC Tong[1], Mahdad Karimi[5], Prudence Boylan[6], Nathan Ryder[7,8], Tracy Johns[6,9], Gurmeet Singh[1,6]
[1]*Menzies School of Health Research, Darwin, Northern Territory, Australia,* [2]*Charles Darwin University, Darwin, Northern Territory, Australia,* [3]*The Royal Women's Hospital, Melbourne, Victoriia, Australia,* [4]*Melbourne University, Melbourne, Victoriia, Australia,* [5]*Western Diagnostic Pathology, Perth, Western Australia, Australia,* [6]*Sexual Assault Referral Centre, Darwin, Northern Territory, Australia,* [7]*University of Newcastle, Newcastle, New South Wales, Australia,* [8]*Centre for Disease Control, Darwin, Northern Territory, Australia,* [9]*Clinical Forensic Medical Services, Canberra, Australian Capital Territory, Australia*

Background/ Introduction

The presence of a sexually transmitted infection (STI) in a young child is regarded as indicative sexual abuse, but understanding what "indicative" means numerically is challenging. This is a particularly difficult problem in remote northern Australian, where the presence of trachoma means that *Chlamydia trachomatis* UGT autoinoculation is conceivable.

Objectives

We aimed to develop a numerical framework to underpin inference of the predictive value of *C. trachomatis* detection and genotype in a paediatric urogenital tract (UGT) specimen to indicate contact with adult sexual networks, and to populate this with data obtained from specimens obtained recently and obtained 25-30 years ago.

Method

We reasoned that a useful parameter is the genotype dependent positive predictive value (PPV) for *C. trachomatis* in a paediatric UGT specimen being closely connected to sexual networks. Trachoma genotypes may circulate in sexual networks, but also be trachoma associated and circulate by mechanisms independent of sexual contact. An excess of trachoma genotypes in paediatric UGT specimens as compared to adult UGT specimens represents autoinoculation from the ocular site to the UGT. We genotyped the *C. trachomatis* in contemporary *C. trachomatis* positive specimens from northern Australia, and also considered the implications of serotyping data from 25-30 years ago.

Results

Two hundred and seventeen *C. trachomatis* positive UGT specimens from remote north Australia were successfully genotyped. Urine specimens were less likely to be typable than vaginal swabs. None yielded trachoma genotypes, indicating that trachoma genotypes are not currently circuiting in sexual networks in the study area. This contrasts with a study in a similar geographical area in the 1980s-1990s, where it was found that 21/44 adult *C. trachomatis* positive UGT specimens contained trachoma serovar B. This indicates that the implications of a trachoma genotype in a specimen from a possibly at risk child can change with time.

Conclusions

Population-wide *C. trachomatis* genotype surveillance can inform service provider responses to detection of *C. trachomatis* in UGT specimens from young children. Trachoma genotypes are not currently circulating in North Australia sexual networks currently, but genotype B was abundant in the same networks 25-30 years ago.

B17 Comparison of immunoassay platforms for serological testing against *Chlamydia trachomatis*

Diana Martin[1], Sarah Gwyn[1,2], Gretchen Cooley[1], Alexandria Mitchell[1], Ryan Wiegand[1]
[1]*Centers for Disease Control, Atlanta, GA, USA,* [2]*IHRC Inc., Atlanta, GA, USA*

Background/ Introduction

Ocular infection with *Chlamydia trachomatis* (CT) causes trachoma, a leading cause of vision impairment and blindness targeted for elimination by 2020. We have been investigating antibody-based testing of Ct antigens as a surveillance tool using multiplex bead assays (MBA) and have adapted tests to ELISA and lateral flow assay (LFA).

Objectives

The aim of this work is to develop and evaluate three different immunoassays (MBA, ELISA, and LFA) to detect antibody responses against the CT antigen Pgp3.

Method

An LFA and ELISA were developed to detect antibodies against Pgp3. The LFA uses Pgp3 on the test line and Pgp3-colloidal gold as a detection reagent to indicate the presence or absence of anti-pgp3 antibodies, while the ELISA uses detection with horseradish peroxidase/TMB. Serum samples collected from communities in Nepal as part of a study of trachoma post-MDA serosurveillance were tested on MBA, ELISA, and LFA. Whole blood specimens were manufactured by spiking an equal volume of study serum into negative control blood cells.

Results

The sensitivity of the LFA against MBA-positive samples was 98% for serum and 87% for blood and specificity was 97% for serum and 100% for blood. Latent class analysis was performed to compare the performance of the tests without using one test as a reference standard. Initial analysis showed the sensitivity (likelihood of a positive test to cluster into a "positive" class) of MBA to be 93.0%, ELISA to be 98.8%, and LFA to be 98.2%. The specificity (likelihood of a negative test to cluster into a "negative" class) of MBA was 98.6%, ELISA was 94.1%, and LFA was 98.2%.

Conclusions

The data presented here show that an LFA has very good sensitivity and specificity. Latent class analysis suggests that MBA, ELISA, and LFA provide comparable data at a population level and therefore may be able to be used interchangeably for large scale surveillance.

B18 Cost-effectiveness analysis of *Chlamydia trachomatis* screening in pregnant women in Brooklyn, New York

Khushal H. Shah, Jared Ditkowsky, Margaret R. Hammerschlag, Stephan Kohlhoff, Tamar A. Smith-Norowitz
SUNY Downstate Medical Center, Brooklyn, NY, USA

Background/ Introduction

C. trachomatis infection during pregnancy is a major public health concern. Asymptomatic infection can result in serious complications affecting fertility and newborn health. Prenatal screening is efficacious in preventing chlamydial morbidity in pregnant women and their infants as well as providing an opportunity to treat sexual partners.

Objectives

We created a decision analysis model to estimate the costs and health-related effects of screening pregnant women for *C. trachomatis* in a high burden setting (Brooklyn, NY).

Method

We created a Markov model which considered a birth cohort of 100,000 individuals entering the population over a 5 year period from a societal perspective. We predicted the number of *C. trachomatis* cases, associated morbidity, and related costs. There were two comparison arms; pregnant women who received *Chlamydia* screening, and those who did not. Morbidity and mortality of a pregnant woman-infant pair with *C. trachomatis* were calculated.

Results

The cost-effectiveness of screening was reliant on the prevalence of *C. trachomatis*; when the rate was above 3.59%, screening was proven to be cost effective. In a high burden location (Brooklyn), the rate can be as high as 6% which would give a savings of $3,189,000. Rates of pelvic inflammatory disease, premature delivery, infantile conjunctivitis and pneumonia were 0.0883%, 0.0139%, 0.0930%, and 0.0464% per year, respectively.

Conclusions

In a high prevalence area, prenatal screening for *C. trachomatis* proved to be cost saving. However, in areas where the prevalence in pregnant women is <3%, screening may not result in cost savings.

B19 Investigation of *Chlamydia felis* polymorphic protein 7 (*pmp7*) as a target for the generation of neutralizing antibodies

Ross Harley, Christine Whiting, Lori Peacock, Fran Whittington, Philippa Lait, Sarinder Day, Chris Helps
University of Bristol, Bristol, UK

Background/ Introduction

chlamydial polymorphic membrane proteins (pmps) are a family of membrane bound proteins that include targets for the generation of host immune responses during chlamydial infection. Cats infected with C. felis generate strong serum antibody responses to some pmp proteins, including pmp7. Thus, pmp7 may be a novel vaccine component candidate.

Objectives

This study aimed to generate polyclonal antiserum against recombinant C. felis pmp7 and to use the antiserum to (i) confirm that pmp7 is expressed during C. felis replication in vitro and (ii) investigate if pmp7-antiserum can neutralize C. felis infectivity in vitro.

Method

Purified, partial length, C. felis recombinant(r) pmp7 was used to generate polyclonal antiserum in a rabbit using a standard immunisation protocol. Antiserum reactivity to rpmp7 was assessed by ELISA and immunoblotting. Detection of pmp7 protein expression during C. felis infection of McCoy cells was performed by immunoblotting and immunofluorescence. Neutralization assays were performed by incubating C. felis inoculum with rpmp7-antiserum prior to inoculation of McCoy cells. The effect on chlamydial replication within cell cultures was analysed by immunofluorescence to enumerate intracellular chlamydial inclusions and by determination of the relative number of C. felis organisms measured using real-time PCR assays.

Results

The presence of anti-rpmp7 antibody in the purified antiserum was confirmed. Immunoblotting of lysates from cell cultures inoculated with C. felis at 2, 24 and 40 hrs post-inoculation (PI) with C. felis provided evidence of expression of pmp7 at 40 hrs PI. Immunolabelling of chlamydial intracellular inclusions by C. felis rpmp7-antiserum indicated the expression of pmp7 within inclusions mainly from 26 hrs PI. Neutralization assay studies found no evidence of an inhibitory effect of the antiserum on the number of chlamydial inclusions or in the relative copy numbers of C. felis present within cell cultures.

Conclusions

We show for the first time that pmp7 protein is expressed during infection with C. felis and that it is expressed within chlamydial inclusions during late stages of the developmental cycle. No evidence was found that rpmp7-antiserum is able to neutralize infection with C. felis in vitro.

B20 Presence of *Chlamydia* spp. on layer farms in the Netherlands

Marloes Heijne[1], Jeanet v.d. Goot[1], Helmi Fijten[1], Hendrik-Jan Roest[1], Ben Wit[2], Kitty Maassen[3]
[1]*Central Veterinary Institute (CVI), part of Wageningen UR, Lelystad, The Netherlands,* [2]*Food and Consumer Product Safety Authority (NVWA), Utrecht, The Netherlands,* [3]*National Institute for Public Health and the Environment (RIVM), Bilthoven, The Netherlands*

Background/ Introduction

Recent publications show *Chlamydia* spp. are highly prevalent in poultry. With around 97 million chickens, poultry is an important part of the Dutch agrifood sector. No data are available on the presence of *Chlamydia* spp. on Dutch poultry farms. Here, we present the first results of a study on layer farms.

Objectives

Gaining insight in the presence of different *Chlamydia* spp. on poultry farms in the Netherlands.

Method

Between March 2015 and January 2016, 154 layer farms were sampled as part of a surveillance for zoonotic pathogens in farm animals. Per farm five pooled samples (twelve scoops of faeces per pool) were collected in one poultry house. If more houses were present, extra samples were collected. From the 154 farms 830 pools were tested in a 23S *Chlamydiaceae* Real-Time PCR. Subsequently samples were tested in a specific *C. psittaci* PCR to confirm presence of *C. psittaci*. Additionally a duplex Real-Time PCR is used to further investigate the presence of *C. gallinacea* and *C. avium*.

Results

169 of the 830 pooled faecal samples tested positive in the *Chlamydiaceae* PCR, but all samples tested negative in the *C. psittaci* PCR. First results of the *C. gallinacea* and *C. avium* PCR show that most of the *Chlamydiaceae* positive samples are positive for *C. gallinacea*. This work is still in progress and the results have to be translated to the farm level.

Conclusions

This is the first report on the presence of *C. gallinacea* in Dutch laying hens. We did not detect *C. psittaci* as indicated in other publications. At the moment it is not clear what the clinical and zoonotic implications of this study are. Further research is needed to elucidate this.

B21 Expanding host reservoir of *Chlamydia*-like organisms

Kati Hokynar[1], Eero J Vesterinen[1,2], Thomas M Lilley[3], Arto T Pulliainen[2], Suvi J Korhonen[1], Jorma Paavonen[1], Mirja Puolakkainen[1]
[1]*University of Helsinki and Helsinki University Hospital, Helsinki, Finland,* [2]*University of Turku, Turku, Finland,* [3]*Bucknell University, Lewisburg PA, USA*

Background/ Introduction

Chlamydia-like organisms (CLOs) are recently identified members of the *Chlamydiales* order. CLOs have been detected in environmental samples and in various hosts like amoebae and arthropods. Our earlier analysis of the fecal bacterial flora of the Daubenton's bat in Finland showed that it contains members of order *Chlamydiales*.

Objectives

In this study we screened bats droppings for the presence of CLOs by targeted molecular methods. In addition, sequence analysis of the 16S rRNA and 23S rRNA encoding genes was used to classify positive specimens and infer their phylogenetic relationships.

Method

DNA was extracted from more than 200 samples of bats droppings and screened withPan-*Chlamydiales*-qPCR, targeting the 16S rRNA gene. Positive samples were examined further by PCR targeting the 23S rRNA gene. Sequencing and phylogenetic analysis of the 16S rRNA and 23S rRNA amplicons were used to classify positive specimens and infer their phylogenetic relationships.

Results

Chlamydiales DNA was detected in 55% of the specimens. Sequence analysis and phylogeny revealed two main groups of CLOs. Of group 1, the 16S sequences matched with *Chlamydia* genus or with uncultured *Chlamydia* from snakes. For the 23S sequences, the best BLAST hit was *C. pneumoniae*, but sequence identity was low (76-89%). Of group 2, the16S sequences matched best with *RhabdoChlamydia* spp. or with uncultured *Chlamydia* identified in ticks, the sequence identities being ≈97%. The best BLAST hits for the 23S sequences from these samples were members of the families *ParaChlamydiaceae*, *Waddliaceae* and *Simkaniaceae*, but with sequence identities of 77-85%.

Conclusions

Bats represent another host for novel members of *Chlamydiales*. From bat droppings, two groups of CLO sequences were identified. Group 1 sequences might represent a novel family within the order *Chlamydiales*, and group 2 sequences likely belong to the family *Rhabdoclamydiaceae*.

B22 Characterisation of chemical mutants with resistance to the *Chlamydia trachomatis* CtHtrA inhibitor, JO146, identifies a possible lipid biology function

Vanissa A. Ong[2], Peter Timms[3], Bryan Wee[2], Wilhelmina Huston[1,2]
[1]*University of Technology Sydney, Sydney, NSW, Australia,* [2]*Queensland University of Technology, Brisbane, QLD, Australia,* [3]*Sunshine Coast University, Maroochydore, QLD, Australia*

Background/ Introduction

CtHtrA is a serine protease and chaperone that likely functions in the cell envelope of *Chlamydia* for protein assembly, maintenance, and degradation during stress response. Previously we demonstrated that CtHtrA is essential for the replicative phase of growth by the identification and application of a specific inhibitor.

Objectives

The objective of this study was to isolate and characterise mutants with resistance to JO146 by the generation of an EMS mutation library in *C. trachomatis* strain D. We used a plaque purified genome sequence *C. trachomatis* D in our laboratory to ensure a clean genetic background.

Method

The *C. trachomatis* D mutation library was generated and confirmed using frequency of rifampicin resistance. A range of EMS doses were tested for frequency of rifampicin resistance and killing of *C. trachomatis* (2 mg/ml was used to generate the library). The libraries of mutants (and a control that was not mutated) were subjected to a series of 26 repeated exposures to JO146 with increasing doses (other selection protocols were tested but either resulted in complete loss of the strains or insufficient selectivity). JO146 resistant mutants were plaque purified from separate libraries and characterised genotypically and phenotypically.

Results

The selection resulted in three independent mutants with reduced susceptibility to JO146. The three mutants all had different non-synonymous variants in CT776 a acyl-ACP synthetase (AasC), and two of them had separate mutations (one being a null) in CT206 a predicted acyl-transferase. The likely (unconfirmed) role of the two loci is in the lipid fatty acid composition by acquisition/integration of fatty acids from the host cell. The mutants produced more infectious progeny than the wild-type, but several other phenotypic traits (persistence, heat stress) were not distinguishable from the wild-type.

Conclusions

The results indicate that either 1. these proteins are the direct target of JO146, 2. the likely lipid bilayer fatty acid composition changes impede chlamydial cell entry by JO146, or 3. HtrA activity is functionally linked to the composition of the lipid bilayer.

B23 Evaluating potential vaccine targets in both the *Chlamydia trachomatis* and *Chlamydia muridarum* intravaginal mouse challenge models

Robin Kaufhold

MRL (West Point, PA), Merck & Co., Inc., Kenilworth, NJ, USA

Background/ Introduction

Identifying relevant animal challenge models adds to the complexity of human vaccine development. Murine challenge models have been the most utilized animal model for vaccine development against the *Chlamydia trachomatis* urogenital serovars. The question arises though as to whether a *C. trachomatis* or a *C. muridarum* model is more applicable.

Objectives

To evaluate the *C. muridarum* and *C. trachomatis* intravaginal mouse challenge models using prior animal studies evaluating potential vaccine candidates.

Method

C57BL/6 mice were immunized with *C. muridarum* or *C. trachomatis* Serovar D elementary bodies (EBs), adjuvant alone, or potential vaccine candidates in combination with adjuvant. Two weeks following the immunization regimen, mice were administered medroxyprogesterone acetate at 10 and 3 days prior to challenge. Mice were intravaginally challenged with *C. muridarum* or *C. trachomatis* Serovar D EBs. Over the course of several weeks the vaginal vault and ectocervix were swabbed and DNA was extracted. The magnitude and duration of *Chlamydia* infection was determined by amplifying a fragment of the chlamydial 16S ribosomal subunit gene in a novel qPCR assay.

Results

In 100% of the *C. muridarum* intravaginal challenge studies EB immunized mice have significant reduction of bacterial shedding by qPCR ($p<0.05$) compared to adjuvant control immunized mice. For the *C. trachomatis* model 79% of the studies have significant reduction of shedding with EB immunized mice ($p<0.05$). In evaluating potential vaccines candidates, MOMP is protective ($P<0.05$) in both challenge models, PmpD p73 Passenger Domain is protective in only the *C. trachomatis* model, and PmpD p82 Translocator Domain and CPAF are not protective in either challenge model.

Conclusions

The *C. muridarum* model is a more reproducible and reliable model with respect to significantly reduced shedding of EB immunized mouse control groups. We have observed that if a potential vaccine candidate significantly reduces shedding in the *C. muridarum* model then it will also reduce shedding in the *C.trachomatis* model.

B24 Expression of *Chlamydia trachomatis ompA, cpaf, tarp* and *tox* genes during cervical infection

Suvi J Korhonen[1,2], Kati C Hokynar[1], Eija Hiltunen-Back[3], Jorma A Paavonen[4], Mirja H Puolakkainen[1,5]

[1]*Department of Virology, Haartman Institute, University of Helsinki, Helsinki, Finland,* [2]*Department of Bacteriology, Helsinki University Hospital, HUSLAB, Helsinki, Finland,* [3]*Clinic of Venereal Diseases, Skin and Allergy Hospital, Helsinki University Hospital, Helsinki, Finland,* [4]*Department of Obstetrics and Gynecology, Helsinki University Hospital and University of Helsinki, Helsinki, Finland,* [5]*Department of Virology and Immunology, Helsinki University Hospital, HUSLAB, Helsinki, Finland*

Background/ Introduction

Gene expression of *Chlamydia trachomatis* in cell culture is fairly well known but gene expression during *in vivo* infection remains somewhat unexplored. Also, it is not known to what extent gene expression *in vitro* correlates to the situation in human infection.

Objectives

Our aim was to study the expression of selected *C. trachomatis* genes (*ompA, cpaf, tarp* and *tox*) involved in virulence and/or bacterial cell structure integrity during *in vivo* infection. Gene expression was analyzed in cervical swabs collected from patients with suspected *C. trachomatis* infection.

Method

Altogether samples from 52 patients (44 *C. trachomatis* positive and 8 *C. trachomatis* negative) were included in this study. Total RNA was extracted from Gen-Probe Aptima swab transport media. cDNA was synthesized and RT-qPCR analysis of *ompA, cpaf, tarp* and *tox* genes was performed. A separate cervical swab was used for *C. trachomatis* culture from the same patients, and gene expression profile of the selected fresh isolates was studied in HeLa229 cell culture with similar methodology.

Results

Among the 44 *C. trachomatis* positive samples, expression of one or several of the investigated genes was demonstrated in nine samples: five expressed *ompA* gene, three expressed *tox* gene, three expressed *tarp* gene and five expressed *cpaf* gene. When the expression profile of selected low passage number isolates from the same patients was studied during *in vitro* infection, all isolates were shown to express *ompA, tox, tarp* and *cpaf* genes. No expression of any of these genes was observed among the eight *C. trachomatis* negative samples.

Conclusions

We detected expression of *C. trachomatis* genes during cervical infection albeit infrequently. The analyzed *C. trachomatis* isolates expressed these genes in *in vitro* infection. This suggests that the differences are likely due to the small amount of chlamydial mRNA in the cervical swabs and not due to differences between isolates.

B25 *Chlamydia*-induced NFkB activation *in vitro*

Cory A. Leonard, Nicole Borel
University of Zurich, Zurich, Zurich, Switzerland

Background/ Introduction

Epithelial cells release inflammatory cytokines in response to chlamydial infection. The release of these cytokines may be regulated, in part, by the pro-inflammatory transcription factor nuclear factor kappa B (NFkB).

Objectives

This study aims to evaluate the effect of porcine and human chlamydial strains on NFkB activation *in vitro* (*Chlamydia pecorum* 1710S, porcine abortion; *C. suis* S45, inapparent intestinal porcine infection; *C. trachomatis* serovar E, human genital serovar).

Method

HeLa cells (human cervical epithelial cell line) were inoculated with *Chlamydia* or exposed to tumor necrosis factor alpha (TNFa; positive control). NFkB activation, as indicated by NFkB nuclear translocation, was determined by immunofluorescence microscopy (IF). Pretreatment of HeLa cells with the eukaryotic protein translation inhibitor cycloheximide (CHX) was used to inhibit *de novo* translation of NFkB inhibitors in order to limit subsequent NFkB de-activation and return to the cytosol, facilitating IF visualization of NFkB nuclear translocation and enabling subsequent semi-quantitative analysis.

Results

C. pecorum centrifugation-assisted inoculation resulted in dose-dependent nuclear translocation of NFkB. Centrifugation was required for *C. pecorum*-dependent NFkB nuclear translocation, which was maximal by 2 hours post inoculation (similar time frame as TNFa-induced control NFkB activation). Mock inoculum, prepared from uninfected HeLa cells and processed as for *Chlamydia* stocks, had no effect on NFkB nuclear translocation. NFkB nuclear translocation was also induced by *C. suis* or *C. trachomatis* inoculation, though the effect was not as pronounced as for *C. pecorum*. CHX enhanced both *Chlamydia*- and TNFa-dependent NFkB nuclear translocation, however, centrifugation had no effect on TNFa-dependent NFkB nuclear translocation.

Conclusions

Chlamydia-dependent NFkB nuclear translocation in HeLa cells is species-dependent and associated with animal- and human-infecting *Chlamydia*e. HeLa cells are Toll-like receptor (TLR)-1, -2, and -4 signaling deficient, therefore observed *Chlamydia*-dependent NFkB nuclear translocation is likely to be TLR-independent. Centrifugation increases chlamydial attachment/uptake and this may potentiate chlamydial NFkB activation.

B26 Genital and anorectal *Chlamydia trachomatis* load in women with a concurrent infection

Jeanne AMC Dirks[2], Geneviève AFS van Liere[1,2], Christian JPA Hoebe[1,2], Nicole HTM Dukers-Muijrers[1,2], Petra F Wolffs[2]

[1]*Public Health Service South Limburg, Department of Sexual Health, Infectious Diseases and Environmental Health, Geleen, The Netherlands,* [2]*Department of Medical Microbiology, School of Public Health and Primary Care, Maastricht University Medical Center (MUMC+), Maastricht, The Netherlands*

Background/ Introduction

Concurrent urogenital and anorectal *Chlamydia trachomatis* (CT) infections are common among women, including women who did not report anal sex. Insight in differences between the genital and anorectal bacterial load in women who reported anal sex and women who did not, could provide insight in CT transmission.

Objectives

To compare genital and anorectal CT load and their association in women who reported anal sex and women who did not report anal sex.

Method

A convenience sample of 112 women ≥16 years old with concurrent genital-anorectal CT who visited the STI clinic was selected. Real-time PCR was used to quantify CT OmpA-gene copies/ml and human leukocyte antigen (HLA)-gene copies/ml to ensure adequate sampling. Paired samples were excluded if HLA could not be detected (n=4). CT load values were log10 transformed for analyses. Students T-tests (continuous) and Chi^2 tests (genital load>anorectal load and genital load< anorectal load) were used to compare genital and anorectal load with the report of anal sex. Linear regression analyses were used to assess the association between genital and anorectal load.

Results

The mean genital load was similar between women who reported anal sex and women who did not (4.8 CT/ml versus 5.2 CT/ml, P=0.14). Anorectal load was significantly higher in women reported anal sex (3.8 CT/ml versus 2.8 CT/ml, P=0.001). Anorectal load was not associated with genital load in both categories (B 0.10, 95% CI -0.15-0.34, P=0.44 and B 0.25, 95% CI -0.10-0.61, P=0.15 respectively). Genital load was higher than anorectal load in 37.5% (N=33) of women who reported anal sex. For women who did not report anal sex this was 62.5% (n=55) (P=0.01).

Conclusions

Genital and anorectal load were not associated, irrespective of the report of anal sex. Anal sex was associated with anorectal load, not with genital load. Genital load was higher than anorectal load in the majority of women.

B27 Spontaneous clearance of urogenital and anorectal *Chlamydia trachomatis* infection is associated with lower bacterial load

Geneviève AFS van Liere[1,2], Jeanne AMC Dirks[2], Nicole HTM Dukers-Muijrers[1,2], Petra F Wolffs[2], Christian JPA Hoebe[1,2]

[1]*Public Health Service South Limburg, Department of Sexual Health, Infectious Diseases and Environmental Health, Geleen, The Netherlands,* [2]*Department of Medical Microbiology, School of Public Health and Primary Care, Maastricht University Medical Center (MUMC+), Maastricht, The Netherlands*

Background/ Introduction

Chlamydia trachomatis (CT) infections can clear without treatment. However, studies on anorectal CT clearance are scarce. Moreover it is unknown whether antibiotic use and bacterial load have an effect on urogenital and anorectal CT clearance.

Objectives

To assess the effect of antibiotic use and bacterial CT load on urogenital and anorectal CT clearance.

Method

All CT positives ≥18 years of age who attended the STI clinic were asked a repeat test when returning for treatment between June 2011 and December 2013. Diagnostic and repeat samples were tested using PCR. Real-time PCR was used to quantify CT OmpA-gene copies/ml and human leukocyte antigen-gene copies/ml to ensure adequate sampling. Paired samples were excluded if HLA could not be detected (n=5) or data on antibiotic use was missing (n=4). CT load values were log10 transformed for analyses. Logistic regression was used to test the association between antibiotic use and clearance.

Results

CT infection was cleared in 10.0%(n=10) of urine samples, in 7.6%(n=19) of vaginal samples and in 15.7%(n=8) of anorectal samples. The number of days between tests (mean 11, SD 6) was not associated with clearance in all sample types (P=0.93, P=0.19 and P=0.66 respectively). Clearance of vaginal samples was associated with antibiotic use between tests (OR 4.2 95% CI 1.1-17.0). CT load in the diagnostic test was lower in persons who cleared the infection versus persons who did not clear the infection (urine samples; 1.2 versus 2.6, P=0.001, vaginal samples; 2.1 versus 5.2, P<0.0001, anorectal samples; 2.0 versus 3.7, P=0.002).

Conclusions

CT clearance was associated with a lower CT load at the time of diagnosis. Possibly these low load infections are in the downward phase when the patients immune system is resolving the infection. Insight is viability of CT infections is needed for further interpretation of these results.

B28 Experimental challenge of pregnant cattle with the putative abortifacient *Waddlia chondrophila*

Nicholas Wheelhouse, Allen Flockhart, Morag Livingstone, Kevin Aitchison, Jeanie Finlayson, Mark Dagleish, <u>David Longbottom</u>
Moredun Research Institute, Edinburgh, UK

Background/ Introduction

Waddlia chondrophila is a *Chlamydia*-related intracellular bacterium which belongs to the Waddliaceae family. *W. chondrophila* has previously been isolated from bovine foetuses in the US and Germany, and serological studies support its putative role in bovine abortion. More recently, *Waddlia* has been implicated in cases of human miscarriage.

Objectives

Given the lack of direct evidence, the current study was carried out to investigate whether experimental challenge of pregnant cattle with *W. chondrophila* would result in abortion and recovery of the organism.

Method

Nine pregnant Holstein-Friesian heifers received 2×10^8 IFU *W. chondrophila* by intravenous challenge at 3 months gestation. Four pregnant negative-control animals underwent mock challenge. Rectal temperatures and bloods were obtained at 4 hourly intervals 24 hrs post-challenge. Two negative control and four *W. chondrophila* challenged animals were necropsied two weeks prior to parturition to allow the aseptic collection of tissues for molecular analyses and recovery of the organism. The remaining animals were allowed to proceed to parturition where placentas were collected and dam and calf were necropsied within 48hrs, for collection of samples.

Results

Gross examination revealed only a single dam, which was euthanised two weeks prior to parturition, to have large amounts of yellow, semi-solid exudate on the surface of the chorioallantois in the inter-cotyledonary zones which occasionally extended onto the outer surface of the placentome. Presence of *W. chondrophila* antigen was confirmed by IHC in the placentomes, and foetal tissues were also positive by real-time PCR. There was no evidence of the organism in any of the other challenged or negative control animals. *W. chondrophila* was recovered from the single positive animal and DNA genome sequencing matched that of the challenge strain.

Conclusions

The current study demonstrated the presence of *W. chondrophila* DNA in the placenta, amniotic fluids and foetus in a near-term heifer, and critically, viable organisms in the placenta, 6 months after intravenous infection. This study therefore demonstrates the disease causing potential of this organism.

B29 Highly diverse MLVA-ompA genotypes of rectal *Chlamydia trachomatis* amongst men who have sex with men in Brighton, UK and evidence for an HIV-related sexual network

Clare Labiran[2], Peter Marsh[1], Judith Zhou[3], Alan Bannister[3], Ian N. Clarke[2], Stephanie Goubet[4], Suneeta Soni[3]

[1]*Public Health England, Southampton, UK,* [2]*University of Southampton, Southampton, UK,* [3]*Brighton and Sussex University Hospital, Brighton, UK,* [4]*University of Brighton, Brighton, UK*

Background/ Introduction

Specific *Chlamydia trachomatis* (CT) ompA genotypes correlate with infection in men who have sex with men (MSM) who mostly have genotypes D, G and J compared with heterosexuals in whom D, E and F are more common. Sexual behaviour and tissue tropism may account for these differences.

Objectives

This prospective study aimed to determine the distribution of genotypes by multi-locus variable number tandem repeat (VNTR) analysis plus analysis of the ompA gene (MLVA-ompA) of rectal CT among MSM attending Brighton GUM Clinic.

Method

Samples were assigned genotypes by PCR and sequencing of the markers of the MLVA-ompA genotyping system. Rectal CT was isolated in cell culture using McCoy cells. Data regarding demographics, HIV status, rectal symptoms, past history of STIs including CT were collected.

Results

1809 MSM attending the clinic between October 2011 and January 2013 took part in the study, 112 (6.2%) of whom had rectal samples which tested positive for CT. 85/112 (75.9%) CT positive rectal samples were assigned 66 different genotypes. Two distinct genotype sub-clusters were identified: Sub-cluster 1 was mainly D, E and F; sub-cluster 2 was D, G, J and L2b (p<0.001). Sub-cluster 1 consisted of more HIV-negative men than sub-cluster 2 (p=0.025). Isolates were successfully cultured from 37 of the 112 specimens, from which 27 otherwise unobtainable (from direct PCR) MLVA-ompA genotypes were gained.

Conclusions

The most prevalent genotypes were G, E and D representing some overlap with the heterosexual distribution in UK. Sub-cluster 1 consisted of more "heterosexual types" and significantly more HIV-negative men than sub-cluster 2.

B30 Kinetic of *Chlamydia abortus* infection in response to estradiol and progesterone in mouse model

Antonio Murcia-Belmonte, Daniel Álvarez, M. Rosa Caro, Jose A. Navarro, M. Carmen Gallego, Francisco Cuello, Nieves Ortega, Antonio J. Buendía, Jesús Salinas
Universidad de Murcia, Murcia, Murcia, Spain

Background/ Introduction

Chlamydia abortus (CA) produces ovine enzootic abortion. Symptoms are not observed until the organism colonizes the placenta, eventually causing abortion. Then, animals become carriers and will shed the organism in the following oestruses. This process could suggest that sex hormones might play an important role on the physiopathology of abortion.

Objectives

The goal of this study is to determinate in a mouse model, the influence of 17β-estradiol and progesterone on the kinetic of the CA infection.

Method

Forty five ovariectomized Swiss OF1 mice were randomly allocated in 3 groups. They were subcutaneously administered either 3 mg of progesterone, 3 μg of 17β-estradiol, or only sesame oil (control group). Animals were challenged intraperitoneally with 5×10^9 inclusion-forming units of CA strain AB7. Animals were sacrificed at 4, 8 and 11 days post-infection (pi). The morbidity was measured as weight loss and samples of liver and spleen were collected each day of sacrifice for chlamydial quantification and histopathological analyses.

Results

The progesterone treated mice showed higher weight loss than estradiol and control groups, recovering their body weight later than the other groups. The isolation of CA was higher in the progesterone group at 4 and 8 days pi than in the other groups. Estradiol group had the lowest presence of CA throughout the study. The inflammatory foci were more evident in the progesterone group in relation to the other groups at 4 and 8 days pi.

Conclusions

The results indicate an effect of progesterone on *Chlamydia abortus* infection, showing an increased morbidity, higher level of isolation and more severe lesions from liver and spleen.

B31 Modulation of chlamydial transcriptional responses after 2-deoxyglucose treatment: evidence for a carbon response

Zachary, T. Tucker, Xiaojing Zheng, <u>Catherine, M. O'Connell</u>
University of North Carolina, Chapel Hill, North Carolina, USA

Background/ Introduction

Previous studies suggest that *Chlamydiae* lack a carbon response. We reported reduced transcription of *glgA* and other conserved plasmid-responsive chromosomal loci in *C. trachomatis* when host production of glucose-6-phosphate (G6P) is limited by treatment with 2-deoxyglucose (2DG). Bacteria were also less proinflammatory, suggesting that virulence may be environmentally regulated.

Objectives

The object of this study was to define the global transcriptional response of *C. trachomatis* to 2DG treatment and investigate the role for glucose sensing in the modulation of virulence.

Method

Profiling of RNA extracted 24 hours after infection of a human oviduct epithelial cell line with *C. trachomatis* D/UW-3/Cx in the presence or absence of 10 mM 2DG was performed via RNA sequencing using the Ion Torrent platform. Differential gene transcription was validated via RT-PCR for both D/UW-3/Cx and L2/434/Bu. The impact of 2DG treatment on the transcriptional responses and growth of *C. trachomatis* strains resistant to a G6P analog KSK-120 that carry mutation(s) in UhpC, the hexose phosphate transporter, was also investigated.

Results

In addition to reduced *glgA* transcripts, we observed elevated transcription (~5 fold) of *sdhC* and *fumC*, encoding enzymes of the TCA cycle. Transcription of *ptsH*, encoding the phosphocarrier protein HPr a component of the phosphoenolpyruvate-dependent sugar phosphotransferase system was also increased. Transcription of *omcA* (20x) and *omcB* (5x) was reduced while *sodM* and *fmt* was elevated (~6x). Surprisingly, growth of M2-C6 carrying a UhpC^{A393T} mutation was severely restricted when supplemented with 10 mM 2DG and no difference in the transcription of these genes was detected. Growth of P9-C22 (UhpC$^{L429I, M315I}$) was not significantly impacted and transcriptional responses were unchanged.

Conclusions

Treatment of *C. trachomatis* with 2DG elicits a carbon-specific response with increased transcription of genes important for energy metabolism. *Chlamydiae* may also interpret this signal as stress, responding with increased *sodM* transcription and strongly reduced expression of *omcA* and *omcB*. Mutations in UhpC impair chlamydial modulation of these responses.

B32 Evaluation of the ovine immune response and protection following vaccination with recombinant proteins MIP and CPAF of *Chlamydia abortus* as novel vaccines for enzootic abortion of ewes (EAE)

Lauren Marie Therese O'Neill[1,2], Bryan Markey[1], Orla Keane[2], Padraig Ross[3], Jarlath Nally[4], Janakiram Seshu[5]

[1]School of Veterinary Medicine, University College Dublin (UCD), Belfield Dublin 4., Ireland, [2]Animal Bioscience Department, Teagasc Grange., Dunsany Co. Meath, Ireland, [3]Central Veterinary Research laboratory, Backweston, Co. Kildare, Ireland, [4]National Animal Disease Center- USDA, Ames, Iowa, USA, [5]University of Texas at San Antonio (UTSA), San Antonio, Texas., USA

Background/ Introduction

Chlamydia abortus is the causative agent of EAE, affecting the placenta of sheep and resulting in late gestation abortions. The disease costs approximately €5 million annually in Ireland. Reports of cases of abortion in flocks associated with the modified live commercial vaccine suggest a need for a safer vaccine.

Objectives

The aim of this study was to use flow cytometry to evaluate the ovine immune response to two recombinant proteins from *C. abortus;* the macrophage infectivity potentiator (MIP) and the *Chlamydia* protease activity factor (CPAF) and to determine their ability to protect ewes against EAE.

Method

Fifty EAE sero-negative ewes were randomly allocated to one of 5 treatment groups. The groups received (1) 100µg of MIP (2) 100µg CPAF (3) 50µg MIP and 50µg CPAF combination (4) phosphate buffered saline or (5) commercial vaccine, 6 months prior to tupping. The animals were inoculated subcutaneously on day 90 of gestation (1×10^6 inclusion forming units of *C. abortus* C95/27). Details of abortions and lambings are being recorded. Blood samples were collected at regular intervals. Flow cytometry was used to assess the following cell surface markers in fresh blood; CD4, CD8, MHCI, MHCII, CD14 and WC1.

Results

Blood samples taken 2 weeks post-infection were compared to pre-infection levels using flow cytometry. Results showed that WC1 significantly increased for CPAF and MIP/CPAF groups while CD14 significantly increased for the control and commercial vaccine groups. MHCII decreased significantly for MIP/CPAF and the commercial vaccine groups while MHCI only increased significantly for the MIP group. CD8 increased in all groups significantly except for the commercial vaccine group and finally CD4 increased in the control and MIP/CPAF groups significantly. Further analysis of data will be presented at the conference.

Conclusions

Flow cytometry analysis demonstrates significant shifts for certain cell surface markers between pre and post *C. abortus* infection levels. The protective abilities of these vaccines and importance behind these shifts will be evaluated at conclusion of lambing to be presented in full in September.

B33 Quantitative immunohistochemical analysis of *C. trachomatis* infected upper reproductive tract tissues in the pigtailed macaque model

Dorothy L Patton, Yvonne T Sweeney, Audrey E Baldessari
University of Washington, Seattle, WA, USA

Background/ Introduction

Chlamydia trachomatis (CT) infection of the upper genital tract (UGT) remains difficult to document in women experiencing sequelae associated with CT infections. The pigtailed macaque (*Macaca nemestrina*) provides a clinically relevant animal model to characterize the immunological cellular responses of the UGT exposed to experimentally induced CT infection.

Objectives

The purpose of this study was to use the macaque model of chlamydial infection to describe and quantify the immune cellular response to UGT chlamydial infection. If a distinct immune profile is pathognomonic for chlamydial infection, quantitative immunohistochemical analysis might be useful as an indirect marker for CT UGT infection.

Method

Nine macaques underwent direct endocervical and intratubal inoculation (n=6 CT-D; n=3 sham inoculant). Four and eight weeks after inoculation, one fallopian tube per animal was surgically removed. UGT tissue pathology was elucidated by gross appearance, H&E staining and by immunohistochemical (IHC) staining for immune cell subtypes CD4 (helper), CD8 (cytotoxic) T-cells, CD20 (B-cells), or CD68 (macrophage). IHC stained UGT tissues from four non-study macaques were evaluated as naïve controls. All IHC stained tissue sections were quantitatively assessed using Visiopharm Software. Mean values for each cell type on the $\log_{10}$ scale were compared between groups using linear mixed models.

Results

IHC staining in CT infected tubal tissues revealed statistically significantly higher levels of each cell subtype at Week 4 compared to controls, followed by a decline (significant in the case of CD4 and CD20) at week 8. Only CD20 staining remained significantly higher in the infected vs control tissues at week 8. Cellular infiltrate was similar in the sham inoculated and naïve control animals. No significant difference in IHC staining was noted among infected tissues when grouped by severity of grossly observable dilatation and fibrosis *in situ*.

Conclusions

CT infected UGT tissues had similar staining profiles, distinct from sham-inoculated animals. An influx of T-cells, B-cells and macrophages was clearly noted 4 weeks after CT was introduced to UGT tissues. With the exception of persistent B cells, the robust response had largely receded by 8 weeks.

B34 Identification and characterization of a *Waddlia chondrophila* effector secreted in the host cytoplasm

Carole Kebbi-Beghdadi, Ludovic Pilloux, Gilbert Greub
University Hospital Center and University of Lausanne, Lausanne, Switzerland

Background/ Introduction

Waddlia chondrophila is a *Chlamydia*-related bacteria now considered as an emerging pathogen causing adverse pregnancy outcomes in humans and abortion in ruminants. Similarly to classical *Chlamydiae*, *W. chondrophila* genome encodes a complete Type 3 Secretion System (T3SS) that enables *Waddlia* to modulate its environment and interact with its host cell.

Objectives

We observed that immunogenic protein WcT3SS_001 is secreted in the host cytoplasm. We intend to experimentally confirm *in silico* predictions and to demonstrate its T3SS-dependent secretion. We will also determine WcT3SS_001 expression pattern and characterize its bacterial and eukaryotic interactants looking for hints about its function in the host cell.

Method

To confirm secretion of WcT3SS_001 by the T3SS, we expressed the protein in a heterologous system (*Yersinia enterocolitica*) where type III secretion can be selectively induced. Furthermore, RNA and protein expression were analyzed during the bacteria replication cycle by RT-qPCR, immunofluorescence/confocal microscopy and western blot. Finally to characterize bacterial and host cell proteins interacting with WcT3SS_001, we expressed the protein in *E. coli* or in human cells and performed pull down and co-immunoprecipitation experiments.

Results

Our results indicated that the *WcT3SS_001* gene is transcribed during the early phase of the cycle and that the protein is produced and secreted in the host cytoplasm 16 to 24 hours post infection. Despite the low amino acid sequence homology between T3SS effectors, we were able to identify in *silico* WcT3SS_001 as a Type 3 secreted protein. We succeeded in expressing this protein, and a T3SS effector of *C. trachomatis* (CT_875) as positive control, in a heterologous system (*Yersinia enterocolitica*) that will allow to assess secretion by the Type 3 system.

Conclusions

Timing of WcT3SS_001 expression suggests a role for this protein in establishing optimal conditions to sustain the bacteria exponential growth. Determining the interacting host cell components will provide valuable insights into the function of this putative T3SS effector and open perspectives for the development of new drugs against *Chlamydiae*.

B35 Multiple approaches to discover new T3SS effectors of *Chlamydiales* bacteria

Ludovic Pilloux, Carole Kebbi-Beghdadi, Antony Croxatto, Gilbert Greub
Center for Research on Intracellular Bacteria (CRIB), Institute of Microbiology, University Hospital Center and University of Lausanne, Lausanne, Switzerland

Background/ Introduction

Bacterial type III secretion system (T3SS) is responsible of the secretion of effector proteins. As demonstrated for classical *Chlamydia*, effectors are able to modulate various host cell functions, facilitating the survival and the replication of the bacteria. However, nothing is known about effectors secreted by *Chlamydia*-related bacteria.

Objectives

This study aims at identifying T3SS effector proteins secreted by *Chlamydia*-related bacteria inside the membrane of the bacterial inclusion or within the host cell cytosol. The second aim is to characterize the role of these effectors especially by identifying their interactants within host cells.

Method

The first approach is based on bioinformatic algorithms that predict T3SS effectors even though no consensus sequence for type III secretion has been identified. We have also developed and optimized two alternative methods to recover bacterial proteins secreted in the host cell cytoplasm. These methods rely (i) on selective permeabilization of the eukaryotic membrane and (ii) on fractionation of host cell components, a technique that also allows to recover bacterial proteins secreted in the inclusion membrane. All the fractions were analysed by mass spectrometry.

Results

The first bioinformatic approach gave a short list of 15 putative T3SS effectors, with a majority of proteins of unknown functions. In parallel, experimental approaches provided complementary lists of others proteins either secreted in the host cell cytosol or translocated into the membrane of the inclusion. Secretion of these proteins by the T3SS was confirmed using a heterologous expression system. Finally, to characterize the role of these secreted proteins, they were further expressed in eukaryotic cells to identify their interactants.

Conclusions

This large screening, based on multiple approaches, led to the identification of new chlamydial secreted effector proteins. This study increased our understanding of chlamydial pathogenesis, which was particularly limited for *Chlamydia*-related bacteria, and opens novel perspectives for new anti-chlamydial drugs.

B36 An indole-producing *Prevotella* sp. isolate attenuates the bactericidal effect of IFNγ on genital *Chlamydia trachomatis* (CT)

Ashok Aiyar, Shardulendra Sherchand, Rebecca Lillis, David Martin, Alison Quayle
LSU Health Sciences Center, New Orleans, USA

Background/ Introduction

IFNgamma protects against CT, by inducing tryptophan degradation, thus starving CT of this essential amino acid. However, high endocervical IFNgamma levels are often observed in CT+ women, suggesting that CT can evade IFNγ's effects. Pertinently, genital CT isolates can salvage indole to make tryptophan, to evade the effect of IFNgamma.

Objectives

Whereas the *Lactobacillus* sp. that dominate the normal vaginal microbiome cannot make indole, some anaerobes that are amplified during bacterial vaginosis (BV) can make indole. Therefore, we tested whether indole-producing anaerobes isolated from BV samples permitted CT to evade the effect of IFNgamma.

Method

This study evaluated the effect of an indole-producing isolate of *Prevotella* sp. isolated from BV patients on the growth of: 1) The "wild-type" genital CT strain D/UW-3/CX; and 2) An isogenic point mutant of CTD/UW-3/CX that cannot express trpB, in the presence and absence of IFNgamma (300U/ml). Experiments were conducted using transformed cervical epithelial cell-line Hela 229. IFNgamma was added concurrent with infection. The number of primary inclusions formed at 42 hpi and the IFU released at that time were used to quantify bacterial growth.

Results

Our results indicate that an indole-producing *Prevotella* sp. isolate can attenuate the effect of IFNg on CT, only if the CT strain used can express tryptophan synthase. Importantly, an indole-negative isolate of *Prevotella* sp. does not block IFNgamma from restricting the growth of CT, and the indole-producing isolate could not rescue *trpB*- CTD/UW-3/CX from growth restriction by IFNgamma.

Conclusions

Indole-producing *Prevotella* sp., isolated from BV patients, attenuate IFNgamma-driven CT eradication, by facilitating salvage tryptophan synthesis. Thus, unfavorable vaginal microbiomes can prevent CT infection resolution by reducing the efficacy of IFNgamma. Consequently, establishing a favorable microbiome that doesn't provide indole is essential for the success of IFNgamma-inducing anti-CT vaccines.

B37 Do subfertile women with *C. trachomatis* antibodies have reduced clinical pregnancy rates, a prospective follow-up- study

Tiina Rantsi[1], Päivi Joki-Korpela[1], Hanna Öhman[2], Mirja Puolakkainen[3], Aini Bloigu[2], Jorma Paavonen[1], Heljä-Marja Surcel[2], Aila Tiitinen[1]

[1]*The Department of Obstetrics and Gynecology/University of Helsinki and Helsinki University Hospital, Helsinki, Finland,* [2]*National Institute for Health and Welfare, Oulu, Finland,* [3]*Virology and Immunology, University of Helsinki and Helsinki University Hospital, Helsinki, Finland*

Background/ Introduction

A number of patients suffering from subfertility have evidence of past chlamydial infection as indicated by *C. trachomatis* antibodies in serum. In addition to tubal factor infertility, it has been suggested that achieving a clinical pregnancy spontaneously is lower among patients with positive *Chlamydia* serology, even without visible tubal pathology.

Objectives

This prospective study consists of subfertile couples referred for infertility investigations to the Department of Obstetrics and Gynecology, Helsinki University Central Hospital. The study investigates if the past *C. trachomatis* infection measured by IgG and IgA antibodies is responsible for reduced pregnancy rates in women with unexplained infertility.

Method

During July 2007 - December 2010, a total 228 women were enrolled for the study. The blood specimens of the participants were collected together with routine samples and further analyzed at the Institute for Health and Welfare in Oulu. The patients were followed from July 2007 to June 2014. Clinical data on participants as well as the results of their examinations, treatments and pregnancy rates were collected. *C. trachomatis* immunoglobulin A (IgA) and immunoglobulin G (IgG) antibodies were studied using commercially available EIA kits (AniLabSystems, Helsinki, Finland). Chi-squared test and Mann-Whitney U-test were used for statistical analysis.

Results

23.7 % (54/228) of the participants had antichlamydial antibodies, 5.7 % (13/228) IgA and 19.7 % (45/228) IgG antibodies. Women with antichlamydial IgA antibodies had history of miscarriages more often than women who were seronegative (30.8% vs. 9.3%, p=0.036). The number of ectopic pregnancies did no differ between the groups. Spontaneous pregnancies occurred more often to women negative for chlamydial serology than to patients with positive markers of infection (36.5% vs 21.4%, p=NS). Time to successful pregnancy was longer among patients with antichlamydial IgG antibodies than that of patients without (1.9 vs. 1.4 years, p=0.011).

Conclusions

Women with positive *C. trachomatis* antibodies did not suffer from unexplained infertility, but time to successful pregnancy was longer with serologic marker of infection. Spontaneous pregnancies occurred less frequently to women positive for chlamydial serology, but IVF treatment was not needed more often.

B38 Cost-effectiveness analysis of *Chlamydia trachomatis* screening in dutch pregnant women

G.I.J.G. Rours[1,2], R.P. Verkooyen[2], R. de Groot[1], H.A. Verbrugh[2], M.J. Postma[3]
[1]Erasmus MC, Dept of Paediatric Infectious Diseases and Immunology, Rotterdam, The Netherlands,
[2]Erasmus MC, Dept of Medical Microbiology and Infectious Diseases, Rotterdam, The Netherlands,
[3]University of Groningen, Unit of PharmacoEpidemiology & PharmacoEconomics, Dept of Pharmacy, Groningen, The Netherlands

Background/ Introduction

Chlamydia trachomatis infections during pregnancy may have serious consequences for women and their offspring. chlamydial infections are largely asymptomatic. Hence, prevention is based on screening.

Objectives

The objective of this study was to estimate the cost-effectiveness of *C. trachomatis* screening during pregnancy in Dutch women.

Method

We used a health-economic decision analysis model, which included potential health outcomes of *C. trachomatis* infection for women, partners and infants, and premature delivery. We estimated the cost-effectiveness from a societal perspective using recent prevalence data from a population-based prospective cohort study among pregnant women in the Netherlands. We calculated the averted costs by linking health outcomes with health care costs and productivity losses. Cost-effectiveness was expressed as net costs per major outcome prevented and was estimated in base-case-, sensitivity- and scenario analysis.

Results

In the base-case analysis the costs to detect 1,000 pregnant women with *C. trachomatis* were estimated at €527,900. Prevention of adverse health outcomes averted €626,800 in medical costs, resulting in net cost savings. Sensitivity analysis showed that net cost savings remained with test costs up to €22 (test price €19) for a broad range of variation in underlying assumptions. Scenario analysis showed even more cost savings with targeted screening for women less than 30 years of age or with first pregnancies only.

Conclusions

Antenatal screening for *C. trachomatis* is a cost-saving intervention when testing all pregnant women in the Netherlands. Savings increase even further when testing women younger than 30 years of age or with pregnancies only.

B39 Lessons learned in mapping the chlamydial inclusion membrane

Elizabeth A Rucks, Macy Olson, Scot P. Ouellette
University of South Dakota, Vermillion, SD, USA

Background/ Introduction

The fundamental cellular processes that support inclusion membrane biogenesis and integrity are not understood. Studding the chlamydial inclusion membrane are Incs, which are proteins containing at least two large hydrophobic transmembrane domains, flanked by termini that are exposed on the host cytosolic face of the chlamydial inclusion.

Objectives

Data examining Inc function are limited because of the difficulty in working with proteins with large hydrophobic regions and the inherent fragility of the inclusion membrane. To circumvent these issues, we have created inducible constructs encoding specific Incs fused to a biotinylating enzyme and transformed them into *Chlamydia*.

Method

Specifically, we have adapted a strategy used in cell biology to map the mitochondrial matrix. The APEX2 method uses a mammalian expression vector, pcDNA3_APEX2-NES, to express a FLAG-tagged mutant soybean ascorbate peroxidase, which will biotinylate interacting and proximal proteins within thirty minutes after addition of its exogenous substrate, biotin-phenol. Constructs are expressed by *Chlamydia* using anhydro-tetracyline at different time points post-infection. Further, purification of protein complexes relies on the affinity for the biotin, not the preservation of protein-protein interactions.

Results

Notably, we have created and successfully expressed $IncA_{transmembranedomain}$-APEX2, $IncA_{fulllength}$-APEX2 and IncF-APEX2 from *Chlamydia*. These constructs localize and biotinylate the inclusion membrane upon addition of biotin-phenol. Since the biotin labeling reaction associated with the APEX2 method takes minutes, we are able to vary the time at which we examine protein-protein interactions. Therefore, we will have an understanding of how dynamic or static these interactions are at the inclusion membrane. Additionally, we are also determining the structural and phenotypic impact of overexpressing Inc constructs at different time points post-infection on the size and integrity of the inclusion membrane.

Conclusions

We have created powerful tools that will allow direct examination of the dynamic composition of the chlamydial inclusion membrane. These studies will allow us to better understand the consequences of disrupting key components that, in turn, will aid the development of strategies to limit chlamydial primary infections or reduce transmission.

B40 Characterization of aberrant bodies subtypes in *Waddlia chondrophila*

Aurélie Scherler, Nicolas Jacquier, Gilbert Greub
Institute of Microbiology, University Hospital Center and University of Lausanne, Lausanne, Switzerland

Background/ Introduction

Waddlia chondrophila is an obligate intracellular bacterium related to *Chlamydia* and considered as a potential agent of abortion in ruminants and miscarriage in humans. In presence of stress stimuli including β-lactam antibiotics or interferon-gamma, the bacterium can enter a non-dividing and non-infectious state characterized by enlarged and persistent aberrant bodies (ABs).

Objectives

This study aimed to assess the impact of various stress stimuli on the biogenesis of ABs in *W. chondrophila*. Their possible differences in DNA, RNA and protein content as well as their morphology after treatment were determined by distinct approaches.

Method

Primate Vero kidney cells were infected with *W. chondrophila* and treated with different stimuli in order to induce the formation of ABs. The ABs morphology and their number were observed by confocal microscopy. Additionally, their DNA replication and transcription pattern were assessed by quantitative PCR and reverse transcription PCR respectively.

Results

All stimuli tested induced the formation of ABs. According to their morphology and to their number per host cell, two main subtypes of ABs can be defined: (i) small and multiples ABs versus (ii) large and rare ABs. DNA replication of *W. chondrophila* was generally not affected by the different stimuli. Finally, distinct groups of mRNA expression patterns of important division proteins (MreB and RodZ) might be characterized according to the different expression of their encoding genes.

Conclusions

The presence of different ABs subtypes seems to indicate distinct mechanism of ABs formation. However, further studies are necessary to understand the molecular mechanisms involved in ABs formation. Indeed, the comprehension of the biological mechanisms triggering the development of this persistent stage may reduce treatment failure against chronic chlamydial infections.

B41 MiRNAs as biomarkers for *Chlamydia*-induced tubal factor infertility

Tankya Simoneaux[1], Yuehao Wu[1], Khamia Ryans[1], Danielle McKeithen[1], Debra Ellerson[2], Zenas George[2], Roshan Pais[1], Francis O. Eko[1], Carolyn M. Black[2], Uriel Blas-Machado[3], Joseph U. Igietseme[1,2], Qing He[1,2], Yusuf O. Omosun[1,2]
[1]Department of Microbiology, Biochemistry & Immunology, Morehouse School of Medicine, Atlanta, Georgia, USA, [2]Centers for Disease Control & Prevention, Atlanta, Georgia, USA, [3]Department of Pathology, College of Veterinary Medicine, University of Georgia, Athens, Georgia, USA

Background/ Introduction

Tubal factor infertility (TFI) accounts for 30% of female infertility, due to obstruction of the reproductive tract caused by several infections including *Chlamydia trachomatis*. Currently, TFI is diagnosed through highly invasive methods; therefore, there is a dire need for noninvasive biomarkers of TFI that could be used in therapy prediction.

Objectives

To identify novel and differentially expressed miRNAs and genes regulated in chlamydial pathogenesis that can predict the risk of developing TFI.

Method

Mice were divided into two groups based on the number of infections: Primary infection, one infection and secondary infection, two infections. Mice were sacrificed and blood samples were collected at one, two, four, and eight weeks after infection. miRNA sequencing, pathology, cytokine analysis and fertility assay were performed.

Results

There were differences in the pathological presentation; re-infected mice had more histological aberrations in the oviduct and uterus. Blood miRNA were differentially expressed in both primary and secondary infections, and the blood miRNA profile was different for the two groups. TargetScan and network analyses showed that the differentially expressed miRNAs in the blood were associated with host response to bacterial invasion, extracellular matrix, adherens junction formation and T cell receptor signaling amongst others. A select miRNAs appear to be useful as biomarkers for chlamydial pathogenesis leading to TFI. In addition, we also discovered novel miRNAs in *Chlamydia* infected mice.

Conclusions

chlamydial disease pathogenesis depends on host factors, which include miRNAs and the genes they control. Here we have shown that miRNAs in the blood can be used as biomarkers for *Chlamydia* disease progression leading to TFI.

B42 Quantitative proteomic analysis of elementary and reticulate bodies from *Chlamydia trachomatis*

Paul JS Skipp[1], Chris Hughes[2], Therese McKenna[2], Richard Edwards[3], James Langridge[2], Annabelle EP Clarke[1], Nicholas R Thomson[4], Ian N. Clarke[1]
[1]University of Southampton, Southampton, UK, [2]Waters Corp, Wilmslow, UK, [3]University of New South Wales, Sydney, Australia, [4]Sanger Institute, Cambridge, UK

Background/ Introduction

The obligate intracellular developmental cycle of *Chlamydia trachomatis* presents significant challenges in defining its proteome. In this study we have applied quantitative proteomics to both the intracellular reticulate body (RB) and the extracellular elementary body (EB) from *C. trachomatis*.We used *C. trachomatis* L2 as a model system.

Objectives

Our primary aim was to obtain the highest possible proteome coverage using exquisitely purified (>99%) EBs and RBs. Our objective was to determine individual protein concentration per bacterial cell (both EB or RB) by careful calibration using particle counting (against known latex bead standards) and accurate quantitative PCR to chromosomal and plasmid targets.

Method

C.trachomatis was grown in BGMK cells. RBs harvested at 15h post infection (PI) were purified by three rounds of gradient centrifugation. This is the earliest possible time to obtain purified RBs in quantity within the limits of the current technology. EBs were purified at 48h PI. We used two-dimensional reverse-phase UPLC to fractionate peptides before mass spectroscopic analysis, providing absolute amount estimates of chlamydial proteins providing absolute amount estimates of chlamydial proteins. The ability to express the data as molecules per cell gave ranking in both abundance and energy requirements for synthesis, allowing meaningful identification of rate-limiting components.

Results

The study assigned 562 proteins with high confidence and provided absolute estimates of protein concentration for 489 proteins. RBs were purified just prior to the commencement of DNA replication, interestingly, the data showed an increase in TTS capacity at 15h PI. Most of the enzymes involved in peptidoglycan biosynthesis were detected along with high levels of muramidase (in EBs) suggesting breakdown of peptidoglycan occurs in the non-dividing form of the microorganism. All the genome-encoded enzymes for glycolysis, pentose phosphate pathway and tricarboxylic acid cycle were identified and quantified; these data supported the observation that the EB is metabolically active.

Conclusions

The availability of detailed, quantitative proteomic data is invaluable for investigations into gene regulation and function. These high quality data are reproducible, robust and reliable for high abundance proteins. However, the subtleties of chlamydial gene regulation are likely to lie within the proteins of low abundance (<10 copies per cell).

B43 Toward more efficient use of the macaque model: Repeat chlamydial infections and unintended transfer of cervical infection to rectal mucosa

Yvonne T Sweeney, Robert J Suchland, Dorothy L Patton
University of Washington, Seattle, WA, USA

Background/ Introduction

The macaque model for *Chlamydia trachomatis* (CT) infection is used to assess the efficacy of multipurpose preventive technologies (MPT) in development. Study design modifications may allow for more effective MPT assessment and for a reduction in the number of research macaques required for multiple studies.

Objectives

In order to re-use animals, it is essential to prove the macaques develop documentable infection when experimentally re-challenged after antibiotic clearance of a prior CT infection. If cervical CT inoculation can unintentionally cross-infect rectal mucosa, it is important to specifically assess rectal secretions when conducting MPT efficacy studies.

Method

Twelve pigtailed macaques underwent direct cervical inoculation (CT serovar E; 5e6 IFU), followed by five weekly exams to detect infection in cervical and rectal secretions, then underwent antibiotic therapy for cure. Three months later the experiment was repeated in these animals with the same (CT E) or different (CT F) isolate. Inoculant was delivered to the face of the cervix/vaginal fornix via 1mL tuberculin syringe. Secretions were collected on dacron swabs. chlamydial infection was detected at each site by culture and by nucleic acid amplification (NAAT: Aptima2) assays. Serology was assessed weekly for CT specific antibodies.

Results

Ten of twelve macaques developed cervical infection (defined here as culture/NAAT positive beyond week 1) after initial exposure. Nine were NAAT positive from rectal swabs at least once; five remained positive for at least three weeks. Eight macaques tested seropositive for CT antibody. After antibiotic clearance, one macaque was removed from the study prior to the second inoculation. Upon repeat inoculation, four of five E, and two of six F exposed macaques tested positive for cervical infection. Rectal crossover was detected in the majority of animals, and CT serum antibody in eight of eleven macaques.

Conclusions

Cervical re-infection was documented, yet none of the factors tested predicted infection in the repeat phase. Re-use of animals requires further investigation. Cervical inoculation was followed by rectal CT detection in most animals. Therefore rectal secretions should be assessed for CT in studies assessing prevention/treatment of cervical *Chlamydia* infection.

B44 Culture-independent genomics supports pathogen discovery for uncultivable bacteria within the genus *Chlamydia*

Alyce Taylor-Brown[1], Nathan L Bachmann[1], Nicole Borel[2], Adam Polkinghorne[1]
[1]*Centre for Animal Health Innovation, Faculty of Science, Health, Engineering and Education, University of the Sunshine Coast, Sippy Downs, Australia,* [2]*Institute of Veterinary Pathology, University of Zurich, Zurich, Switzerland*

Background/ Introduction

Molecular studies have revealed considerably more diversity in the phylum *Chlamydiae* than was previously thought. A significant barrier to characterising these novel *Chlamydiae* is the requirement for culturing. We recently identified a range of novel uncultured *Chlamydiae* in captive snakes in Switzerland, however, nothing is known about their biology.

Objectives

Using a metagenomics approach, the aim of this study was characterise the genome of a novel chlamydial species (Uncultured *Chlamydia sp.* 2742-308) from a captive snake, to expand our knowledge of the additional diversity and biology of the genus *Chlamydia.*

Method

Total genomic DNA extracted from a choana swab from a captive snake underwent host methylated DNA depletion. The selectively enriched DNA was then subjected to multiple displacement amplification. Whole genome sequencing was carried out on the resulting enriched DNA sample on an Illumina MiSeq using 150 bp paired-end reads. Reads were filtered using Trimmomatic prior to *de novo* assembly using SPAdes. BLASTx analysis was conducted to identify chlamydial contigs. Automated and manual annotation was carried out using RAST and Artemis, respectively. Phylogenetic relationships were assessed based on concatenation of 40 conserved proteins.

Results

We identified two genomic contigs: a 1,113,133 bp contig, and a 7,504 bp contig, representing the chromosome and plasmid of *Chlamydia sp.* 2742-308, respectively. The 998 predicted coding regions include an expanded repertoire of outer membrane proteins (pmps and omps), some of which exhibited frameshift mutations, as well as several chlamydial virulence factors such as Tarp and *mip*. Notably, no evidence of a traditional chlamydial plasticity zone was identified. Phylogenetically, *Chlamydia sp.* 2742-308 forms a clade with *Chlamydia pneumoniae* and *Chlamydia pecorum*, distinct from former *Chlamydophila spp.*

Conclusions

Genomic characterisation of a novel uncultured *Chlamydiae* from a reptilian host has expanded our understanding of the diversity and biology of a genus that was thought to be the most well-characterised in this unique phylum. It is anticipated that this method will be suitable for characterisation of other novel *Chlamydiae.*

B45 The number, organization and size of polymorphic membrane protein coding sequences as well as the most conserved Pmp protein differed within and across *Chlamydia* species

Sarah Van Lent[1], Heather Huot Creasy[2], Garry Myers[2,3], Daisy Vanrompay[1]
[1]*Ghent University, Ghent, Belgium,* [2]*University of Maryland, Baltimore, USA,* [3]*University of Technology, Sydney, Australia*

Background/ Introduction

Variation is a central trait of the polymorphic membrane protein (Pmps) family. The number of pmp coding sequences (CDS) differ between *Chlamydia* species, but it is unknown if the number of pmp CDSs is constant within a *Chlamydia* species.

Objectives

The number, organization and size of pmp CDSs were determined in *C. trachomatis*, C. *pneumoniae*, C. abortus and C. psittaci genomes. Conserved proteins are hypothesized to be indispensable for the pathogenesis of bacteria. Therefore, the conservation of the Pmp proteins was determined both within and across the above-mentioned *Chlamydia* species.

Method

The pmp CDSs were annotated in 16 *C. trachomatis*, 6 C. *pneumoniae*, 2 C. abortus and 16 C. psittaci genomes by a Hidden Markov Model. The pmp CDSs and intergenic CDS regions were drawn to scale for all analyzed genomes. The protein sequences of each Pmp subtype were aligned and the percentage of conserved amino acids was calculated both within and across *Chlamydia* species.

Results

The size of CDSs of pmpA, pmpB and pmpH was conserved among all analyzed genomes, while the size of the expanded subtypes pmpE/F and pmpG, but remarkably also of subtype pmpD coding sequences differed among the analyzed genomes. PmpD, PmpA, PmpH and PmpA were the most conserved polymorphic membrane proteins in *C. trachomatis*, C. *pneumoniae*, C. abortus and C. psittaci, respectively. PmpB was the most conserved Pmp across the four analyzed *Chlamydia* species.

Conclusions

PmpD is not the most conserved Pmp across *Chlamydia* species, and not the most conserved Pmp protein in all *Chlamydia* species and in some C. abortus and C. psittaci strains PmpD was shorter due to a deletion. Is PmpD really essential for the pathogenesis of C. psittaci and C. abortus?

B46 *Chlamydia psittaci* **reference genes for normalization of expression data differ depending on the culture conditions and selected time points during the chlamydial replication cycle**

Sarah Van Lent, Daisy Vanrompay
Ghent University, Ghent, Belgium

Background/ Introduction

RT-qPCR is a major tool to better understand the pathogenesis of bacteria. However, the accuracy and reproducibility of RT-qPCR is dependent on many settings. The use of reference genes is the preferred method to reduce non-biological variation. Nevertheless, normalization is the most problematic and ignored part of RT-qPCR.

Objectives

So far, stably expressed genes for normalization of RT-qPCR data in *Chlamydia* have only been determined for the human pathogen *C. trachomatis*. In this study, we present the selection and validation of reference genes for RT-qPCR studies in C. psittaci during the normal developmental cycle and during penicillin-induced persistence.

Method

C. psittaci Cal10 was cultivated in Hela 229 cells, both in normal culture medium and in medium inducing the persistant state (by penicillin). The expression level of ten potential reference genes was determined at 2, 6, 12, 18, 24, 32 and 48 hpi by RT-qPCR. Data analyses were carried out with geNorm software on normal, penicillin and normal + penicillin samples.

Results

16S rRNA was the most abundantly expressed, while enoA and fumC were the least abundant transcripts. radA and tyrS transcript levels showed the lowest and enoA and fumC transcript levels the highest variation in Cq-values. The wide range of transcript levels of candidate reference genes confirmed that no single candidate reference gene was constantly expressed at the different analyzed settings. This implicated the need for using multiple reference genes. The genes tyrS, gidA, map and 16S rRNA ranked among the most stably expressed genes. The final selected reference genes differed according to the bacterial growth status, and the time points.

Conclusions

Our data confirmed the finding that the best-suited reference genes differ among experimental conditions, as the most stably expressed reference gene varied for each experimental group. 16S rRNA was suggested as reference gene in only 8 out of the 12 tested conditions.

B47 The relation between *Chlamydia trachomatis* IgG and IgA responses in vaginal secretions, the CT-DNA status, and clinical symptoms

Dewi J. de Waaij[1], Marlon de Gast[1], Remco P.H. Peters[2], Servaas A. Morré[1], Joke Spaargaren[1], Sander Ouburg[1]
[1]*VU University Medical Center, Amsterdam, The Netherlands,* [2]*ANOVA, Johannesburg, South Africa*

Background/ Introduction

Systemic *Chlamydia trachomatis* (CT) IgG antibody detection has a clear role in triage of women for excluding tubal pathology or triage women to laparoscopy. The role of immunoglobulin responses in vaginal secretions has not been studied extensively for their potential role in *e.g.* clinical progression.

Objectives

To assess the relation between *Chlamydia trachomatis* IgG and IgA responses in vaginal secretions, the CT-DNA status, and clinical symptoms.

Method

Dry vaginal swabs were obtained from 604 South African women. Eligible women were defined as being 18 to 49 years old who reported to be sexually active during the previous six months. Local vaginal IgA and IgG titres were determined by pELISA (Medac) and were assessed in relation to the CT-DNA status (Presto-PCR (GMT)) and clinical factors. Categorical data were compared between groups using Chi-square test and the Mann-Whitney U test for continuous data. A *p*-value <0.05 was considered statistically significant.

Results

Of the 604 women, 95 were CT DNA positive. Thirty percent of the DNA positive women were IgA positive and 70% were IgG positive. Of the CT DNA negative women, 32% and 68% were considered IgA and IgG positive, respectively (IgG *p*=0.47;IgA *p*=0.31). Of the CT DNA positive women, 26 (27%) reported symptoms and from the CT DNA negative women, 175 (34%) women reported symptoms. IgA positivity was found in 15% (n=4) in CT DNA positive symptomatic women and IgG positivity in 69% (n=18). In CT DNA negative women, 39% (n=69) were IgA positive and 66% (n=115) were IgG positive.

Conclusions

No significant differences were observed in Ig titers between CT DNA positive and negative women. Local IgA levels may not necessarily increase during *C. trachomatis* infections. The results suggest that IgG is the more prevalent immunoglobulin in vaginal secretions or that higher titers persist longer.

B48 Vertical transmission of *Chlamydia trachomatis*

Minna Honkila[1,2], Erika Wikström[2,3], Marjo Renko[1,2], Heljä-Marja Surcel[3], Tytti Pokka[1,2], Irma Ikäheimo[4], Matti Uhari[1,2], Terhi Tapiainen[1,2]
[1]Department of Children and Adolescents, Oulu University Hospital, Oulu, Finland, [2]PEDEGO Research Unit - Research Unit for Pediatrics, Dermatology, Clinical Genetics, Obstetrics and Gynecology, University of Oulu, Oulu, Finland, [3]National Institute for Health and Welfare, Oulu, Finland, [4]Nordlab Oulu, Oulu University Hospital, Oulu, Finland

Background/ Introduction

Occurrence of symptomatic *Chlamydia trachomatis* infection in newborns is rare even though its prevalence among pregnant women would indicate else.

Objectives

To clarify this discrepancy we evaluated the vertical transmission of *C. trachomatis* from mothers to newborns based on our data and two earlier studies.

Method

Children < 4 years with a possible *C. trachomatis* infection were identified from two national health registers in 1/1/1996 - 12/31/2011. The copies of medical records were obtained from the health care institutions in order to verify the infection. Mothers of the *C. trachomatis* infected children were identified and their serum samples were analyzed for the *C. trachomatis* antibodies.

Results

Altogether 206 children < 4 years of age had a possible *C. trachomatis* infection during the study period, which represents an occurrence of 0.22 per 1000 live births (95% CI 0.19-0.25). The occurrence was 0.13 per 1000 live births (95% CI 0.11-0.16) for microbiologically confirmed *C. trachomatis* cases < 3 months (N=123). Altogether 35% (35/99) of maternal serum samples were negative for *C. trachomatis* antibodies in the first trimester of pregnancy. Vertical transmission rate was 0.8% among NAAT positive mothers and 14.7% among mothers who had seroconversion for *C. trachomatis* antibodies between pregnancies.

Conclusions

Vertical transmission rate of *C. trachomatis* infection is 1% among all NAAT positive pregnant women and 15% among those who have recently acquired infection. One third of the maternal infections leading to an infected newborn are acquired during pregnancy.

B49 Development and Evaluation of an Improved Enzyme-Linked Immunosorbent Assay for the Detection of Antibodies to *Chlamydia trachomatis* Plasmid-Encoded Pgp3

Catherine E Winstanley[1], Kyle H Ramsey[2], Peter Marsh[3], Ian N. Clarke[1]
[1]*University of Southampton, Southampton, Hampshire, UK,* [2]*Midwestern University, Chicago, Illinois, USA,* [3]*Public Health England, Southampton General Hospital, Southampton, Hampshire, UK*

Background/ Introduction

Measurement and understanding the seroprevalence of urogenital *Chlamydia trachomatis* infections has been hindered by the lack of a rigorously validated and relevant ELISA. Previous ELISAs based on *C. trachomatis* plasmid-encoded Pgp3 have been described but lack standardisation and critical controls or use an irrelevant Pgp3 as the capture antigen.

Objectives

We aimed to develop an improved sensitive and specific indirect ELISA based on recombinant Pgp3 derived from a urogenital strain of *C. trachomatis*, serovar E, using a rigorous validation protocol.

Method

Recombinant Pgp3 derived from urogenital *C. trachomatis* serovar E (pSW2) expressed as a fusion protein with an N-terminal glutathione s-transferase (GST) tag was used as the capture antigen. For assay validation, serum samples were collected from 166 adult patients diagnosed as positive or negative for urogenital *C. trachomatis* infection by nucleic acid amplification testing (NAATs). All sera were assayed against GST as a negative control.

Results

We determined overall sensitivity and specificity to be 68.18% and 98.0%, respectively. Sensitivities for female and male samples were 71.93% and 64.15%, respectively. Comparison of samples from these patients diagnosed positive for *C. trachomatis* by NAAT and patients diagnosed negative by NAAT revealed statistical significance ($p = {<}0.0001$). We further validated our ELISAs by demonstrating that sera from mice urogenitally infected with *C. trachomatis* produce measureable responses to recombinant Pgp3.

Conclusions

We have developed and validated a sensitive and specific ELISA to detect anti-Pgp3 antibodies as an indicator of past and current infection to *C. trachomatis* using a urogenital derivation of Pgp3. It is anticipated that this assay will be used for seroepidemiological analysis of urogenital *C. trachomatis* in populations.

B50 *Chlamydia trachomatis* infection during high-risk pregnancy is not associated to increased inflammation markers in vaginal content.

Valeria Paula Gualtieri[1], Andrea Carolina Entrocassi[1], Cecilia Ramos[2], María Lucía Gallo Vaulet[1], Estela Acosta[2], Julia Junges[2], María D'Errico[2], Cecilia Varela[2], Ramón Alberto De Torres[1], Marcelo Rodriguez Fermepin[1], Carlos Ortega Soler[3]
[1]Universidad de Buenos Aires, Unidad de Estudios de Chlamydiae y otras infecciones del tracto genital, Cátedra de Microbiología Clínica, Facultad de Farmacia y Bioquímica., Ciudad de Buenos Aires, Buenos Aires, Argentina, [2]HSEMI Hospital Subzonal Especializado Materno Infantil "Ana Goitia", Avellaneda, Buenos Aires, Argentina, [3]Universidad de Buenos Aires, Facultad de Medicina., Ciudad de Buenos Aires, Buenos Aires, Argentina

Background/ Introduction

An association between *Chlamydia trachomatis* and adverse pregnancy outcomes as premature rupture of the membranes (PROM), stillbirth or low birth weight, has been found by either serological or molecular studies. It's been proposed that the possible cause for these complications could be the immunological reaction caused by a chlamydial infection.

Objectives

This study was designed to search for IL-1 beta and inflammatory response in vaginal content in association to *Chlamydia trachomatis* infection among pregnant women with obsteric high risk. Obstetric high risk has been defined for this purposes as risk of PROM, preterm labour, low birth weight, or history of stillbirth.

Method

From August 2013 to August 2014, every woman attending a high-risk obstetrics unit at a public hospital in Buenos Aires has been offered to participate in this study. After signing an informed consent, patients having high-risk pregnancies were included in the study. *Chlamydia trachomatis* and *Trichomonas vaginalis* were detected in cervicovaginal lavage and urine samples by molecular techniques. Inflammatory response was determined by counting leukocites, considering inflammatory response as positive when leukocytes/epithelial cell ratio was >1. IL-1 beta level was measured on vaginal content by EIA. Bacterial vaginosis was also studied by Nugent score along with additional microscopy criteria (BACOVA).

Results

Fifty two high-risk pregnant women were included in the study. *Chlamydia trachomatis* was detected in 10/52. For *C. trachomatis* infected patients, IL-1 beta in vaginal content ranged from <1 pg/mL to 316 pg/mL, 6/10 with values under 50pg/mL, having no significant differences with non infected pregnant women. Inflammatory response was positive in 7/10, two of them were also positive for *T.vaginalis* infection, and 4 had bacterial vaginosis. Only one of the *Chlamydia trachomatis* positive patients had PROM, but was also infected by *Trichomonas vaginalis*. No preterm labour or stillbirths were found among chlamydia infected women.

Conclusions

The role of *C.trachomatis* in adverse pregnancy outcomes has been extensively discussed. Despite the associations described, mechanisms leading to complications are yet to be described. The factors analyzed in this study could not been associated to chlamydial infection so far. Additional immunological factors should be proposed to be further studied.

B51 Inhibition of protein translation during infection with *C. trachomatis*

Tina Tzivelekidis[1], Larisa Volceanov[1], Oliver Schilling[2], Georg Häcker[1]
[1]Institute of Medical Microbiology and Hygiene, Freiburg i. Brsg, Germany, [2]Institute of Molecular Medicine and Cell Research, Freiburg i. Brsg, Germany

Background/ Introduction

Chlamydia trachomatis causes numerous changes to the cell, and it is believed that it achieves this in a large part by the secretion of effector molecules although instances are rare where a given protein has been clearly linked to a known effect.

Objectives

We examined the hypothesis that proteolysis, possibly triggered by chlamydial protease CPAF, is responsible for a number of the cell-biological effects of chlamydial infection.

Method

To gain greater insights we established a proteomic map of degradation and synthesis of host cell proteins during chlamydial infection using SILAC-labelling. Pathway analysis suggested a particular reduction in proteins involved in ribosomal function. We therefore specifically tested for host cell protein synthesis during chlamydial infection using Click-IT-labelling, ribosomal profiling and analysis of polysomal (actively translated) mRNA by RT-PCR and microarray.

Results

We found a substantial reduction of *de novo*-protein synthesis in HeLa cells infected with *C. trachomatis* from about 24 h p.i. This reduction was coincident with an increase in the 80S ribosome-fraction (possibly corresponding to 'stalled' ribosomes) and a minor reduction in the polysomal fraction by ribosomal profiling. Interestingly ectopic expression of CPAF in human cells reproduced the 80S-increase. Preliminary analysis of polysomal mRNA suggests specificity in protein translation during infection.

Conclusions

C. trachomatis reduces protein synthesis of the infected cell, very likely through targeting of ribosomal protein translation. This may be relevant to countering a host response to infection and may explain numerous cell-biological effects in chlamydial infection.

POSTERS: LATE BREAKERS

LB1 *Chlamydia* infection induces expansion of unconventional T cells expressing CD11c

Jamal Qualai[1], Lin-Xi Li[2], Jon Cantero[1], Antoni Tarrats[3], Stephen J. McSorley[4], Meritxell Genescà[1]

[1]Mucosal Immunology Unit, Institut d'Investigació en Ciències de la Salut Germans Trias i Pujol, AIDS Research Institute IrsiCaixa-HIVACAT, Can Ruti Campus, Badalona, Catalunya, Spain, [2]Department of Microbiology and Immunology, University of Arkansas for Medical Sciences, Little Rock, Arkansas, USA, [3]Department of Obstetrics and Gynecology, University Hospital "Germans Trias i Pujol," Can Ruti Campus, Badalona, Catalunya, Spain, [4]Center for Comparative Medicine, Department of Anatomy, Physiology and Cell Biology, School of Veterinary Medicine, University of California, Davis, Davis, California, USA

Background/ Introduction

In the search for new surrogate markers of genital mucosal immunity in women, we have detected an increase of CD11c on T cells associated to vaginal *Chlamydia* infection in mice, as well as during symptomatic bacterial vaginitis in women (Qualai et al. PLos One, 2016).

Objectives

To address the phenotype of blood and genital tract-derived T cells expressing CD11c during acute vaginal *Chlamydia* infection in mice and to compare them with T cells expressing CD11c[+] T cells from women.

Method

We first performed microarray and Gene Set Enrichment Analysis of activated effector T cells expressing CD11c derived from naïve female mice. Next, we performed flow cytometry analyses of blood and genital tract obtained from C57BL/6 mice vaginally infected with *Chlamydia muridarum* Within the CD11c+ T cells we analyzed the expression of several NK-associated molecules (NK1.1, DX5, NKG2A, NKp46), specific T cell phenotypes (CD8α, CD1d-restricted iNKT cells, γδTCR) and adhesion molecules (CD103, CCR10). Finally, we examined CD11c expression in both, circulating and cervical T cells from healthy young women, and defined the migratory and interferon (IFN)-g secretory capacity of these cells.

Results

Microarray analyses of CD11c+T cells demonstrated enrichment for natural killer-associated genes. Murine CD11c[+]T cells displayed markers associated with non-conventional T cells, including gdT cells and invariant natural killer T cells. However, in women, only gdT cells and CD8[+]T cells were enriched within the CD11c fraction of blood and cervical tissue. Further, only in female mice, NK1.1 and CD103 expression was tightly associated with CD11c+T cells. In women, these CD11c[+] cells were highly activated and had greater IFN-g secretory capacity than CD11c[-] T cells. Furthermore, circulating CD11c+ T cells were associated with the expression of multiple adhesion molecules.

Conclusions

These data suggest that CD11c expression distinguishes circulating T cells during bacterial infection with innate capacity and mucosal homing potential. Although CD11c was also induced after systemic *Chlamydia* infection in mice, its increase in response to genital tract disorders may represent a novel surrogate marker of mucosal immunity in women.

LB2 Natural killer cells decrease T Regulatory Cells response during both chlamydial respiratory primary infection and reinfection

Hong Wang[1], Jing Li[1], Xiaojing Dong[1], Xi Yang[2], Weiming Zhao[1]
[1]Shandong University, Jinan, Shandong, China, [2]University of Manitoba, Winnipeg, Manitoba, Canada

Background/ Introduction

Recent studies suggested Treg involved in tissue pathology during chlamydial infection. As an important component in innate immunity, NK cells has been show plays an important role in modulating the function of other immune cells, however the influence of the cells on Treg remain unclear in *Chlamydia* infection.

Objectives

This prospective study aimed to investigate the modulating effect and mechanism of NK cells on Treg during intracellular bacterial lung infection of *Chlamydia muridarum* in mice.

Method

Mice were infected or reinfected with *Chlamydia muridarum* after treatment with NK cell-depleting antisera (anti-asialo GM1). Treg response, Treg differentiation-related cytokines and tissue inflammation were assessed.

Results

Our data showed *Chlamydia muridarum* lung infection induced an expansion of Treg. During both primary infection and reinfection model, NK cell-depleted mice showed significantly increased Treg in cell number and related transcription factor (Foxp3) expression in local (lung) and secondary lymphoid organs (spleen and draining lymph node) than control mice, which was in line with severe disease after respiratory infection. Furthermore, we found the change of IL-6 and TGF-β levels in the NK cell-depleted mice would prefer the development of Treg.

Conclusions

These results demonstrate NK cells have an important modulating effect during both the primary and secondary chlamydial infection, which contribute to the severe disease.

LB3 Estimating local *Chlamydia* incidence and prevalence using surveillance data

Joanna Lewis[1,2], Peter J. White[1,2]

[1]*NIHR Health Protection Research Unit in Modelling Methodology and MRC Centre for Outbreak Analysis and Modelling, Department of Infectious Disease Epidemiology, Imperial College London, London, UK,* [2]*Modelling and Economics Unit, Public Health England, London, UK*

Background/ Introduction

Understanding patterns of *Chlamydia* prevalence is important for addressing inequalities and assessing interventions. Population-based surveys are expensive; the best UK data come from the Natsal national surveys which are necessarily infrequent, and not powered to compare prevalence in different localities. Estimates at finer spatial and temporal scales are required.

Objectives

We aimed to estimate *Chlamydia* prevalence from numbers of tests and diagnoses reported in surveillance data.

Method

Our method is based on a simple model for the infection, testing and treatment processes and informed by the literature on infection natural history and treatment seeking behaviour. By combining this information with surveillance data we obtain estimates of *Chlamydia* screening rates, incidence and prevalence. We validate and illustrate the method by application to national and local-level data from England.

Results

Estimates of national prevalence by sex and age group agree with results from the Natsal-3 survey. They could be improved by additional information on the number of diagnoses that were symptomatic. There is substantial local-level variation in prevalence, with more infection in deprived areas. Incidence in each sex is strongly correlated with prevalence in the other. Importantly, we find that positivity (the proportion of tests which were positive) does not provide a reliable proxy for prevalence.

Conclusions

This approach provides a powerful tool to identify prevalence trends with time and location, and understand the effects of control strategies. Estimates could be more accurate if surveillance systems recorded which patients were symptomatic and the duration of symptoms before care-seeking.

LB4 Evaluation of Surveillance Tools for Trachoma in Four Districts in Nepal

West SK[1], Zambrano A[1], Munoz B[1], Sharma, S[2], Mishra, S[2], Dize L[1], Crowley K[3], Rotondo L[3]

[1]Dana Center for Preventive Ophthalmology, Johns Hopkins University, Baltimore MD; [2]Nepal Netra Jyoti Sangh, Kathmandu,Nepal; [3]RTI Inernational, Washington DC.

Background/Introduction:

As countries eliminate trachoma, surveillance is necessary to determine absence of re-emergence. The World Health Organization recommends population-based prevalence surveys in children two years after mass drug administration(MDA) ceases. Two years may be insufficient to observe re-emergence, and more data are needed on tools, besides clinical assessment, for surveillance.

Objectives:

first, to determine the prevalence of trachoma in children age 1-9 years in districts 2, 4, 6 and 8 years after MDA had ceased; second, to determine the benefit of a test for infection and test for antibodies to *C. trachomatis* antigen pgp3.

Methods:

In 4 districts in Nepal, 15 randomly selected clusters within each were chosen. In each cluster, 50 randomly selected children ages 1-9 years old were examined for TF. Eye swabs were taken from all children to test for *C. trachomatis* using the Cepheid platform (Cepheid, Sunnyvale, CA). Dried blood spots were collected to determine antibody positivity to the *C. trachomatis* antigen pgp3. Blood was processed on the Luminex platform following standard procedures. Data were analyzed as simple frequencies, and age stratified proportions

Results:

The survey enrolled over 3,000 children ages 1-9 years. Overall, 9 cases of trachoma were found in the 4 districts, and 3 cases of infection. There was no evidence of an increase in trachoma with number of years since last MDA. No district had TF prevalence >5%. Pgp3 antibody positivity was 2.4% in the first two districts and did not increase with age. There was no clustering of antibody positivity within communities.

Conclusions:

Our surveillance surveys, designed as proposed by WHO, showed no evidence for re-emergence of trachoma in four districts of Nepal. The low level and lack of increase by age in seroprevalence of antibodies to *C. trachomatis* pgp3 deserves further investigation as a marker of interruption of transmission.

LB5 A history of enzyme detection assays to diagnose Chlamydia trachomatis infection highlights how useless the CE mark is

Schachter, J.

Department of Laboratory Medicine, University of California, San Francisco, USA

A recent editorial (Schachter, STI, 2016) pointed out that despite vigorous marketing campaigns, enzyme detection assays to diagnose Chlamydia trachomatis (CT) infection did not work.

The first such test, in the US, was "MicroZyme the Easy Test", Diversified (Diagnostics Inc. (DDI)) circa 1990. In 1995 its President and founder was sentenced to 5 years in jail after the FDA accused him (among other things) of being behind a scheme to market ineffective diagnostic kits, including altering study data to show their Chlamydia test was more effective than actual results demonstrated.

Between 2004 and 2015 the same technology, with minor format changes, was being sold in Europe and elsewhere in the world (where the FDA had no regulatory powers). The assays were marketed under many names, including HandiLab-C, Sumatest, Biovei, The BioChekSwab test, and SELFCheck Chlamydia. Assay. All these tests were developed and/or manufactured by companies located near San Francisco. None had FDA clearance, thus could not be sold in the US. It was easier to obtain a CE mark, with approval for point of care professional use and over the counter sale. In 2006 I saw one of these assays on sale in a Boots pharmacy, and a Tesco supermarket. In 2016, it was possible to buy one on the internet in the UK. And it is sad to read the users' reviews. One wonders how the user who celebrated an enzyme detection test that found him/her negative for chlamydia would feel if he/she knew that two peer reviewed papers found a sensitivity of 0 (all positives by nucleic acid amplification were negative by enzyme detection) for chlamydia detection. Five evaluations found sensitivity <20%.

The CE mark is more about manufacturing regulations, safety and conformity, and provides no assurance of diagnostic accuracy. Obviously, poor performing tests can get a CE mark. Who can blame the young person who buys a test, feeling that if it is being sold by a reputable company, and has a CE mark it should provide a reliable result. The CE mark will change, but currently, in this context, the CE mark is providing a disservice.

AUTHOR INDEX

Acosta, Estela	197	Belaw, Yeshigeta	118
Ades, A.E.	82	Benfield, Thomas	76
Ades, Tony E	68	Bergström, Sven	21
Aeby, Sébastien	52	Bertelli, Claire	50, 52
Agerholm, Jørgen S	37	Biondi, Roberta	100
Agyemang, David	134	Biritwum, Nana	134
Aitchison, Kevin	175	Birkelund, Svend	97, 125
Aiyar, Ashok	183	Black, Carolyn M	32, 101, 112, 126, 133, 188
Akkuratov, Evgeny	135	Blas-Machado, Uriel	112, 126, 188
Alami, Aziz	44, 157	Bloigu, Aini	69, 184
Alexander, Neal	66	Blomquist, Paula B	68, 98
Almqvist, Fredrik	21	Bochkareva, Olga	135
Althaus, Christian L	137	Bogaards, Johannes A	74
Álvarez, Daniel	95, 177	Bøje, Sarah	37
Amato-Gauci, Andrew	70	Borel, Nicole	41, 45, 47, 100, 146, 152, 172, 191
Amaya, Michelle I	110	Bouazza, Mohamed	44, 157
Amraoui, Abdelouahed	44, 157	Boucrot, Emmanuel	161
Ananaba, Godwin A	112	Boylan, Prudence	163
Andersen, Peter	28, 37, 131	Bradshaw, Catriona S	113, 114, 115
Andersson, Patiyan	8, 57, 148, 163	Branley, James	129
Andreasen, Aura	143	Braun, Kristin M	22
Arkatkar, Tanvi	12	Brenner, Nicole C	163
Arulanandam, Bernard P	12	Bressan, Alessia	160
Asche, Valerie L	57	Bridle, Andrew	51
Astachonok, Andrey	132	Brinkworth, Amanda J	7
Bachmann, Nathan L	46, 47, 51, 129, 191	Brode, Sven	31
Bahnan, Wael	21	Brooks, David G	111
Bailey, Robin L	59, 116, 117, 120, 128, 130, 134	Brothwell, Julie A	4, 6, 11
Bakajika, Didier	134	Brown, Naj	27
Baldessari, Audrey E	180	Bruisten, Sylvia	38
Bandea, Claudiu	32	Bryant, Clare	31
Banniettis, Natalie	96	Brzozowski, Marek	27
Bannister, Alan	176	Buendía, Antonio J	95, 177
Bannister, Stephanie	153	Bulir, David C	33, 121
Banzola, Nicoletta	107	Burr, Sarah E	59, 116, 117, 120, 128
Baptista, Graciela	102	Burskaya, Valentina	135
Baraitser, Paula	89	Burton, Matthew J	8, 56, 116, 117, 130
Barisani-Asenbauer, T	118	Busch, Carrie E	110
Barnes, Mathilda	109	Butcher, Robert	58
Barnes, Perry	109	Butt, Julia	9
Bastidias, Robert	23	Cai, Jinshan	144
Baud, David	140	Cantero, Jon	200
Bavoil, Patrik M	43	Cao, Xiaoan	144
Bébéar, Cécile	138, 149, 150, 151	Carabeo, Rey A	7, 17, 22
Becker, Elisabeth	5	Carneiro da Silva, Joanna	43

Caro, M Rosa	95, 177	Day, Sarinder	166
Carter, Darrick	27	Deák, Judit	154
Cassama, Eunice	116, 120, 128,	Dean, Deborah	46, 124
Castillo-Ramirez, S	46	DeAngelis, Daniela	82
Cekovska, Zaklina	162	de Barbeyrac, Bertille	138, 149, 150, 151
Cenacchi, Giovanna	100	De-Barsy, Marie	52
Cevenini, Roberto	107, 123	Debrah, Oscar	134
Chalabi, Hadeel	118	Decré, Dominique	150
Chamberlain, Holly	39	Deenen, René	18
Chambers, James P	12	de Gast, Marlon	194
Chaplin, Andrey	135	de Groot, R	185
Charlois, Cécile	150	de la Maza, Luis M	128
Chee, Ronnie	31	Delarocque-Astagneau, E	138
Chen, Hongyu	109	De Livera, Alysha M	114, 115
Chen, Marcus Y	113, 114, 115	Del Río, Laura	95
Chong, Sylvia	33, 121	de Moraes, Isabel	99
Chotikanatis, Kobkul	96	den Daas, Chantal	141
Chow, Christine	111, 153	Derrick, Tamsyn	56, 59, 116, 117, 130
Cirkovic Velickovic, Tanja	118	D'Errico, María	197
Clare, Simon	31	De Torres, Ramón Alberto	197
Clarke, Annabelle EP	189	de Vries, Henry John C.	38, 85
Clarke, Ian N.	8, 57, 67, 120, 136, 176, 189, 196	de Waaij, Dewi J	194
Clarkson, John	153	Dhotte, Philippe	150
Clark, Taane G	120	Didelot, Xavier	46
Cochrane, Sarah	98	Di Francesco, Antonietta	41, 152
Coers, Jorn	11	Di Pietro, Marisa	160
Coler, Rhea	27	Dirks, Jeanne AMC	173, 174
Coll, Francesc	120	Ditkowsky, Jared	165
Collingro, Astrid	49	Dize, Laura	109, 203
Compri, Monica	107	Dojiri, Stacey	124
Cooley, Gretchen	66, 164	Donati, Manuela	100, 152
Corbel, Michael J	105	Dondog, Bollorma	142
Courtright, Paul	66	Dong, Xiaojing	201
Cousins, Emma	153	Douglas, Fiona P	57
Crowley, K	203	Druzhkin, Ivan V	104
Croxatto, Antony	182	Dubbink, Jan Henk	155, 156
Cuello, Francisco	177	Dubrovina, Svetlana	158
Cutcliffe, Lesley T	57, 120	Dukers-Muijrers, Nicole	74, 75, 77, 173, 174
Dagleish, Mark	175	Dumoux, Maud	19
Dahlberg, Jenny	64	Dunbar, Kevin J	68, 111, 153
Dakka, Nadia	44, 157	Eder, Thomas	18
Danson, Amy E	99	Edwards, Richard	189
D'Antuono, Antonietta	107	Edwards, Tansy	106
Darville, Toni	39	Eko, Francis O	32, 101, 112, 126, 133, 188
Davies, Bethan	76	Elder, Matthew	31

Elfving, Karin 64
Elkheir, Balgesa 118
Ellerson, Debra 32, 126, 188
Ellis, Lou 31
Elmdaghri, Naima 44, 157
Elofsson, Mikael 23
Elyazouli, Loubna 44, 157
Entrocassi, A C 102, 197
Eppings, Lisanne 75
Eriksson, Tiina 127
Erneholm, Karin 37
Faal, Nkoyo 128
Fairley, Christopher K 114, 115
Favaroni, Alison 5
Fearnley, Nicola R 111
Fedotov, Edward A 104
Feodorova, Valentina A 103, 104, 105
Fields, Kenneth A 13
Fijten, Helmi 167
Filardo, Simone 160
Filaretov, Vsevolod 135
Finethy, Ryan 11
Finlayson, Jeanie 175
Fisher, Derek 24
Fitzmaurice, Tim 31
Flockhart, Allen 175
Flueckiger, Rebecca M 106
Follmann, Frank 28, 37, 131
Ford, Charlotte 161
Foschi, Claudio 107, 123
Franco, Octavio 100
Fredlund, Hans 64
Frolund, Maria 76
Fulcher, Leslie 39
Fuller, Sebastian S 111, 153
Gallego, M Carmen 95, 177
Gallo Vaulet, María Lucía 102, 197
Garcia, Victor 137
Garland, Suzanne M 163
Gaston, Hill JS 31
Gaydos, Charlotte A 103, 104, 105, 109
Gekara, Nelson 31
Gelfand, Mikhail S 135
Genescà, Meritxell 200
Geisler, Will M. 30, 92

George, Zenas 32, 188
Gibbs, Sue 38
Giebel, Amanda M 11
Giffard, Philip M 8, 57, 148, 163
Goller, Jane L 114, 115
Goncalves, Adriana 59, 116, 117
Goodall, Jane C 31
Goodier, Martin R 59, 116
Good, James 21
Goria, Natalia Malen 102
Gottstein, Zeljko 139
Goubet, Stephanie 176
Grdanoska, Tatjana 162
Green, Marc 153
Greub, Gilbert 20, 48, 50, 52, 140, 181, 182, 187
Gualtieri, Valeria Paula 102, 197
Guentzel, M Neal 12
Gupta, Rishein 12
Guy, Rebecca J 114, 115
Gwyn, Sarah 66, 164
Gylfe, Åsa 23
Häcker, Georg 198
Hadad, Ronza 64
Hadfield, James 8, 57
Hallam, Steven J 49
Hall, Catherine L 111, 153
Ham, Kendra K 110
Hammerschlag, M R 96, 110, 165
Harding-Esch, Emma M 111, 153
Harley, Ross 166
Harrison, Kelly 3
Harrison, Mark A 111
Harris, Simon R 8, 57, 122, 145
Hässig, Michael 152
Hay, Phillip E 111
Hayward, Richard D 15, 19, 128, 161
Heegaard, Niels HH 131
Hefty, Scott 3
Hegemann, Johannes 5
Heijne, Janneke CM 74, 90, 141
Heijne, Marloes 167
HEJAJI, Hicham 44, 157
Helps, Chris 166
Hendenström, Mattias 23
Hénin, Nadège 149, 151

He, Qing	32, 101, 112, 126, 188	Jungersen, Gregers	37
Herrmann, Björn	64	Junges, Julia	197
Hiltunen-Back, Eija	171	Kabona, George	106
Hocking, Jane S	61, 113, 114, 115	Käding, Nadja	18
Hoebe, Christian JPA	74, 75, 77, 173, 174	Kares, Saara	127
Hoenderboom, Bernice M	63	Karimi, Mahdad	163
Hoffmann, Karolin	152	Kaufhold, Inga	18
Hoheisel, Jörg D	9	Kaufhold, Robin	170
Hokynar, Kati C	168, 171	Kaye, Paul	27
Holland, M J	28, 56, 59, 116, 117, 120, 128, 130	Keane, Orla	179
Holt, Deborah C	148, 163	Kebbi-Beghdadi, Carole	52, 181, 182
Holtzman, Michael	16	Keck, Jonathon	12
Holzinger, Dana	142	Kessimer, Mehmet	39
Honkila, Minna	195	Khryanin, Alexey	119
Horner, Patrick J	68, 82, 98	Kiathanapaiboon, Amy	39
Horn, Matthias	49	Kim, Hoyon	124
Horvatek Tomic, Danijela	138	Kim, Jeeho	39
Houghton, Joanna	59, 116, 117	Kishi, Fumio	108
Hovis, Kelley	43	Kock, Marleen M	156
Hsia, Ru-ching	43	Kohlhoff, Stephan	96, 165
Hufnagel, Katrin	9, 142	Köhrer, Karl	18
Hughes, Chris	189	Konnova, Svetlana S	104
Hughes, Gwenda	143	Korhonen, Suvi J	168, 171
Huot-Creasy, Heather	43, 192	Köstlbacher, Stephan	49
Hu, Shuai	11	Kounali, Daphne	68
Huston, Wilhelmina	113, 169	Kretzschmar, Mirjam E	141
Hutton, Susan I	57	Krstic, Maja	118
Igietseme, Joseph U	32, 101, 112, 126, 133, 188	Labiran, Clare	176
Ikäheimo, Irma	195	Labrie, Scott	3
Imounga, Laure	151	Lacey, Charles	27
Inic-Kanada, Aleksandra	118	Laghi, Luca	123
Isaksson, Jenny	64	Lait, Philippa	166
Jack, Kelvin	58	Land, Jolande A	159
Jacquier, Nicolas	20, 52, 187	Langridge, James	189
Jalal, Hamid	8	Laroucau, Karine	41, 122
Janier, Michel	150	Larsson, Inger	64
Jankoska, Gordana	162	La Ruche, Guy	151
Janssen, Kevin JH	75	La Salle, Sophie	16
Jeffries, David	130	Last, Anna R	116, 120, 128
Jelocnik, Martina	41, 47, 129	Laurier-Nadalié, Cécile	149, 151
Johns, Tracy	163	Lawrence, Amba	113
Joki-Korpela, Päivi	69, 184	Laye, Mass	128
Joof, Hassan	59, 66, 116, 117, 128	Lee, Amanda	121
Joseph, Kahaliah	32	Le Hen, Isabelle	138, 150
Joseph, Sandeep J	46, 124	Lehtinen, Matti	127

Le Mesurier, Richard T	58	Ma, Ruilin	144
Leonard, Cory A	45, 172	Macleod, John	82
Le Roy, Chloé	151	Massae, Patrick	56, 166, 130
Levels, Luuk	77	Mastromarino, Paola	160
Levi, Aurora	100	Mathews, John D	57
Levkut, Martin	45	May, Margaret	76
Lewallen, Susan	66	McClure, Myra	24, 68
Lewis, Joanna	202	McIntyre, James A	155, 156
Liang, Steven	33, 121	McIvor, Ruthy	113
Li, Jing	201	McKeithen, Danielle N	112, 126, 188
Li, Lin-Xi	200	McKenna, Therese	189
Lilley, Thomas M	168	McSorley, Stephen J	200
Lilliebridge, Rachael A	163	Mensah, Ernest	134
Lillis, Rebecca	183	Mercer, Catherine H	137
Linley, Ezra	67	Miao, Beiping	9
Livingstone, Morag	122, 145, 175	Michel, Angelika	9
Li, Zhaocai	144	Migchelsen, Stephanie J	66
Longbottom, David	41, 122, 145, 175	Mihailovic, Jelena	118
Lorenzen, Emma	37	Mihajlov, Kiril	162
Lou, Zhongzi	144	Miller, Terry	51
Lowndes, Catherine M	111, 153	Mishra, S	203
Low, Nicola	87, 137	Mitchell, Alexandria	164
Lucchesi, Mayk	75	Mojica, Sergio A	23, 43
Luczak, Soeren	5	Molina, Sandra	59
Lueong, Smiths	9	Moncada, Jeanne	8
Lukac, Maja	139	Moore, Sophie	59
Maassen, Kitty	167	Morré, Servaas A	63, 155, 156, 158, 159, 194
Mabey, David CW	8, 54, 58, 59, 66, 106 116, 117, 120, 128, 130	Morrison, Richard P	11
		Morrison, Sandra G	11
MacIntyre, Sheila	99	Motin, Vladimir L	103, 104, 105
Madden, Victoria	39	Mouritson, Lars	109
Magnino, Simone	100	Mtengai, Karim	56
Mahony, James B	33, 121	Mtuy, Tara	116, 130
Makalo, Pateh	59, 66, 128, 166, 167	Mueller, Konrad E	13
Malisa, Aiweda	116	Mueller, Linda	50, 52
Manam, Srikanth	16	Mullender, Margriet	38
Marangoni, Antonella	107, 123	Munoz, B	203
Mårdh, Otilia	70, 143	Muramatsu, Matthew K	6
Mårdh, Per-Anders	78	Murcia-Belmonte, Antonio	95, 177
Markey, Bryan	179	Murthy, Ashlesh K	16
Marsh, Peter	8, 67, 176, 196	Mußmann, Marc	49
Marti, Hanna	46, 124	Myers, Garry	129, 192
Martin, David	183	Nabicassa, Meno	116, 120, 128
Martin, Diana	66, 164	Nagarajan, Uma	39
Martin, Oliver	19	Nagy, Tamas	32

Ñahui Palomino, R A	123	Perusko, Marija	118
Nally, Jarlath	179	Peterson, Greg	3
Nans, Andrea	161	Peters, Remco PH	155, 156, 194
Nardini, Paola	107, 123	Petrovska, Milena	162
Natunen, Kari	127	Peuchant, Olivia	149, 151
Navarro, Jose A	177	Phelan, Jody	120
Ndeikoundam, Ndeindo	151	Phillips, Daniel	43
Nelson, David E	4, 6, 11, 117	Phillips, Laura	153
Ngondi, Jeremiah	106	Phillips, Sam	113
Nicholson, Bruce J	16	Pickering, Harry	128
Nielsen, Mads Lausen	97, 125	Piepenburg, Olaf	111
Nogueira, Ana T	22	Pillonel, Trestan	50, 52
Nowak, Barbara	51	Pilloux, Ludovic	52, 181, 182
O'Connell, Catherine M	39, 178	Pleijster, Jolein	159
Öhman, Hanna	69, 184	Pohl, Jan	32
Olsen, Anja W	28, 37, 131	Pokka, Tytti	195
Olson, Macy	186	Pokorzynski, Nicholas D	7
Omosun, Yusuf O	32, 101, 126, 188	Poleshchuk, Nikolay	132
O'Neill, Colette	57, 136	Polkinghorne, Adam	41, 47, 51, 129, 146, 191
O'Neill, Lauren M T	179	Polyanina, Tatiana I	103, 104, 105
Ong, Vanissa A	169	Pond, Marcus J	111
Opondo, Charles	106	Postma, MJ	185
Ortega, Nieves	95, 177	Poulsen, Thomas B G	97, 125
Ortega Soler, Carlos	197	Powell, Emily	39
Østergaard, Ole	131	Pramar, Surendra	8
Ouburg, Sander	63, 155, 156, 158, 159, 194	Price, Malcolm J.	82
Ouchi, Kazunobu	108	Prukner-Radovcic, Estella	139
Ouellette, Scot P	10, 186	Pullan, Rachel	106
Paavonen, Jorma A	69, 127, 168, 171, 184	Pulliainen, Arto T	168
Paes, Wayne	27	Puolakkainen, Mirja H	69, 127, 168, 171, 184
Pais, Roshan	101, 126, 188	Putman, Tim E	6
Palmer, Christine D	59, 116, 117	Qi, Weihong	51
Panovski, Nikola	162	Qualai, Jamal	200
Panum, Inge	76	Quayle, Alison	81, 183
Papa, Valentina	100	Quilicot, Ana Marquiza	139
Parisi, Antonio	102	Quinn, Thomas C	103, 104, 105
Parisi, Dolores	102	Quiruelas, Sonia	102
Parker, Mathew J	111	Radouani, Fouzia	44, 157
Parolin, Carola	123	Rajaram, Krithika	11
Partin, James	32	Ramadhani, Athumani M	56, 116, 130
Patel, Rajul R	111	Ramos, Cecilia	197
Patton, Dorothy L	180, 190	Ramsey, Kyle H	16, 35, 136, 196
Pawlita, Michael	9, 142	Randell, Scott	39
Peacock, Lori	166	Rantsi, Tiina	69, 184
Pedrosa, Antonio T	17	Rattei, Thomas	18

Ravel, Jacques 43, 138
Read, Timothy D 46, 124
Reed, Matthew S 32
Reed, Steve 27
Renko, Marjo 195
Reshetnikov, Oleg 119
Ristivojevic, Petar 118
Rizzo, Mabel 102
Roberts, C H 58, 59, 66, 116, 117, 120, 128, 130
Rockey, Daniel D 6
Rodriguez Fermepin, M 102, 197
Roest, Hendrik-Jan 167
Rosenkrands, Ida 28, 131
Ross, Padraig 179
Rotondo, L 203
Rours, GIJG 185
Rowland-Jones, Sarah 128
Rubangakene, Peter Paul 66
Rubanik, Luidmila 132
Rucks, Elizabeth A 186
Rucks, Lisa A 10
Rueden, Kelsey J 10
Rupp, Jan 18
Russell, Raedeen S 101, 133
Ryans, Khamia 112, 126, 188
Ryder, Nathan 163
Sachse, Konrad 122
Sadiq, S Tariq 93, 111, 153
Sait, Michelle 122, 145
Salamin, Nicolas 50
Salinas, Jesús 95, 177
Salin, Olli 23
Saltykov, Yury V 103, 104, 105
Sarovich, Derek S 57
Schachter, Julius 8, 204
Scherler, Aurélie 187
Schiavoni, Giovanna 160
Schilling, Oliver 198
Schmidt, Nis 18
Schmitt, Markus 142
Schröter, Juliane 142
Schuerer, Nadine 118
Seghrouchni, Fouad 157
Senyonjo, Laura 134
Seshu, Janakiram 179

Sessa, Rosa 160
Seth-Smith, Helena MB 8, 47, 51, 57, 122, 145, 146
Shah, Khushal H 165
Sharma, S 203
Sharratt, Paula 111
Shelyakin, Pavel 135
Shenton, Daniel P 153
Sherchand, Shardulendra 183
Shima, Kensuke 18
Sigalova, Olga 135
Silver, Jim 21
Simms, Elizabeth 121
Simms, Ian 82
Simoneaux, Tankya 112, 126, 188
Simpson, Julie 115
Singh, Gurmeet 116
Skilton, Rachel J 136
Skipp, Paul JS 189
Smid, Joost H 137
Smiljanic, Katarina 118
Smith-Norowitz, Tamar A 165
Sokana, Oliver 58
Soldan, Kate 68, 82
Solomon, Anthony W 8, 58
Soni, Suneeta 176
Southisombath, K 66
Spaargaren, Joke 158, 159, 194
Sperandio, Clément 149
Spiteri, Gianfranco 70, 143
Stanic-Vucinic, Dragana 118
Starnbach, Michael N. 26
Stary, Angelika 72
Stein, Barry D 4, 6, 11
Stein, Elisabeth 118
Stensballe, Allan 125
Stepanauskas, Ramunas 49
Struthers, Helen E 155, 156
Stuchlik, Olga 32
Suchland, Robert J 11, 190
Sultanakhmedov, Edgar S 103, 104, 105
Sunduru, Naresh 23
Surbevska, Biljana 162
Surcel, Heljä-Marja 69, 127, 142, 184, 195
Sweeney, Yvonne T 180, 190
Szigeti, Aviva 96

Tabrizi, Sepehr N	113, 163	Vaughan, Lloyd	51
Tamarelle, Jeanne	138	v.d. Goot, Jeanet	167
Tanturovski, Dragan	162	Vecchio Nepita, Edoardo	100
Tapiainen, Terhi	195	Verbrugh, HA	185
Tarrats, Antoni	200	Verkooyen, RP	185
Taylor-Brown, Alyce	41, 51, 191	Vernay-Vaisse, Chantal	150
Teng, Andy	128	Versteeg, Bart	38
Thiébaut, Anne	138	Verweij, Stephan P	155
Thompson, Christopher C	24	Vesterinen, Eero J	168
Thomson, N R	8, 47, 57, 120, 122, 128, 145, 189	Viollier, Patrick H	20
Thumu, Sirisha	96	Vitali, Beatrice	123
Tiitinen, Aila	69, 184	Vodstrcil, Lenka	113
Timms, Peter	41, 47, 113, 169	Volceanov, Larisa	198
Titenko, Anastasiia	119	Vouga, Manon	52, 140
Toh, Evelyn	11, 117	Walsh, Martin	99
Tong, Steven YC	57, 163	Wang, Hong	201
Topf, Maya	19	Wang, Yibing	136
Touati, Arabella	149, 150, 151	Wanninger, Sabrina	146, 152
Tourlomousis, Pani	31	Ward, Helen	76
Trajkovska Dokic, Elena	162	Waterboer, Tim	9, 142
Trifunovic, Sara	118	Watson, Kim A	99
Tsang, Allen	79	Webster, Steve J	31
Tucker, Zachary, T	178	Wee, Bryan	169
Turner, Katy ME	76, 82	Weiss, Helen A	130
Turpitt, Johanna	111	Welton, Nicky J.	82
Turyaguma, Patrick	66	West, Sheila K	203
Tzivelekidis, Tina	198	Westh, Henrik	76
Uhari, Matti	195	Wheelhouse, Nicholas	175
Unemo, Magnus	8, 64	White, Peter J	202
Upendo, Mwingira	106	Whiting, Christine	166
Utz, Sergey R	103, 104, 105	Whittington, Fran	166
Valdivia, Raphael	2, 23	Wickstrum, Jason	3
Van Benthem, Birgit HB	63, 74	Wiegand, Ryan	164
van Bergen, Jan EAM	63	Wikström, Erika	195
van den Broek, Ingrid VF	63	Willhauck-Fleckenstein, M	9, 142
van den Broek, Lenie	38	Wills, Gillian	68
Van Der Pol, Barbara	91	Wilson, Janet	84
van der Eem, Lisette	156	Wilson, Judith	148
van Ess, Eleanne F	158, 159	Wilson, Kathy	43
Van Lent, Sarah	192, 193	Winstanley, Catherine E	67, 136, 196
van Liere, Geneviève AFS	74, 77, 173, 174	Winther, Robert	97
van Oeffelen, Aloysia AM	63	Wit, Ben	167
Vanrompay, Daisy	192, 193	Wolffs, Petra FG	75, 173, 174
van Wees, Daphne A	141	Wolf, Katerina	13
Varela, Cecilia	197	Woodhall, Sarah C	68, 98, 143

Worthington, Karen	113
Wu, Yuehao	126, 188
Wyrick, Priscilla	39
Yanatori, Izumi	108
Yang, Xi	201
Yu, JiehJuen	12
Zaitsev, Sergey S	103, 104, 105
Zambrano, A	203
Zerden, Mathew	39
Zhang, Yong	16
Zhao, Weiming	201
Zhavnerko, Genady	132
Zheng, Xiaojing	178
Zhou, Jizhang	144
Zhou, Judith	176